Welcome
to HEINLE ESL/ELT!

P9-EMN-899
CENGAGE Learning

CONTENTS

Spotlight on:

Heinle is a part of Cengage Learning

Icon Key

 NCLB No Child Left Behind Recommendation

 SPECIAL EDUCATION Special Education Recommendation

 CONTENT Content Area Instruction Recommendation

 CNN CNN® Video

 International English

Understanding the way the world learns English.

Standards
Test Preparation
Learner Persistence
Content
Multi-level
Emergen...
Realia
Everyday Communication
Context
Consistency
Adequate Yearly Progress

For over thirty years, HEINLE has been developing successful materials for English learners by listening to and working closely with the educators who use them. Understanding the specialized needs of English language teachers and instructors—and the students they teach—has helped us provide products that are innovative, effective, and motivating for students everywhere!

◀ **These great products can be seen throughout this catalog.**

Visit us online at elt.heinle.com

Quick and easy test creation with complete teacher control!

Available with most Heinle programs, Exam*View*® *Assessment Suite* test-generating software allows teachers to create and customize tests in three easy steps.

ExamView®
Assessment Suite

Features

Test Manager

With the Exam*View*® Test Manager you can:

✔ Manage your class roster and assignments

✔ Retrieve results from online tests

✔ Generate detailed and flexible reports

Test Layout Styles

The Exam*View*® Style Gallery now delivers even more test layout styles, allowing you to match state or national standardized test formats.

Point Values

Want to make each True/False worth one point and an essay worth thirty points? No problem! Now you can control how the test is scored.

Now you can:

✔ Customize tests

✔ Scramble test questions

✔ Add questions for any problem-area skill

Step 1.
Name the test or quiz.

Step 2.
Select the book and chapter(s).

Step 3.
Choose the number and type of test items.

Question Type	Available to Select	Number to Select
True/False	6	2
Multiple Choice	5	2
Completion	23	4
Matching	6	6
Short Answer	10	3
Total	50	17

You're done!

3

Technology based on today's needs.

At Heinle we understand the role innovative technology plays in supporting our print materials. Our wide range of online and software-based technology products provide students with more opportunities for engaging, personalized learning—and help teachers make better use of their valuable time by offering an easy, effective way to manage their courses.

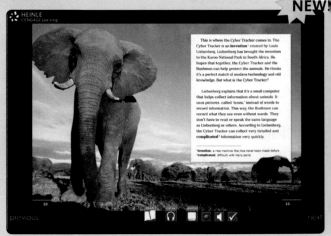

E-Support for Teacher Materials

Teachers can save time by planning lessons online with the Online Lesson Planners for *Stand Out*. This new tool that accompanies our best-selling adult education series, *Stand Out,* provides teachers with complete, customizable lesson plans with three pacing options for every lesson. See p. 38.

E-Books and Online Workbooks for Students

Students can enjoy the convenience of our e-materials, including *Milestones* E-books, *Visions* E-books, *Footprint Reading Library* Online E-Books, and the *World English* Online Video Workbooks. The *Milestones* and *Visions* E-books feature each entire student book online in Flash format. The *Footprint Reading Library* E-Books include all readers, audio, and video in the series as well as comprehension and video activities. The *World English* Online Video Workbooks contain all video clips and automatically graded exercises. See pp. 8, 14, 18, and 42.

Demo activities are available at elt.heinle.com/technology

MilestonesTracker Online Assessment and Remediation System

Provide complete assessment and remediation support! *MilestonesTracker* provides fully automated, interactive online assessment and remediation support for Heinle's new *Milestones* program. This innovative product features customized learning paths for students and powerful school-, district-, and state-level reporting for teachers. See p. 12.

Also See Exam*View*® Assessment Suite p 3.

Grammar Café

Add new life to your grammar class! *Grammar Café* is a revolutionary online grammar course that blends words, sounds, images, and more to heighten your students' understanding of important grammar concepts. Offering both a self-paced student-led mode and an assignment-based instructor-led mode, *Grammar Café* includes grammar lessons, activities, and assessment and is an ideal complement to any grammar or writing text. See p. 58.

Teaching with Video

Video accompanies many of our print materials to add an exciting real-world dimension to learning:

Stand Out Lifeskills Video Program

This program creates engaging opportunities for students to become even more successful learners of English. Eight clips per DVD support and reinforce many of the lifeskill competencies covered in the series. See p. 39.

Video material from National Geographic Digital Media

Three of our best-selling series—the *Footprint Reading Library*, *Reading Explorer,* and *World English*—feature accompanying video material from National Geographic Digital Media. This video material motivates students and aids in visual learning. See pp. 18, 42, and 62.

Each of these programs is powered by ...

MyELT is an Internet-based learning management system designed just for English language teachers and students. Instructors use *MyELT* to assign Heinle online learning content, track student grades, create student progress reports, and more. Students use *MyELT* to complete the online activities, monitor their own learning progress, and review as necessary.

5

CURRICULUM CHART: K – 12

CORE PROGRAMS	READING	GRAMMAR	CONTENT	WRITING	TECHNOLOGY	DICTIONARIES & TEST PREPARATION
PRE-LITERACY						
Milestones Intro p. 8 Visions Intro: Literacy and Language p. 14 Visions Basic p. 14	The Heinle Phonics & Intervention Kit p. 13	Basic Grammar in Action p. 59			MilestonesTracker p. 12 Milestones Independent Practice CD-ROM p. 8 Visions Online Remediation p. 15 Visions Intro/Basic Student CD-ROMs p. 14 The Heinle Picture Dictionary CD-ROM p. 32	The Heinle Picture Dictionary for Children p. 31 The Heinle Picture Dictionary p. 32
BEGINNING						
Milestones Intro p. 8 Milestones A p. 8 Visions Intro: Literacy and Language p. 14 Visions A p. 14	Milestones Intro Reading Library p. 16 The Heinle Phonics & Intervention Kit p. 13 The Heinle Reading Library: Mini-Reader Collection p. 16 Foundations Reading Library p. 20	Grammar Expert Basic p. 59 Grammar in Context Basic p. 52 Grammar Connection 1 p. 54	Gateway to Science p. 34 Reading Explorer 1 p. 62 World English Intro p. 42 US Citizen, Yes, 3/e p. 47	Great Sentences for Great Paragraphs p. 72 Step-by-Step Writing 1 p. 21	MilestonesTracker p. 12 Milestones E-Book p. 8 Milestones Independent Practice CD-ROM p. 8 Visions E-Book p. 14 Visions Online Remediation p. 15 The Heinle Picture Dictionary CD-ROM p. 32 Collins COBUILD Basic Dictionary of American English CD-ROM p. 25 Reading Explorer Student CD-ROM p. 62	The Heinle Picture Dictionary for Children p. 31 Collins COBUILD Basic Dictionary of American English p. 25 The Heinle Picture Dictionary p. 32 Collins COBUILD English/Spanish Glossary p. 30
EARLY-INTERMEDIATE						
Milestones B p. 8 Visions B p. 14 Voices in Literature Bronze p. 22	The Heinle Reading Library p. 16 Facts & Figures, 4/e p. 65 Themes for Today, 2/e p. 66 Stories Worth Reading 1 p. 69 Weaving It Together 1, 3/e p. 74 Strategies for Test-Taking Success: Reading p. 21 Footprint Reading Library p. 18	Visions Grammar Practice A p. 14 Grammar Expert 1 p. 59 Grammar in Context 1, 4/e p. 52 More Grammar Practice 1 p. 59 The New Grammar in Action 1 p. 59 Grammar Connection 2 p. 54	Gateway to Science p. 34 Strategies for Test-Taking Success: Math p. 21 Reading Explorer 2 p. 62 World English 1 p. 42 US Citizen, Yes, 3/e p. 47	Great Paragraphs p. 72 Step-by-Step Writing 1 p. 21 Weaving It Together 1, 3/e p. 74 Strategies for Test-Taking Success: Writing p. 21 Top 10 p. 78	MilestonesTracker p. 12 Milestones E-Book p. 8 Milestones Independent Practice CD-ROM p. 8 Visions E-Book p. 14 Visions Online Remediation p. 15 Visions A – C Student CD-ROM p. 14 The Heinle Picture Dictionary CD-ROM p. 32 Collins COBUILD School Dictionary of American English CD-ROM p. 27 Reading Explorer Student CD-ROM p. 62 Footprint Reading Library Online E-Book p. 18	Collins COBUILD School Dictionary of American English p. 27 Collins COBUILD Basic Dictionary of American English p. 25 Collins COBUILD English/Spanish Student's Dictionary of American English p. 30 The Heinle Picture Dictionary for Children p. 31 The Heinle Picture Dictionary p. 32 Collins COBUILD English/Spanish Glossary p. 30 Strategies for Test-Taking Success p. 21
INTERMEDIATE						
Milestones B p. 8 Visions B p. 14 Voices in Literature Silver p. 22	The Heinle Reading Library p. 16 Thoughts & Notions, 2/e p. 65 Insights for Today, 3/e p. 66 Stories Worth Reading 2 p. 69 Weaving It Together 2, 3/e p. 74 Strategies for Test-Taking Success: Reading p. 21 Footprint Reading Library p. 18 The Classic Graphic Novel Collection p.20	Visions Grammar Practice B p. 14 Grammar Expert 2 p. 59 Grammar in Context 2, 4/e p. 52 More Grammar Practice 2 p. 59 The New Grammar in Action 2 p. 59 Grammar Connection 3 p. 54 Grammar Dimensions p. 50	Gateway to Science p. 34 Strategies for Test-Taking Success: Math p. 21 Reading Explorer 3 p. 62 World English 2 p. 42	From Great Paragraphs to Great Essays p. 72 Step-by-Step Writing 2 p. 21 Weaving It Together 2, 3/e p. 74 Strategies for Test-Taking Success: Writing p. 21 Top 10 p. 78	MilestonesTracker p. 12 Milestones E-Book p. 8 Milestones Independent Practice CD-ROM p. 8 Visions E-Book p. 14 Visions Online Remediation p. 15 Visions A – C Student CD-ROM p. 14 Collins COBUILD School Dictionary of American English CD-ROM p. 27 Reading Explorer Student CD-ROM p. 62 Footprint Reading Library Online E-Book p. 18	Collins COBUILD School Dictionary of American English p. 27 Collins COBUILD English/Spanish Student's Dictionary of American English p. 30 Collins COBUILD English/Spanish Glossary p. 30 Strategies for Test-Taking Success p. 21
HIGH-INTERMEDIATE						
Milestones C p. 8 Visions C p. 14 Voices in Literature Gold p. 22	The Heinle Reading Library p. 16 Cause & Effect, 4/e p. 65 Issues for Today, 3/e p. 66 Weaving It Together 3, 3/e p. 74 Strategies for Test-Taking Success: Reading p. 21 Footprint Reading Library p. 18 The Classic Graphic Novel Collection p.20	Visions Grammar Practice C p. 14 Grammar Expert 3 p. 59 Grammar in Context 3, 4/e p. 52 More Grammar Practice 3 p. 59 The New Grammar in Action 3 p. 59 Grammar Connection 4 p. 54 Grammar Dimensions p. 50	Strategies for Test-Taking Success: Math p. 21 Reading Explorer 4 p. 62 World English 3 p. 42	Great Essays p. 72 Step-by-Step Writing 3 p. 21 Weaving It Together 3, 3/e p. 74 Strategies for Test-Taking Success: Writing p. 21 Top 20, 2/e p. 78	MilestonesTracker p. 12 Milestones E-Book p. 8 Milestones Independent Practice CD-ROM p. 8 Visions E-Book p. 14 Visions Online Remediation p. 15 Visions A – C Student CD-ROM p. 14 Collins COBUILD School Dictionary of American English CD-ROM p. 27 Reading Explorer Student CD-ROM p. 62 Footprint Reading Library Online E-Book p. 18	Collins COBUILD School Dictionary of American English p. 27 Collins COBUILD English/Spanish Student's Dictionary of American English p. 30 Collins COBUILD English/Spanish Glossary p. 30 Strategies for Test-Taking Success p. 21
ADVANCED & TRANSITION						
Milestones C p. 8 Visions C p. 14	The Heinle Reading Library p. 16 Concepts & Comments, 2/e p. 65 Concepts for Today, 2/e p. 66 Topics for Today, 3/e p. 66 Weaving It Together 4, 3/e p. 74 Strategies for Test-Taking Success: Reading p. 21 Footprint Reading Library p. 18	Grammar in Context 3, 4/e p. 52 Grammar Connection 5 p. 54 Grammar Dimensions p. 50	Strategies for Test-Taking Success: Math p. 21	Greater Essays p. 72 Step-by-Step Writing 4 p. 21 Weaving It Together 4, 3/e p. 74 Strategies for Test-Taking Success: Writing p. 21 Top 20, 2/e p. 78	MilestonesTracker p. 12 Milestones E-Book p. 8 Milestones Independent Practice CD-ROM p. 8 Collins COBUILD School Dictionary of American English CD-ROM p. 27 Reading Explorer Student CD-ROM p. 62 Footprint Reading Library E-Book p. 18	Collins COBUILD School Dictionary of American English p. 27 Collins COBUILD English/Spanish Student's Dictionary of American English p. 30 Collins COBUILD English/Spanish Glossary p. 30 Strategies for Test-Taking Success p. 21

LEVEL GUIDE

	Page Number	Pre-Literacy/Newcomer	Low-Beginning	Beginning	Early-Intermediate	Intermediate	High-Intermediate	Advanced	Transition
NEWCOMER/PRE-LITERACY									
Heinle Phonics & Intervention Kit, The **NEW!**	13	•	•						
Milestones: Intro **NEW!**	8	•	•						
New Arrival English	22	•							
Visions: Basic, Intro	14	B,I	B,I						
CORE PROGRAMS									
Go for it!, 2/e: 1, 2, 3, 4	22				1	2	3,4		
Launch into Reading: 1, 2, 3	22					1	2	3	3
Making Connections: 1, 2, 3	22		1	1	2	2	3	3	
Milestones: Intro, A, B, C **NEW!**	8	Intro	I,A	A	B	B	B	C	C
Shooting Stars: 1, 2, 3, 4, 5, 6	22		1,2	1,2	3,4	5,6	5,6		
Visions: Basic, Intro, A, B, C	14	B,I	B,I,A	A	B	B	C	C	C
Voices in Literature: Bronze, Silver, Gold	22		B	S	S	G	G		
CONTENT									
Gateway to Science	34		•	•	•				
World English: Intro, 1, 2, 3 **NEW!**	42		Intro	1	2	2	3		
Reading Explorer: 1, 2, 3, 4 **NEW!**	62			1	2	2	3	4	
Strategies for Test-Taking Success: Writing, Reading, Math	21			W,R,M	W,R,M	W,R,M	W,R,M	W,R,M	
DICTIONARIES									
Collins COBUILD Basic Dictionary of American English **NEW!**	25		•	•					
Collins COBUILD School Dictionary of American English	27				•	•	•		
Heinle's Basic Newbury House Dictionary of American English, 2/e	36		•	•	•				
Heinle's Newbury House Dictionary with Integrated Thesaurus, 4/e	36				•	•	•		
Heinle Picture Dictionary, The	32		•	•	•				
Heinle Picture Dictionary for Children, The	31	•	•	•	•				
SKILLS PRACTICE									
More Grammar Practice: 1, 2, 3	59			1	2	2	3		
Skillbuilder: 1, 2	22			1	2	2	2	2	
Step-by-Step Writing: 1, 2, 3	21			1	1,2	2	3		
Visions Grammar Practice: Intro, A, B, C	14	Intro	I,A	A	B	B	C	C	C
INDEPENDENT READING									
Classic Graphic Novel Collection, The **NEW!**	20						•		
Footprint Reading Library **NEW!**	18				•	•	•	•	•
Foundations Reading Library	20		•	•					
Heinle Reading Library, The: Academic Content Collection	16			•	•	•	•	•	
Biography Collection	16			•	•	•	•	•	
Illustrated Classics Collection	16			•	•	•	•	•	
Milestones Introductory Reading Library **NEW!**	16	•	•						
Mini-Reader Collection	16	•	•						

Steps to student success!

MILESTONES Intro – C

Neil J. Anderson, Jill Korey O'Sullivan, Jennifer Trujillo

LEVEL: Proficiency: pre-literacy to transition
Interest: middle school/high school
Readability (by grade): 0 – 8
  Introductory: 0 – 4
  Level A: 4 – 6
  Level B: 5 – 7
  Level C: 6 – 8

Lexile scores available upon request

Using a unique embedded assessment plan along with a balanced blend of literature and content readings, *Milestones* ensures that students are mastering skills and standards before being introduced to new ones. This consistent, research-based approach will lead your students to success on state exams as well as language acquisition and content knowledge crucial for academic success!

- **Embedded assessment** helps prevent problems with skills and standards before they occur.

- **Academic vocabulary** instruction, practice, and assessment prepare students for success inside and outside the classroom.

- **Differentiated instruction** for every reading selection through adapted readings, point-of-use suggestions, and multi-level questioning strategies ensures access for all students.

- **Complete remediation support** through *MilestonesTracker* and Exam*View*® provides a standards-aligned review, practice activities, and assessments for all unmastered skills and standards.

- **Phonics and intervention strategies** through *The Heinle Phonics & Intervention Kit* offer extensive support for struggling readers.

Ask about our Online Professional Development!

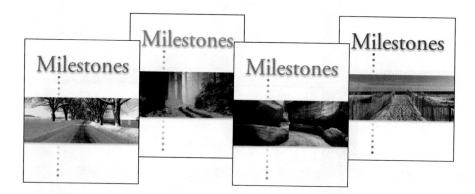

NEW!

Ensure skills and standards mastery!

SERIES COMPONENTS

For students:
Student Editions
NEW! E-Books
Workbooks with Test Preparation
Independent Practice CD-ROMs
Milestones Introductory Reading Library

For teachers:
Teacher's Editions
Assessment Books
Audio Programs
Teacher's Resource CD-ROMs with Exam*View*®
MilestonesTracker Online Assessment and Remediation System
The Heinle Phonics & Intervention Kit
Graphic Reader Blackline Master Companions
ELT Advantage: *Online Professional Development* courses, p. 111 (Ask your Heinle representative for course correlations.)

See pp. 137-138 for Milestones *ISBN/Price listings*

For a guided tour, visit
elt.heinle.com/milestones

Your colleagues say…

"*You have put together a great book!* Milestones *really hits areas that other textbooks do not!*"

—*Tanya M. Castro, ESL Teacher, Pharr–San Juan–Alamo Independent School District, Texas*

"*Your design shines! The activities are very teachable, in a logical order that is approachable to the students and they cover a great deal of information.*"

—*Karen Davis-Ernst, Teacher, Bakersfield, California*

Milestones *has* EVERYTHING *you need to help your students succeed!*

Research-based Learning Strategies

Clearly defined **Objectives** and **Focus Questions** direct student learning.

Academic Vocabulary and **Academic Content** are introduced for support across all disciplines.

Reading Strategies and **Academic Vocabulary** are clearly introduced and practiced to assist in comprehension.

"**Checkpoints**" ensure students are on the road to skills and standards mastery.

"**Reading Checks**" verify comprehension.

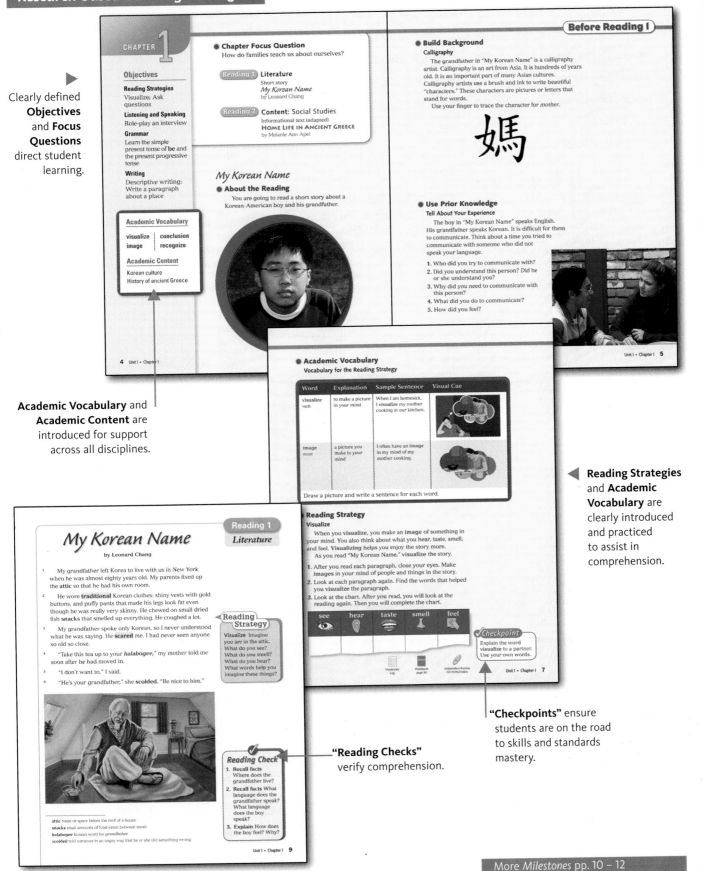

CHAPTER 1

Objectives

Reading Strategies
Visualize; Ask questions

Listening and Speaking
Role-play an interview

Grammar
Learn the simple present tense of **be** and the present progressive tense

Writing
Descriptive writing: Write a paragraph about a place

Academic Vocabulary

| visualize | conclusion |
| image | recognize |

Academic Content

Korean culture
History of ancient Greece

● **Chapter Focus Question**
How do families teach us about ourselves?

Reading 1 **Literature**
Short story
My Korean Name
by Leonard Chang

Reading 2 **Content: Social Studies**
Informational text (adapted)
HOME LIFE IN ANCIENT GREECE
by Melanie Ann Apel

My Korean Name
● **About the Reading**
You are going to read a short story about a Korean-American boy and his grandfather.

4 Unit 1 • Chapter 1

Before Reading 1

● **Build Background**
Calligraphy
The grandfather in "My Korean Name" is a calligraphy artist. Calligraphy is an art from Asia. It is hundreds of years old. It is an important part of many Asian cultures. Calligraphy artists use a brush and ink to write beautiful "characters." These characters are pictures or letters that stand for words.
Use your finger to trace the character for *mother*.

媽

● **Use Prior Knowledge**
Tell About Your Experience
The boy in "My Korean Name" speaks English. His grandfather speaks Korean. It is difficult for them to communicate. Think about a time you tried to communicate with someone who did not speak your language.
1. Who did you try to communicate with?
2. Did you understand this person? Did he or she understand you?
3. Why did you need to communicate with this person?
4. What did you do to communicate?
5. How did you feel?

Unit 1 • Chapter 1 5

● **Academic Vocabulary**
Vocabulary for the Reading Strategy

Word	Explanation	Sample Sentence	Visual Cue
visualize *verb*	to make a picture in your mind	When I am homesick, I visualize my mother cooking in our kitchen.	
image *noun*	a picture you make in your mind	I often have an image in my mind of my mother cooking.	

Draw a picture and write a sentence for each word.

● **Reading Strategy**
Visualize
When you **visualize**, you make an **image** of something in your mind. You also think about what you hear, taste, smell, and feel. Visualizing helps you enjoy the story more.
As you read "My Korean Name," visualize the story.
1. After you read each paragraph, close your eyes. Make images in your mind of people and things in the story.
2. Look at each paragraph again. Find the words that helped you visualize the paragraph.
3. Look at the chart. After you read, you will look at the reading again. Then you will complete the chart.

see	hear	taste	smell	feel

✓**Checkpoint**
Explain the word **visualize** to a partner. Use your own words.

Vocabulary Log

Workbook page 30

Independent Practice CD-ROM/Online

Unit 1 • Chapter 1 7

My Korean Name

by Leonard Chang

Reading 1
Literature

1 My grandfather left Korea to live with us in New York when he was almost eighty years old. My parents fixed up the **attic** so that he had his own room.

2 He wore **traditional** Korean clothes: shiny vests with gold buttons, and puffy pants that made his legs look fat even though he was really very skinny. He chewed on small dried fish **snacks** that smelled up everything. He coughed a lot.

3 My grandfather spoke only Korean, so I never understood what he was saying. He **scared** me. I had never seen anyone so old so close.

4 "Take this tea up to your *halabogee*," my mother told me soon after he had moved in.

5 "I don't want to," I said.

6 "He's your grandfather," she **scolded**. "Be nice to him."

Reading Strategy
Visualize Imagine you are in the attic. What do you see? What do you smell? What do you hear? What words help you imagine these things?

✓**Reading Check**
1. **Recall facts** Where does the grandfather live?
2. **Recall facts** What language does the grandfather speak? What language does the boy speak?
3. **Explain** How does the boy feel? Why?

attic room or space below the roof of a house
snacks small amounts of food eaten between meals
halabogee Korean word for *grandfather*
scolded told someone in an angry way that he or she did something wrong

Unit 1 • Chapter 1 9

More *Milestones* pp. 10 – 12

Milestones *has* EVERYTHING *you need to help your students succeed!*

Outstanding Vocabulary Support

Milestones includes three opportunities for vocabulary instruction, practice, and assessment in EVERY chapter.

✔ **Academic Vocabulary**—for cross-curricular support

✔ **Vocabulary From the Reading**—for reading comprehension

✔ **Vocabulary Development**—for strategies inside and outside of the classroom

Introduce

Academic Vocabulary

| visualize | conclusion |
| image | recognize |

Academic Content

Korean culture
History of ancient Greece

For NEW vocabulary teaching strategies and assessment materials from Dr. Robert Marzano, see page 112-113.

Exclusive to
Milestones:
Dr. Robert Marzano

"...one of the most crucial services that teachers can provide, particularly for students who do not come from academically advantaged backgrounds, is systematic instruction in important academic terms."

—*Robert J. Marzano*
(Milestones *Vocabulary Advisor*)
and Debra J. Pickering, 2005

Instruct

● **Academic Vocabulary**
Vocabulary for the Reading Strategy

Word	Explanation	Sample Sentence	Visual Cue
visualize *verb*	to make a picture in your mind	When I am homesick, I **visualize** my mother cooking in our kitchen.	
image *noun*	a picture you make in your mind	I often have an **image** in my mind of my mother cooking.	

Draw a picture and write a sentence for each word.

Every vocabulary lesson incorporates Dr. Marzano's six-step process for teaching new vocabulary.

1. Provide a description, explanation, or example of a new term.

2. Ask students to restate the description, explanation, or example in their own words.

3. Ask students to construct a picture, symbol, or graphic representing the term.

4. Engage students periodically in activities that help them add to their knowledge of the terms in their notebooks.

5. Periodically ask students to discuss the terms with one another.

6. Involve students periodically in games that allow them to play with terms.

Practice

3. Look at the chart. After you read, you will look at the reading again. Then you will complete the chart.

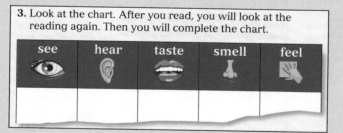

see	hear	taste	smell	feel

Assess

Academic Vocabulary	What do these academic vocabulary words mean? • **image, visualize** • **conclusion, recognize**	7 14

Embedded Assessment

Milestones provides explicit and systematic instruction to ensure proficiency and mastery of skills and standards with numerous opportunities to monitor progress.

Here's how it works:

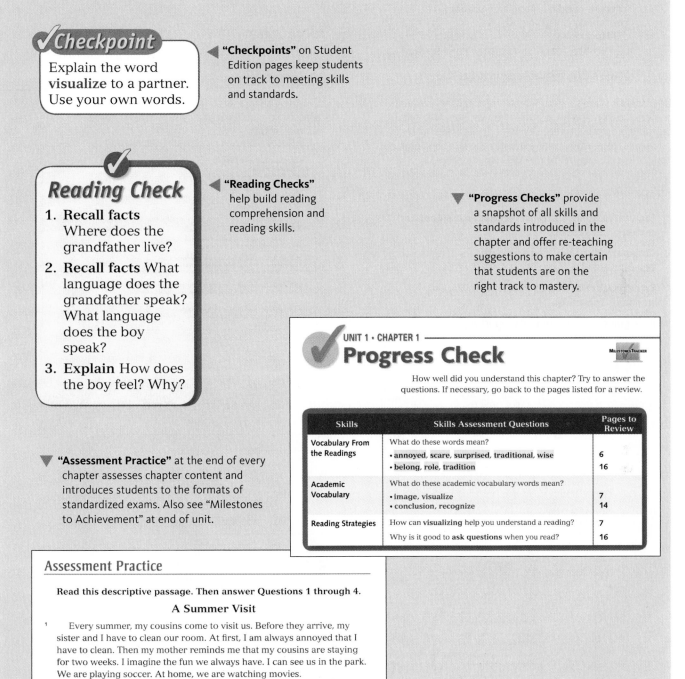

✓ Checkpoint

Explain the word **visualize** to a partner. Use your own words.

"Checkpoints" on Student Edition pages keep students on track to meeting skills and standards.

✓ Reading Check

1. **Recall facts** Where does the grandfather live?

2. **Recall facts** What language does the grandfather speak? What language does the boy speak?

3. **Explain** How does the boy feel? Why?

"Reading Checks" help build reading comprehension and reading skills.

"Progress Checks" provide a snapshot of all skills and standards introduced in the chapter and offer re-teaching suggestions to make certain that students are on the right track to mastery.

UNIT 1 · CHAPTER 1

✓ Progress Check

MILESTONES TRACKER

How well did you understand this chapter? Try to answer the questions. If necessary, go back to the pages listed for a review.

Skills	Skills Assessment Questions	Pages to Review
Vocabulary From the Readings	What do these words mean?	
	• annoyed, scare, surprised, traditional, wise	6
	• belong, role, tradition	16
Academic Vocabulary	What do these academic vocabulary words mean?	
	• image, visualize	7
	• conclusion, recognize	14
Reading Strategies	How can **visualizing** help you understand a reading?	7
	Why is it good to **ask questions** when you read?	16

"Assessment Practice" at the end of every chapter assesses chapter content and introduces students to the formats of standardized exams. Also see "Milestones to Achievement" at end of unit.

Assessment Practice

Read this descriptive passage. Then answer Questions 1 through 4.

A Summer Visit

1   Every summer, my cousins come to visit us. Before they arrive, my sister and I have to clean our room. At first, I am always annoyed that I have to clean. Then my mother reminds me that my cousins are staying for two weeks. I imagine the fun we always have. I can see us in the park. We are playing soccer. At home, we are watching movies.

2   This year, my cousins arrive in the afternoon on the train. When Maya gets off the train, I am surprised to see how tall she is. She is one year younger than me, but now she is a lot taller. I feel short and a little shy as we walk home. When we arrive at our apartment, we first start cooking tamales,

More *Milestones* p. 12

Complete assessment and remediation support!

MILESTONESTRACKER

Online Assessment and Remediation System

NEW!

MILESTONESTRACKER

LEVEL: Proficiency: pre-literacy to transition
Interest: middle school/high school
Readability (by grade): 0 – 8

Introductory: 0 – 4
Level A: 4 – 6

Level B: 5 – 7
Level C: 6 – 8

Lexile scores available upon request

MilestonesTracker is a groundbreaking online assessment and remediation system for use with Heinle's new *Milestones* learning program. Powered by *MyELT*, *MilestonesTracker* evaluates, re-teaches, and reinforces the skills and concepts taught in each chapter of the *Milestones* textbooks.

MilestonesTracker offers:

- Fully automated, interactive, **online assessment and remediation support**

- **Customized student learning paths** for all unmastered skills and standards

- **Extra practice activities** to enhance skills and standards knowledge

- **At-a-glance state standards** reporting for teachers

Here's how it works:

For the teacher:

Teachers can generate individual student or full classroom standards and skills mastery reports, as well as district level reports.

Performance Summary
Mrs. Juanita Sanchez
Washington High School

ESOL 1   **Total Students:** 18

Term: Fall 07

Learning Objective	# Students Proficient	Class Average
R.4.1.3 Use knowledge of root words to determine the meaning of unknown words within a passage.	18	87.8%
R.4.2.1 Identify structural patterns found in informational text (e.g., compare and contrast, cause and effect, sequential or chronological order, proposition and support) to strengthen comprehension.	17	86.7%
R.4.2.2 Use appropriate strategies when reading for different purposes (e.g., full comprehension, location of information, personal enjoyment).	14	83.9%
W.4.1.3 Identify and use regular and irregular verbs, adverbs, prepositions, and coordinating conjunctions in writing and speaking.	17	86.7%

For the student:

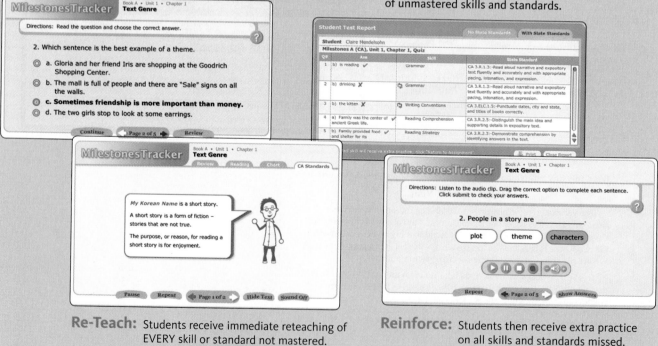

Assess: Students take a test online.

Evaluate: Students see an instant graded report and a list of unmastered skills and standards.

Re-Teach: Students receive immediate reteaching of EVERY skill or standard not mastered.

Reinforce: Students then receive extra practice on all skills and standards missed.

Outstanding phonics and language development support!

THE HEINLE PHONICS & INTERVENTION KIT

LEVEL: Proficiency: pre-literacy to low-beginning
Interest: middle school/high school
Readability (by grade): 0 – 3

Lexile scores available upon request

The Heinle Phonics & Intervention Kit provides extensive phonics and phonemic awareness support for pre-literacy and newcomer students as well as for struggling readers. The kit can be used as a stand-alone program or as a supplement to other Heinle programs for differentiated instruction in multi-level classrooms.

- The kit offers **extensive support and strategies** for struggling readers.

- **66 Decodable Readers** with 9,000 words of decodable text provide instruction and practice of all sounds in the English language.

- **Four-color Transparencies** represent visual interpretations of each sound.

- A **Teacher's Guide** includes pacing options, practice activities, and assessments for everything taught in the kit.

- The **Audio Program** features support of every sound and word introduced and practiced on the Transparencies.

NEW!

The Heinle Phonics & Intervention Kit
- Extensive support for struggling readers
- Teacher's Guide
- Full-color Transparencies
- Audio Program
- 66 Decodable Readers for every sound in the English language

Based on current and confirmed research!

COMPONENTS
66 Decodable Readers
Transparencies
Teacher's Guide
Audio Program

See p. 132 for The Heinle Phonics & Intervention Kit *ISBN/Price listings*

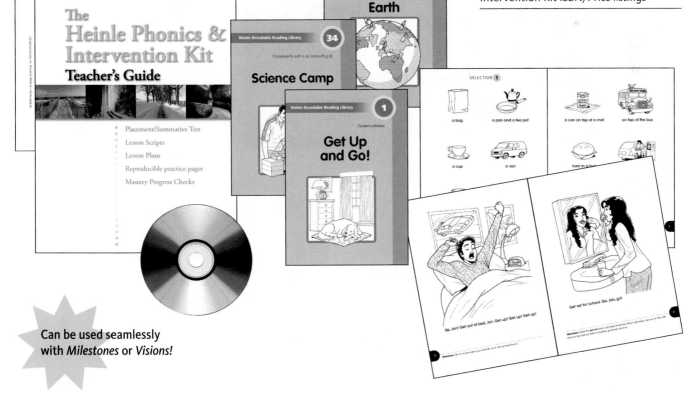

Can be used seamlessly with *Milestones* or *Visions!*

From pre-literacy to transition, **Visions** *has it all!*

VISIONS Intro – C

Literacy, Language, Literature, Content

Mary Lou McCloskey, Lydia Stack, Jill Korey O'Sullivan, Christy M. Newman

LEVEL: Proficiency: pre-literacy to transition
Interest: elementary/middle/high school
Reading (by grade): 0 – 6

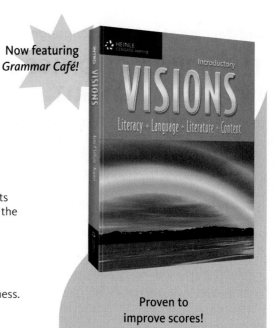

Now featuring *Grammar Café!*

Proven to improve scores!

Visions, Heinle's best-selling language development and reading program, supports students from pre-literacy through transition into mainstream classrooms. Using the Into, Through, Beyond methodology (shown on the following page), *Visions* helps guide your students through every lesson to ensure skills development and academic success!

- **Intro level** for non-schooled and low-beginning students provides systematic language development, as well as instruction in phonics and phonemic awareness.

- **High-interest, level appropriate literature and content readings** motivate students.

- **Scaffolding throughout all four books** follows a three-pronged approach to reading and meeting the standards: Into, Through, and Beyond.

- **Writing activities** reinforce and recycle strategic skills.

- **Assessment CD-ROMs with Exam***View*® test-generating software are aligned with state standards and state exams—and help teachers teach for remediation.

- **Staff Development Handbook and Video** allow for easy program implementation.

- **Student CD-ROMs** offer extra, interactive skills practice.

Correlated to state standards!

SERIES COMPONENTS

For students:
Student Editions
NEW! E-Books
Activity Books
Student Handbook
Grammar Practice Books
Grammar Café, see p. 58
The Heinle Reading Library, see p. 16
Student CD-ROMs

For teachers:
Teacher Editions
Teacher Resource Books
Teacher Resource CD-ROM
Assessment CD-ROMs with Exam*View*®
Assessment Programs
Audio CDs
NEW! Remediation Tool
Transparencies
Staff Development Video
CNN® Video (DVD or VHS)
Staff Development Handbook
Placement Test
NEW! Online In-service
Grammar Practice Answer Keys
ELT Advantage: *Online Professional Development* courses, p. 111
(Ask your Heinle representative for course correlations.)

See pp. 142-143 for Visions *ISBN/Price listings*

elt.heinle.com/visions

Need a shorter option? Choose *Visions Basic.*

Caroline Linse, Jane A. Yedlin

Ideal for:
✔ intensive programs
✔ remediation
✔ summer school
✔ tutoring

Into: Clearly defined objectives and background-building activities help students access the reading.

Through: Point-of-use reading strategies help build reading fluency and comprehension.

Beyond: Word study, grammar, writing, and cross-content activities reinforce and extend skills introduced through the readings.

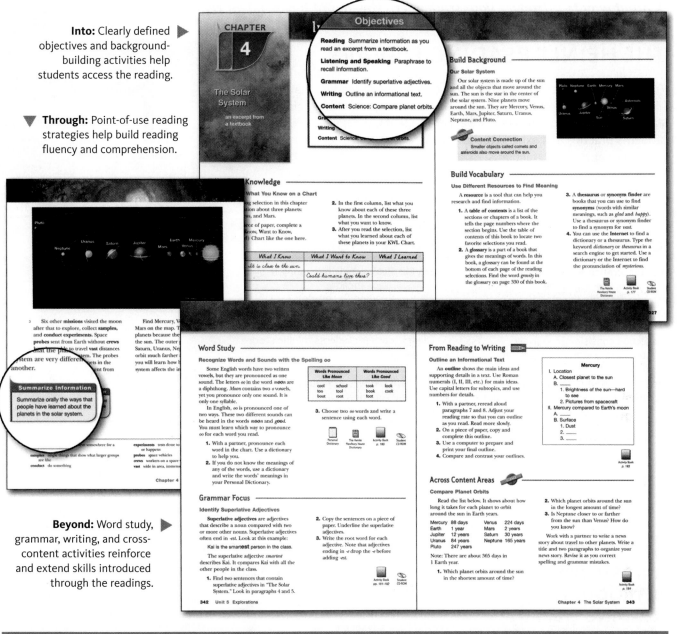

Visions *offers online solutions for teachers and students!*

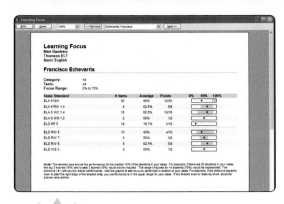

For virtual tours of the *Visions Remediation Tool* and *Visions Online In-Service* visit
elt.heinle.com/visions

NEW!

Visions Remediation Tool offers a better—and easier—way to assess skills and standards mastery and provide instant remediation.

Visions Online In-Service trains new and seasoned teachers to use the complete *Visions* program effectively, including how to integrate each component.

A great way to introduce your students to the joys of independent reading!

THE HEINLE READING LIBRARY

The Heinle Reading Library includes five collections of readers that feature high-interest works of fiction, non-fiction, and adapted literary classics. Written for newcomer through advanced students, the collection helps students practice and expand reading skills, develop fluency, and meet independent reading standards.

The Heinle Reading Library:

MINI-READER COLLECTION

LEVEL: Proficiency: newcomer to
low-beginning
Reading (by grade): 1 – 3

The Heinle Reading Library: Mini-Reader Collection consists of ten lively, contemporary stories designed for students to practice sounds, letters, grammar, and vocabulary in new contexts. Features include color photos on every page, built-in worksheets, and audio recordings of every reader. Linked by level to *Visions Intro*.

Readers
Audio CDs

The Heinle Reading Library: **NEW!**

MILESTONES INTRODUCTORY READING LIBRARY

LEVEL: Proficiency: newcomer to
low-beginning
Reading (by grade): 1 – 3

The *Milestones Introductory Reading Library* contains 21 leveled readers correlated to the themes in *Milestones Introductory*. These colorful, high-interest, low-level readers are a perfect compliment to *Milestones Introductory*. Independent reading support aids reading fluency while full-color illustrations on each page increase reading comprehension.

Readers

Lexile scores available upon request.

The Heinle Reading Library:

BIOGRAPHY COLLECTION

LEVEL: Proficiency: beginning to
advanced
Reading (by grade): 3 – 7

This latest addition to *The Heinle Reading Library* teaches students the life stories of great American heroes while enhancing reading skills. This important foundation offers a unique approach to teaching American culture while expanding fluency.

Readers
Audio CDs

The Heinle Reading Library:

ACADEMIC CONTENT COLLECTION

LEVEL: Proficiency: beginning to
advanced
Reading (by grade): 3 – 7

Featuring full color photos and organizational aids such as diagrams, graphs, and maps, the *Academic Content Collection* helps students master non-fiction reading. It includes three levels of expository readers designed to introduce academic language for independent, extensive reading. The readers are linked by level to *Visions A, B,* and *C* and are supported by Workbooks, Audio CDs, and a Teacher Guide.

Readers
Workbooks
Audio CDs
Teacher Guide with reproducible Masters

The Heinle Reading Library:

ILLUSTRATED CLASSICS COLLECTION

LEVEL: Proficiency: beginning to
advanced
Reading (by grade): 3 – 7

Popular with students and teachers, *The Heinle Reading Library: Illustrated Classics Collection* helps English language learners access the world's greatest literature through three leveled collections of adapted literary classics. Each book helps students practice and expand reading skills, develop fluency, and meet independent reading standards.

- **Adapted classic literature** gives students opportunities for independent, extensive reading.

- **Full-page illustrations** on every other page reinforce the facing page narrative.

- **Linked by level to *Visions* and *Milestones,*** each reader can also be used as a stand-alone product.

- **Workbooks and Audio CDs** help build comprehension and practice skills.

Readers
Workbooks
Audio CDs
Teacher Guide

The Heinle Reading Library by level

Newcomer/ Low-beginning	Level A (Beginning/Early-intermediate)	Level B (Intermediate)	Level C (Early-advanced)

Mini-Reader Collection

First Day of School

Here is My Family

After School Work

Teenagers in the Morning

Saturday Afternoon

Friends at Lunch

Working at the Supermarket

Career Day at School

Holiday Scrapbook

Joel's Senior Yearbook

Milestones Introductory Reading Library

Bad Dog? Good Dog!

Go Jimmy Go!

Goodbye, Hello!

I Always Win!

My Mom, The Movie Star

No, You Can't!

Old Boat, New Boat

Quiz Night

Singer Wanted

SK8 for Jake

Slam Dunk for Mark

The Bear's Mouth

The Cave

The Golden Monkey

The New Guitar

The Shipwreck

The Tickets

Think Daniela!

Trouble at the Zoo

Where's Lorena?

Who's Best?

Biography Collection

Level A
Benjamin Franklin
Clara Barton

Level B
Eleanor Roosevelt
Jackie Robinson

Level C
Martin Luther King, Jr.
George Washington
Babe Ruth

Academic Content Collection

Level A
The Pilgrims
Rain Forests
The Solar System
The Hopi
How Do I Become a Firefighter?
Frida Kahlo

Level B
Arctic
The Oregon Trail
Space Travel
Anne Frank
Alexander Graham Bell
Photosynthesis

Level C
Dolphins
Life in a Cave
The Navajo
The Statue of Liberty
Tony Hawk
Energy

Illustrated Classics Collection

Level A
The Legend of Sleepy Hollow
Aesop's Fables
The Strange Case of Dr. Jekyll and Mr. Hyde
The Red Badge of Courage
The Invisible Man
Moby Dick
Dracula
The Phantom of the Opera
Tales of Mystery and Terror
The Three Musketeers
The Time Machine
The Adventures of Tom Sawyer
The Adventures of Huckleberry Finn
Sherlock Holmes and the Case of the Hounds of the Baskervilles
Pollyanna
Jane Eyre

Level B
Treasure Island
David Copperfield
Ivanhoe
Journey to the Center of the Earth
Pride and Prejudice
The Call of the Wild
Oliver Twist
Anne of Green Gables
The Man in the Iron Mask
Heidi
The Secret Garden
The Mutiny on the HMS Bounty
King Arthur and the Knights of the Round Table
The House of the Seven Gables
The Prince and the Pauper
The Merry Adventures of Robin Hood

Level C
The Adventures of Sherlock Holmes
The Swiss Family Robinson
20,000 Leagues Under the Sea
Black Beauty
Little Women
A Christmas Carol
The Count of Monte Cristo
The Wind in the Willows
Great Expectations
White Fang
Rebecca of Sunnybrook Farm
The War of the Worlds
A Little Princess
Gulliver's Travels
The Hunchback of Notre Dame
A Tale of Two Cities
Frankenstein

Sold in 5-Packs, 25-Packs, and complete Library Sets, ask your Heinle representative for other packaging options.

See pp. 132-135 for The Heinle Reading Library *ISBN/Price listings*

Read, Listen, and Watch over 100 titles!

FOOTPRINT READING LIBRARY

Robert Waring, *Series Editor*

LEVEL: early-intermediate to transition

The *Footprint Reading Library* is a unique collection of graded content readers designed to help students develop language and reading skills. Featuring audio recordings of each reader, as well as video from National Geographic Digital Media, students can read, listen, and watch for full skills support.

NEW!

Featuring video from National Geographic Digital Media!

- **Photographs and organizational aids** such as diagrams, graphs, tables, maps, and charts assist students in reading non-fiction and expository readings.

- **Activities integrated into each reader** aid comprehension and help apply information.

- **"After You Read"** and **assessment reading** sections at end of each book assess comprehension and recycle key vocabulary and concepts.

- **Audio recordings of EVERY reader** help develop pronunciation, intonation, and listening skills.

- **Video from National Geographic Digital Media** motivates students and aids in visual learning.

- **NEW! Online E-books for every** *Footprint* **reader** feature embedded video from National Geographic Digital Media, vocabulary and pronunciation activities, integrated comprehension checkpoints, audio support, and answer keys to make comprehension fun.

For a complete list of titles by theme, see pp. 126-129.

This series is grouped by vocabulary level into five themes for easy curriculum integration:

- ✓ Incredible Animals
- ✓ Fascinating Places
- ✓ Remarkable People
- ✓ Exciting Activities
- ✓ Amazing Science

SERIES COMPONENTS

Readers
Audio CDs
DVDs (with videos from National Geographic Digital Media)
NEW! Online E-Books
Teacher's Manuals
Assessment CD-ROMs with Exam*View*®

Sold in 5-Packs, 25-Packs, and complete Library Sets

See pp. 126-129 for Footprint Reading Library *pricing. Contact your Heinle representative for other packaging options.*

For a guided tour, visit **elt.heinle.com/footprint**

Words to Know

This story is set in the United States (U.S.). It happens in the Columbia River Gorge, in the states of Oregon and Washington.

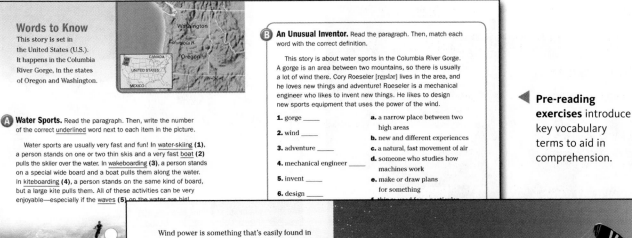

A **Water Sports.** Read the paragraph. Then, write the number of the correct underlined word next to each item in the picture.

Water sports are usually very fast and fun! In water-skiing **(1)**, a person stands on one or two thin skis and a very fast boat **(2)** pulls the skier over the water. In wakeboarding **(3)**, a person stands on a special wide board and a boat pulls them along the water. In kiteboarding **(4)**, a person stands on the same kind of board, but a large kite pulls them. All of these activities can be very enjoyable—especially if the waves **(5)** on the water are big!

B **An Unusual Inventor.** Read the paragraph. Then, match each word with the correct definition.

This story is about water sports in the Columbia River Gorge. A gorge is an area between two mountains, so there is usually a lot of wind there. Cory Roeseler [reːslər] lives in the area, and he loves new things and adventure! Roeseler is a mechanical engineer who likes to invent new things. He likes to design new sports equipment that uses the power of the wind.

1. gorge _____
2. wind _____
3. adventure _____
4. mechanical engineer _____
5. invent _____
6. design _____

a. a narrow place between two high areas
b. new and different experiences
c. a natural, fast movement of air
d. someone who studies how machines work
e. make or draw plans for something

◀ **Pre-reading exercises** introduce key vocabulary terms to aid in comprehension.

Wind power is something that's easily found in the gorge which divides Washington and Oregon. That makes the Columbia River Gorge one of the best places in the world to kiteboard. However, for inventor Cory Roeseler, the gorge is more than just a place to have fun; it's a place where he can test his new inventions.

Roeseler has always loved water sports. When he was a teenager, he was the first person to 'test pilot,' or try out, the sport of kite-skiing. Usually, people water-ski behind a boat. However, Roeseler decided to use wind power to ski behind a kite. It worked! Later, he became a mechanical engineer. Then, in the 1990s, he invented and designed a lot of water sports equipment. Eventually, he became famous in the area of water sports.

Sequence the Events

What is the correct order of the events? Write numbers.

_____ invented water sports equipment

_____ became famous

_____ was a test pilot for kite-skiing

_____ became mechanical engineer

After You Read

1. On page 4, how does Cory Roeseler feel about the wind?
   A. uncomfortable
   B. happy
   C. unsure
   D. nervous

2. In paragraph 1 on page 7, the word 'experience' means:
   A. fly
   B. use
   C. do
   D. be

3. How does the kite help Roeseler?
   A. It catches the wind and provides lift.
   B. He uses it to pull his boat.
   C. It keeps him warm.
   D. It reduces his speed.

▲ **"After You Read"** assessment questions reinforce understanding of vocabulary and content.

▲ **Online E-books** of each reader feature point-of-use vocabulary activities and embedded video from National Geographic Digital Media.

NEW!

THE CLASSIC GRAPHIC NOVEL COLLECTION

Brigit Viney

LEVEL: intermediate

This revolutionary new series of graphic novels re-tells classic literature for learners of English. The fresh blend of accessible storytelling and captivating artwork ensures that students will want to return to these stories time and again.

- Graded at the intermediate level, the series is great for mainstream **literature preparation.**

- An **Audio CD** for each text offers full recordings of the story featuring professional actors and sound effects.

- Perfect for **Reader's Theater!**

Readers
Teacher's Manuals
Workbooks
Audio CDs

Sold in 5-Packs and 25-Packs

elt.heinle.com/classicalcomics

The Classic Graphic Novel Collection

Frankenstein
Great Expectations
Henry V
Macbeth
Jane Eyre

FOUNDATIONS READING LIBRARY

Robert Waring, Maurice Jamall

LEVEL: low-beginning to beginning

Foundations Reading Library is a series of colorful, high-interest, low-level readers written for grades 6 – 12. Carefully sequenced vocabulary and grammar are presented contextually through the adventures of a group of teens living in a small U.S. town.

- **Seven levels, with six readers per level,** are graded by vocabulary words.

- **Full-color illustrations** on each page support comprehension.

- **Adventure, drama, detective, and romance stories** capture teens' interest.

- **Systematic recycling** and extension of vocabulary, phrases, and expressions are found throughout each reader and across the collection.

- **Carefully-controlled grammar** points cover those most typically taught at the low level.

- **Opportunities for reading practice** and building reading fluency are provided.

- **Activity Books** (including tests), **Lesson Planners,** and an **Audio Program** for each level are available.

Readers (single titles or collection volumes)
Activity Books
Audio CDs
Lesson Planners
Level Collection Volumes

Sold in 5-Packs, 25-Packs and complete Library Sets

Level collections containing all six stories in one volume are also available! See pp. 129-130 for details.

STRATEGIES FOR TEST-TAKING SUCCESS: WRITING, READING, MATH

Christy M. Newman, Judith Diamond

LEVEL: Proficiency: early-intermediate to transition
Reading (by grade): 3 – 6

Strategies for Test-Taking Success is an innovative test preparation series designed to help all students develop effective test-taking skills and strategies, regardless of their English language proficiency or academic level. Each book in the *Strategies* series focuses on a major testing discipline.

- Effective multi-level instruction provides **scaffolding for foundational skills** while teaching and practicing advanced ones.

- **Accessible language** with concrete examples and practical activities support and clarify concepts, while higher order thinking skills are developed.

- Preparation materials represent a **matrix of skills and standards** common to all secondary standardized tests.

- **Pretest** helps teachers evaluate students' current skills and record areas of need on a Skill Chart.

- **"Keys to Understanding"** highlights signal words, questions, and special test-taking pointers.

- After each lesson, a **practice section reviews skills,** progressing from controlled and supported to productive and open-ended.

- **Review Tests** and **two Cumulative Practice Tests** simulate real tests and real test questions.

- **ExamView® test-generating software** allows teachers to create tests in minutes, giving students additional practice opportunities.

- *Strategies for Test-Taking Success* can be used to **assess students' mastery of content standards,** and for **re-teaching and remediation.**

Student Editions
Strategies for Test-Taking Success series: Assessment CD-ROM with ExamView®

STEP-BY-STEP WRITING 1 – 3

A Standards-Based Approach

Linda Lonon Blanton

LEVEL: beginning to high-intermediate

Step-by-Step Writing: A Standards-Based Approach is a three-level series uniquely designed to cover the same genres across all levels. It covers standards-based writing genres, conventions, and organizational strategies. Through a variety of activities, students progress from words to sentences to paragraphs, developing the skills and confidence required for successful composition writing and improved test scores.

- **Standards-based writing and test-taking skills** are taught through a step-by-step approach with the use of writing models, grammar activities, graphic organizers, revision/editing practice, checklists, and timed writings.

- **A comprehensive approach to writing** allows teachers to handle a range of ability and proficiency levels while exploring various genres including narrative, expository, technical, persuasive, response to literature, and letters and correspondence.

- **Teacher's Guide** contains differentiated instruction strategies, additional writing prompts, graphic organizers, and answer keys.

- **Technology skills** are integrated through online research activities and word processing skills.

- **Assessment CD-ROM featuring ExamView®** helps teachers create customizable, standards-aligned exams.

Student Editions
Teacher's Guides
Assessment CD-ROMs with ExamView®

VOICES IN LITERATURE Bronze, Silver, Gold

Mary Lou McCloskey, Lydia Stack

LEVEL: Proficiency: beginning to advanced
Interest: middle/high school
Reading (by grade): 4 – 8

Voices in Literature integrates authentic literature and fine art illustrations with rich, active, and interactive classroom learning experiences. English learners will develop listening, speaking, reading, and writing abilities for use in their daily lives and in grade-level academic work.

- **Student texts feature rich, engaging literature** in a broad range of themes.

- **Skillbuilders** provide support in literacy, phonics, grammar, usage, mechanics, and writing with plenty of opportunities for practice.

- **Student Journals** offer expanded writing opportunities, enhanced lesson activities, and exciting end-of-selection projects to ensure that multiple skills are addressed.

- **Teacher's Guides** provide standards and skills at-a-glance charts, multi-level teaching options, and more.

- **Assessment Package** offers summative and cumulative assessment instruments with end-of-unit and final tests.

For students:
Student Editions
Skillbuilders
Student Audio Tapes
For teachers:
Teacher's Guides
Student Journals with Activity Masters
Assessments
Skillbuilder Listening & Speaking Audio Tapes
Teacher's Guide to Using the Heinle ESL/ELD Program

For integrated skills instruction incorporating content areas,
see *Making Connections*, p. 22.

BUILDING BRIDGES 1 – 3
Content and Learning Strategies
for ESL

**Anna Uhl Chamot,
J. Michael O'Malley, Lisa Küpper**
LEVEL: beginning to advanced

GO FOR IT! 1 – 4
Second Edition

David Nunan
LEVEL: beginning to
intermediate

LAUNCH INTO READING 1 – 3
LEVEL: intermediate to transition

MAKING CONNECTIONS 1 – 3
An Integrated Approach
to Learning English

**Mary Lou McCloskey, Lydia Stack,
Carolyn Kessler, Linda Lee,
Mary Ellen Quinn,
Jean Bernard-Johnston**
LEVEL: literacy to advanced

NEW ARRIVAL ENGLISH
Literacy and School Orientation

Jane Yedlin, Caroline Linse
LEVEL: literacy/newcomer

SHOOTING STARS 1 – 6
LEVEL: low-beginning to
high-intermediate

LEVEL GUIDE

AMERICAN ENGLISH DICTIONARIES	PAGE NUMBER	LOW-BEGINNING	BEGINNING	HIGH-BEGINNING	LOW-INTERMEDIATE	INTERMEDIATE	HIGH-INTERMEDIATE	ADVANCED
Collins COBUILD Advanced Dictionary of American English	29							•
Collins COBUILD Advanced Dictionary of American English, English/Japanese	30						•	•
Collins COBUILD Advanced Dictionary of American English, English/Korean	30						•	•
Collins COBUILD Basic Dictionary of American English NEW!	25		•	•	•			
Collins COBUILD English/Español Glossary	30				•	•	•	
Collins COBUILD English/Spanish Student's Dictionary of American English	30				•	•	•	
Collins COBUILD Intermediate Dictionary of American English	28				•	•	•	
Collins COBUILD School Dictionary of American English	27				•	•	•	
Collins Escolar *PLUS* Dictionary, 2/e	30				•	•	•	
Gateway to Science	34		•	•	•	•		
Heinle Picture Dictionary, The	32	•	•	•	•			
Heinle Picture Dictionary for Children, The	31	•	•	•	•			
Heinle's Basic Newbury House Dictionary of American English, 2/e	36	•	•	•	•			
Heinle's Newbury House Dictionary of American English with Integrated Thesaurus, 4/e	36				•	•	•	

COLLINS COBUILD DICTIONARIES
of American English

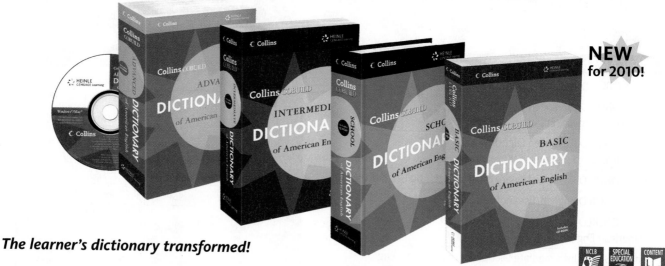

NEW for 2010!

The learner's dictionary transformed!

LEVEL: beginning to advanced

More than simple reference books, the Collins COBUILD dictionaries are pedagogically rich, engaging, full-color, language learning tools. While any good learner's dictionary will help a student understand the meaning of a word, the COBUILD dictionaries go beyond by showing students how to use the word appropriately.

> **for|mu|la** /fɔrmyələ/ (**formulae** /fɔrmyəli/ or **formulas**) **1** N-COUNT A **formula** is a plan that is invented in order to deal with a particular problem. ❏ …*a formula for peace.* **2** N-COUNT A **formula** is a group of letters, numbers, or other symbols which represents a scientific or mathematical rule. ❏ *This mathematical formula describes the distances of the planets from the Sun.* **3** N-COUNT In science, the **formula** for a substance tells you what amounts of other substances are needed in order to make that substance. ❏ *They have the same chemical formula.* [from Latin]

◀ Full-sentence definitions help learners use words correctly.

Offering a complete student resource package, each dictionary contains:

- ✔ Unparalleled vocabulary support
- ✔ Outstanding reference tools
- ✔ Full-sentence definitions
- ✔ Interactive CD-ROM

Search entire contents of dictionary with sound and activities on the Interactive CD-ROM. ▶

Your colleagues say...

"These dictionaries should be in every classroom in the country. Then the task of looking up word meanings would not be so odious, frustrating, and nonproductive... The entries in COBUILD really communicate a word's meaning—rather than giving you some telegraphic bits to try to put together, or defining a word with a different form of the same word."

—*Margaret McKeown, University of Pittsburgh*

☼ Collins | COBUILD

The Bank of English™ is the original and most current computerized corpus of authentic American English. This robust research tool was used to create each definition. All sample sentences are drawn from the rich selection that the corpus offers, which allows for level-appropriate sentences.

For a guided tour, **visit elt.heinle.com/collins**

The complete vocabulary resource for beginning learners!

THE COLLINS COBUILD BASIC DICTIONARY of American English

LEVEL: beginning to low-intermediate

The *Collins COBUILD Basic Dictionary of American English* makes vocabulary acquisition efficient and effective by offering beginning-level students extra support in language learning through clear, level-appropriate definitions, COBUILD's unparalleled vocabulary support, and a level-appropriate, controlled vocabulary list.

Unique features specially designed to address the needs of beginning English language learners:

◀ **"Spelling Partners"** present common words that are spelled the same but have different meanings for a broader range of comprehension.

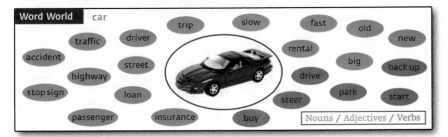

▲ **"Word World"** boxes expand students' vocabulary by presenting target words and domain-related vocabulary.

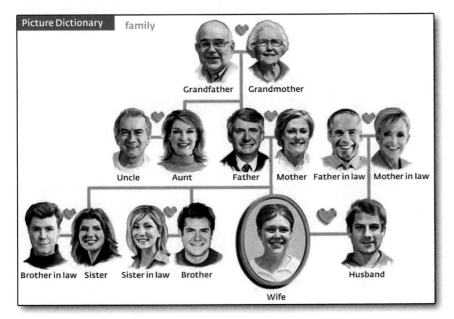

▲ **"Picture Dictionary"** boxes illustrate vocabulary and concepts for a deeper understanding.

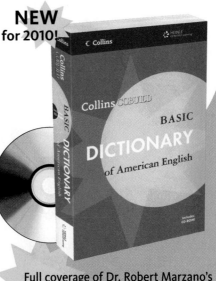

NEW for 2010!

Full coverage of Dr. Robert Marzano's basic vocabulary terms!

COMPONENTS

Softcover with CD-ROM (est. 600 pp.)
Interactive CD-ROM (dual platform)
ELT Advantage: *Making the Most of Learner's Dictionaries* by Michela Clari, p. 111

See p. 124 for Collins COBUILD Basic Dictionary of American English *ISBN/Price listings*

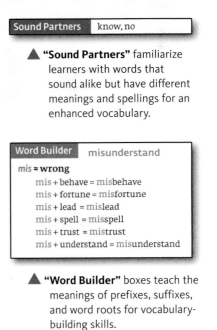

Sound Partners know, no

▲ **"Sound Partners"** familiarize learners with words that sound alike but have different meanings and spellings for an enhanced vocabulary.

Word Builder misunderstand

*mis ≈ **wrong***
  mis + behave = misbehave
  mis + fortune = misfortune
  mis + lead = mislead
  mis + spell = misspell
  mis + trust = mistrust
  mis + understand = misunderstand

▲ **"Word Builder"** boxes teach the meanings of prefixes, suffixes, and word roots for vocabulary-building skills.

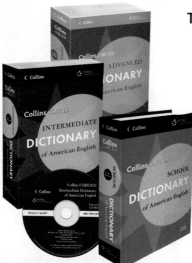

The unique features of the

Collins COBUILD School,

Intermediate, and

Advanced Dictionaries of American English

are designed to

address the specific needs of

intermediate to advanced

English language learners.

Six vocabulary builders support vocabulary development:

Word Web wave

As **wind** blows across water, it makes **waves**. It does this by giving energy to the water. If the waves hit an object, they bounce off it. Light also moves in waves and acts the same way. We can see an object only if light waves bounce off it. Light waves have different **frequencies**. Wave frequency is usually the measure of the number of waves per second. **Radio waves** and **microwaves** are examples of low-frequency light waves. **Visible light** has medium-frequency light waves. **Ultraviolet radiation** and **X-rays** are high-frequency light waves.

THE ELECTROMAGNETIC SPECTRUM

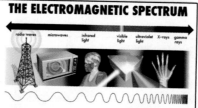

▲ **"Word Webs"** present related vocabulary within a context for a broader understanding of language and concepts.

Picture Dictionary color

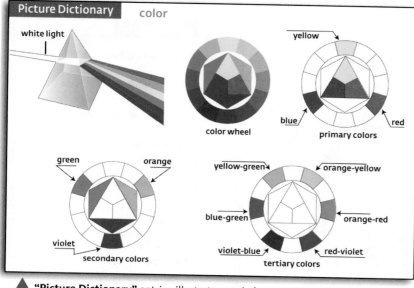

white light

color wheel

primary colors

secondary colors

tertiary colors

▲ **"Picture Dictionary"** entries illustrate vocabulary and concepts for enhanced comprehension.

Word Link geo ≈ earth : geography, geology, geothermal

▲ **"Word Links"** teach prefixes, suffixes, and word roots for increased language awareness.

Word Partnership Use *moment* with:

ADV.	a moment **ago, just a** moment [1]
N.	moment **of silence,** moment **of thought** [1]
V.	**stop for a** moment, **take a** moment, **think for a** moment, **wait a** moment [1]
ADJ.	**an awkward** moment, **a critical** moment, **the right** moment [2]

▲ **"Word Partnerships"** show high-frequency word patterns that increase students' ability to use language appropriately.

Thesaurus *talk* Also look up:

N.	argument, conversation, dialogue, discussion, interview, negotiation; *(ant.)* silence [1]
V.	chat, discuss, gossip, say, share, speak, tell; *(ant.)* listen [1]

▲ **"Thesaurus"** entries offer both synonyms and antonyms to expand vocabulary.

Usage **less** and **fewer**

Less is used to describe general amounts (or noncount nouns). *Less snow fell in December than in January.* *Fewer* is used to describe amounts of countable items. *Maria is working fewer hours this semester.*

▲ **"Usage"** notes explain shades of meaning and clarify cultural references, bringing the learner's language closer to that of a native speaker.

The ideal choice for middle and high school students!

COLLINS COBUILD SCHOOL DICTIONARY of American English

LEVEL: low-intermediate to high-intermediate

The *Collins COBUILD School Dictionary of American English* is an intermediate level dictionary designed to help students succeed both in the classroom and on state examinations.

- Thousands of academic vocabulary terms help prepare students for state examinations.
- Word origins help students gain a rich understanding of the words they are looking up.

Perfect academic vocabulary builder!

COMPONENTS

Softcover (1232 pp.) with CD-ROM
Hardcover (1232 pp.) with CD-ROM
Interactive CD-ROM (dual platform)
ELT Advantage: *Making the Most of Learner's Dictionaries* by Michela Clari, p. 111

CD-ROM Site License available**
**For pricing or to purchase, call Technology Services at 800-423-0563.

See p. 124 for Collins COBUILD School Dictionary of American English *ISBN/Price listings*

For a guided tour, visit
elt.heinle.com/collins

Features:

200 "Word Webs"

950 "Word Links"

75 "Picture Dictionary" boxes

700 "Word Partnerships"

500 "Thesaurus" entries

30 "Usage" notes

See pages 24 and 26 for other Collins COBUILD dictionary features.

27

The most up-to-date intermediate dictionary on the market!

COLLINS COBUILD INTERMEDIATE DICTIONARY of American English

LEVEL: low-intermediate to high-intermediate

Ideal for English language learners who need an intermediate level dictionary, the *Collins COBUILD Intermediate Dictionary of American English* provides full sentence definitions, each created using a controlled vocabulary, and reviewed by a team of classroom teachers to ensure that they are appropriate for learners at this level.

Perfect for college and adult intermediate learners!

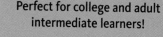

COMPONENTS

Softcover (1232 pp.) with CD-ROM
Interactive CD-ROM (dual platform)
ELT Advantage: *Making the Most of Learner's Dictionaries* by Michela Clari, p. 111

CD-ROM Site License available**
**For pricing or to purchase, call Technology Services at 800-423-0563.

See p. 124 for Collins COBUILD Intermediate Dictionary of American English *ISBN/Price listings*

For a guided tour, visit **elt.heinle.com/collins**

Features:

200 "Word Webs"
950 "Word Links"
75 "Picture Dictionary" boxes
700 "Word Partnerships"
500 "Thesaurus" entries
30 "Usage" notes

Dictionary page excerpt (page 184):

conviction ... **cooking**

1 V-T If someone **is convicted of** a crime, they are found guilty of it in a court of law. ❑ *He was convicted of murder.* ❑ *There was insufficient evidence to convict him.* **2** N-COUNT A **convict** is someone who is in prison. ❑ *...escaped convicts.*

con|vic|tion /kənvɪkʃ°n/ (**convictions**) **1** N-COUNT A **conviction** is a strong belief or opinion. ❑ *It is our firm conviction that a step forward has been taken.* **2** N-COUNT If someone has a **conviction**, they have been found guilty of a crime in a court of law. ❑ *He will appeal against his conviction.*

Word Link vict, vinc ≈ conquering : convict, convince, invincible

con|vince /kənvɪns/ (**convinces, convincing, convinced**) **1** V-T If someone or something **convinces** you **to** do something, they persuade you to do it. ❑ *He convinced her to go ahead and marry Bud.* **2** V-T If someone or something **convinces** you **of** something, they make you believe that it is true or that it exists. ❑ *I soon convinced him of my innocence.* ● **con|vinced** /kənvɪnst/ ADJ ❑ *He was convinced that I was part of the problem.*

Thesaurus convince Also look up :
V. argue, brainwash, persuade, sell, talk into, win over; (ant.) discourage **1** **2**

con|vinc|ing /kənvɪnsɪŋ/ ADJ If someone or something is **convincing**, you believe them. ❑ *There is no convincing evidence that power lines cause cancer.* ● **con|vinc|ing|ly** ADV ❑ *He argued convincingly.*

con|voy /kɒnvɔɪ/ (**convoys**) N-COUNT A **convoy** is a group of vehicles or ships traveling together. ❑ *...a U.N. convoy carrying food and medical supplies.*

con|vul|sion /kənvʌlʃ°n/ (**convulsions**) N-COUNT If someone has **convulsions**, they suffer uncontrollable movements of their muscles. ❑ *5 percent suffered convulsions.*

cook /kʊk/ (**cooks, cooking, cooked**) **1** V-T/V-I When you **cook** a meal, you prepare and heat food so it can be eaten. ❑ *I have to go and cook dinner.* ❑ *...some basic instructions on how to cook a turkey.* ❑ *Let the vegetables cook gently for about 10 minutes.* ❑ *Chefs at the restaurant once cooked for President Kennedy.* ● **cook|ing** N-UNCOUNT ❑ *Her hobbies include dancing and cooking.* **2** N-COUNT A **cook** is a

person who prepares and cooks food. ❑ *They had a butler, a cook, and a maid.* ❑ *I'm a terrible cook.* ▸ **cook up** PHR-VERB If someone **cooks up** a dishonest scheme, they plan it. [INFORMAL] ❑ *They cooked up the plan between them.* → see Picture Dictionary: **cook**

Usage cook and make
Cook is used when referring to the preparation of food using a process involving heat. If preparation only involves assembling ingredients which may have previously been cooked, then *make* is used. "Who made this salad? It's delicious!" "Oh, I just threw it together while I was cooking/making the rest of the dinner."

Thesaurus cook Also look up :
V. heat up, make, prepare **1**
N. chef **2**

cook|book /kʊkbʊk/ (**cookbooks**) N-COUNT A **cookbook** is a book that contains recipes for preparing food.

cook|er /kʊkər/ (**cookers**) N-COUNT A **cooker** is the same as a **stove**. [BRIT]

cook|ery /kʊkəri/ N-UNCOUNT **Cookery** is the activity of preparing and cooking food. [mainly BRIT]

cookie /kʊki/ (**cookies**) **1** N-COUNT A **cookie** is a small sweet cake. **2** N-COUNT A **cookie** is a piece of computer software which enables a website you have visited to recognize you if you visit it again. [COMPUTING] → see **dessert**

cookie cut|ter (**cookie cutters**) also **cookie-cutter** **1** N-COUNT A **cookie cutter** is a tool that is used for cutting cookies into a particular shape. ❑ *...heart-shaped cookie cutters.* **2** ADJ A **cookie-cutter** style is one in which the same approach is always used and there are not enough individual differences. ❑ *Too many cookie-cutter houses were built.*

cookie sheet (**cookie sheets**) N-COUNT A **cookie sheet** is a flat piece of metal on which you bake foods such as cookies in an oven.

cook|ing /kʊkɪŋ/ **1** N-UNCOUNT **Cooking** is food which has been cooked. ❑ *...classic French cooking.* **2** N-UNCOUNT **Cooking** is the activity of

Picture Dictionary cook

boil, steam, roast, fry, stir fry, bake, microwave, toast, barbecue, broil

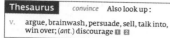
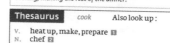

See p. 124 for Collins COBUILD Intermediate Dictionary of American English ISBN/Price listings

See pages 24 and 26 for other Collins COBUILD dictionary features.

The complete language-learning resource!

COLLINS COBUILD ADVANCED DICTIONARY of American English

LEVEL: advanced

The *Collins COBUILD Advanced Dictionary of American English* offers students at an advanced level the challenging language development tools that they need. The dictionary also includes a list of common words found on the TOEFL® and TOEIC® examinations.

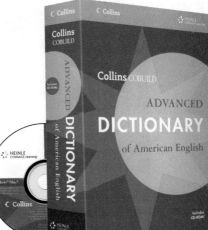

Perfect vocabulary booster for advanced students!

COMPONENTS

Softcover (1680 pp.) with CD-ROM
Interactive CD-ROM (dual platform)
ELT Advantage: *Making the Most of Learner's Dictionaries* by Michela Clari, p. 111

CD-ROM Site License available**
**For pricing or to purchase, call Technology Services at 800-423-0563.

See p. 124 for Collins COBUILD Advanced Dictionary of American English *ISBN/Price listings*

For a guided tour, visit
elt.heinle.com/collins

Features:

250 "Word Webs"

1,500 "Word Links"

50 "Picture Dictionary" boxes

1,150 "Word Partnerships"

725 "Thesaurus" entries

100 "Usage" notes

Dictionary sample page

metamorphosis   824   methodology

metamorphose and emerge onto land. □ *She had been metamorphosed by the war.* → see also **metamorphosis**

Word Link   morph = form, shape : *amorphous*, meta*morphous*, *morphology*

Word Link   osis = state or condition : *halitosis*, *hypnosis*, *metamorphosis*

meta|mor|pho|sis /mɛtəmɔrfəsɪs/ (**metamorphoses**) N-VAR When a **metamorphosis** occurs, a person or thing develops and changes into something completely different. [FORMAL] □ *...his metamorphosis from a Republican to a Democrat.* → see **amphibian**

Word Link   meta = beyond, change : *metabolism*, *metamorphosis*, *metaphor*

meta|phor /mɛtəfɔr/ (**metaphors**) N-VAR A **metaphor** is an imaginative way of describing something by referring to something else which is the same in a particular way. For example, if you want to say that someone is very shy and frightened of things, you might say that they are a mouse. □ *...the avoidance of violent expressions and metaphors like 'kill two birds with one stone.'* N-VAR If one thing is a **metaphor for** another, it is intended or regarded as a symbol of it. □ *The divided family remains a powerful metaphor for a society that continued to tear itself apart.* PHRASE If you **mix your metaphors**, you use two conflicting metaphors. People do this accidentally, or sometimes deliberately as a joke. □ *To mix yet more metaphors, you were trying to run before you could walk, and I've clipped your wings.*

meta|phori|cal /mɛtəfɔrɪkᵊl/ ADJ You use the word **metaphorical** to indicate that you are not using words with their ordinary meaning, but are describing something by means of an image or symbol. □ *It turns out Levy is talking in metaphorical terms.* • **meta|phori|cal|ly** ADV □ *You're speaking metaphorically, I hope.*

meta|physi|cal /mɛtəfɪzɪkᵊl/ ADJ **Metaphysical** means relating to metaphysics. [usu ADJ n] □ *...metaphysical questions like personal responsibility for violence.*

Word Link   physi = of nature : *metaphysics*, *physical*, *physician*

meta|phys|ics /mɛtəfɪzɪks/ N-UNCOUNT **Metaphysics** is a part of philosophy which is concerned with understanding reality and developing theories about what exists and how we know that it exists.

me|tas|ta|size /mɛtæstəsaɪz/ (**metastasizes, metastasizing, metastasized**) V-I If cancer cells **metastasize**, they spread to another part of the body. [MEDICAL] □ *A checkup revealed a small tumor on the left lower lobe of his lung, but it had not yet metastasized.* □ *...when diagnosis is delayed until cancer has metastasized to other parts of the body.*

mete /mit/ (**metes, meting, meted**)
▸ **mete out** PHRASAL VERB To **mete out** a punishment means to order that someone should be punished in a certain way. [FORMAL] □ *His father meted out punishment with a slipper.*

me|teor /mitiər/ (**meteors**) N-COUNT A **meteor** is a piece of rock or metal that burns very brightly when it enters the earth's atmosphere from space.
→ see Word Web: **meteor**

me|teor|ic /mitiɔrɪk/ ADJ If you use **meteoric** when you are describing someone's career, you mean that they achieved success very quickly. □ *...his meteoric rise to fame.*

me|teor|ite /mitiəraɪt/ (**meteorites**) N-COUNT A **meteorite** is a large piece of rock or metal from space that has landed on earth. → see **meteor**

me|teoro|logi|cal /mitiərəlɒdʒɪkᵊl/ ADJ **Meteorological** means relating to meteorology. [ADJ n] □ *...adverse meteorological conditions.*

me|teor|ol|ogy /mitiərɒlədʒi/ N-UNCOUNT **Meteorology** is the study of the processes in the earth's atmosphere that cause particular weather conditions, especially in order to predict the weather. • **me|teor|olo|gist** /mitiərɒlədʒɪst/ (**meteorologists**) N-COUNT □ *Meteorologists have predicted mild rains for the next few days.* → see **forecast**

Word Link   meter = to measure : *kilometer*, *meter*, *perimeter*

me|ter /mitər/ (**meters, metering, metered**) N-COUNT A **meter** is a device that measures and records something such as the amount of gas or electricity that you have used. □ *He was there to read the electricity meter.* V-T To **meter** something such as gas or electricity means to use a meter to measure how much of it people use, usually in order to calculate how much they have to pay. □ *Only a third of these households thought it reasonable to meter water.* N-COUNT A **meter** is the same as a **parking meter**. N-COUNT A **meter** is a metric unit of length equal to 100 centimeters. □ *She's running the 1,500 meters here.*

metha|done /mɛθədoʊn/ N-UNCOUNT **Methadone** is a drug that is sometimes prescribed to heroin addicts as a substitute for heroin. □ *...the danger of patients overdosing on methadone.*

me|thane /mɛθeɪn/ N-UNCOUNT **Methane** is a colorless gas that has no smell. Natural gas consists mostly of methane.

metha|nol /mɛθənɔl/ N-UNCOUNT **Methanol** is a colorless, poisonous liquid, used as a solvent and fuel. □ *...so-called alternative fuels such as ethanol and methanol.*

meth|od /mɛθəd/ (**methods**) N-COUNT A **method** is a particular way of doing something. □ *The pill is the most efficient method of birth control.* → see **experiment, science**

Thesaurus   method   Also look up:
N.   manner, procedure, process, system, technique

Word Partnership   Use **method** with:
ADJ.   alternative/traditional method, best method, effective method, new method, preferred method, scientific method
N.   method of payment, teaching method
V.   develop a method, use a method

me|thodi|cal /məθɒdɪkᵊl/ ADJ If you describe someone as **methodical**, you mean that they do things carefully, thoroughly, and in order. □ *Da Vinci was methodical in his research, carefully recording his observations and theories.* • **me|thodi|cal|ly** /məθɒdɪkli/ ADV [ADV with v] □ *She methodically put the things into her suitcase.*

Meth|od|ism /mɛθədɪzəm/ N-UNCOUNT **Methodism** is the beliefs and practices of Methodists.

Meth|od|ist /mɛθədɪst/ (**Methodists**) N-COUNT **Methodists** are Protestant Christians who follow the teachings of John Wesley and who have their own branch of the Christian church and their own form of worship.

meth|od|ology /mɛθədɒlədʒi/ (**methodologies**) N-VAR A

Word Web   meteor

As an **asteroid** flies through **space**, small pieces called **meteoroids** sometimes break off. When a meteoroid enters the earth's **atmosphere**, we call it a **meteor**. As the earth passes through asteroid belts we see spectacular **meteor showers**. Meteors that reach the earth are called meteorites. Scientists believe a huge meteorite struck the earth about 65 million years ago. It left a pit in Mexico called the Chicxulub **Crater**. It's about 150 miles wide. The crash caused earthquakes and tsunamis. It may also have produced a change in the earth's environment. Some believe this event caused the dinosaurs to die out.

See pages 24 and 26 for other Collins COBUILD dictionary features.

NEW!

COLLINS COBUILD ENGLISH/SPANISH STUDENT'S DICTIONARY
of American English

(Collins COBUILD Inglés/Español Diccionario Para Estudiantes Latinoamericanos)

LEVEL: low-intermediate to high-intermediate

The *Collins COBUILD English/Spanish Student's Dictionary of American English* is specially designed for Spanish-speaking learners of English who need the extra support of their native language. This bilingual learner's dictionary provides Spanish translations for all definitions, senses, examples, and explanatory terms to complement the English material and to provide additional support to the learner when they encounter a difficult word or expression.

Softcover with CD-ROM (1008 pp.)

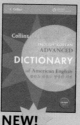

ac|claim /əkleɪm/ (acclaims, acclaiming, acclaimed) **1** v-т If someone or something is acclaimed, they are praised enthusiastically. *aclamar, aplaudir, vitorear* [FORMAL] ❑ *The restaurant has been widely acclaimed for its excellent French food. El restaurante se ha hecho famoso por su excelente comida francesa.* ❑ *He was acclaimed as America's greatest filmmaker. Lo aclamaron como el más grande cineasta estadounidense.* ● ac|claimed ADJ *aplaudido, aclamado* ❑ *She has published six highly acclaimed novels. Ha publicado seis novelas muy aplaudidas.* **2** N-UNCOUNT Acclaim is public praise for someone or something. *aplauso, ovación, aclamación* [FORMAL] ❑ *Angela Bassett has won acclaim for her excellent performance. Angela Bassett se ha ganado el aplauso por sus excelentes interpretaciones.*

▲ Spanish translations are provided for all definitions.

COLLINS COBUILD ENGLISH/ESPAÑOL GLOSSARY

Level: low-intermediate to high-intermediate
Softcover (400 pp.)

Perfect for test preparation!

The *Collins COBUILD English/Español Glossary* is a perfect reference tool designed to assist students with:

- Learning new academic vocabulary words found in all disciplines as well as standardized exams.

- Understanding homework assignments.

- Success in test-taking.

OTHER BILINGUAL DICTIONARIES

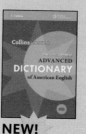

NEW!

COLLINS COBUILD ADVANCED DICTIONARY OF AMERICAN ENGLISH, ENGLISH/JAPANESE

Level: high-intermediate to advanced
Softcover with CD-ROM (1712 pp.)

COLLINS COBUILD ADVANCED DICTIONARY OF AMERICAN ENGLISH, ENGLISH/KOREAN

Level: high-intermediate to advanced
Softcover with CD-ROM (1744 pp.)

NEW!

COLLINS ESCOLAR *PLUS* DICTIONARY, 2/e

(English/Portuguese/Português/Inglês)

Level: low-intermediate to high-intermediate
Softcover (1056 pp.)

NEW!

See pages 24 and 26 for a full introduction to the COBUILD dictionaries.

Pictures plus a world of fun!

THE HEINLE PICTURE DICTIONARY FOR CHILDREN

Jill Korey O'Sullivan

LEVEL: Proficiency: pre-literacy to low-intermediate
Reading (by grade): K – 3

The Heinle Picture Dictionary for Children is the only children's dictionary that presents vocabulary within thematic readings and offers opportunities for multi-level practice of every word introduced to help develop English language skills.

■ **1,100 words are taught contextually** through colorful illustrations and photographs, readings, and activities in eight thematic units.

■ Students encounter words in context through engaging **"Rhyme Time"** and **"Fun Facts"** readings.

■ **"Playing with Words" offers fun activities** in which students increase semantic understanding and develop their language skills.

■ **Multi-level Lesson Planner** provides three different 'mini-lessons' for each level focusing on vocabulary, phonics, and language development.

■ The *Sing-Along with The Heinle Picture Dictionary for Children* **Audio CD** presents 63 original songs that reinforce words introduced in the lessons.

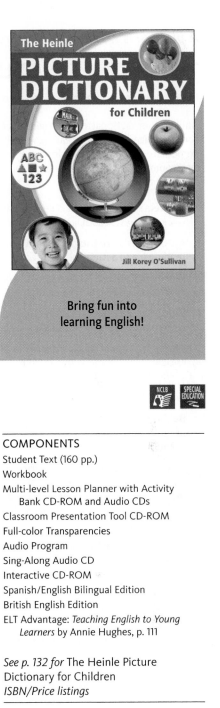

Bring fun into learning English!

"Rhyme Time" and **"Fun Facts"** readings present vocabulary in context.

Vocabulary words appear directly next to the corresponding image.

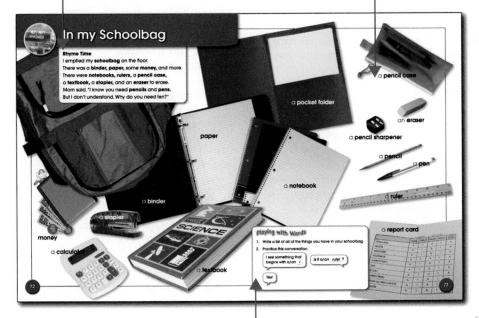

"Playing with Words" activities give students opportunities to demonstrate their language development and apply semantic awareness.

COMPONENTS
Student Text (160 pp.)
Workbook
Multi-level Lesson Planner with Activity Bank CD-ROM and Audio CDs
Classroom Presentation Tool CD-ROM
Full-color Transparencies
Audio Program
Sing-Along Audio CD
Interactive CD-ROM
Spanish/English Bilingual Edition
British English Edition
ELT Advantage: *Teaching English to Young Learners* by Annie Hughes, p. 111

See p. 132 for The Heinle Picture Dictionary for Children *ISBN/Price listings*

For a guided tour, visit
elt.heinle.com/hpdc

Your colleagues say...

❝*...this book is very engaging—not just 'another' dictionary. It's colorful, informative, age appropriate, and FUN."*

—*Melissa Jones,
Jupiter Elementary School, FL*

A picture is worth 4,000 words!

THE HEINLE PICTURE DICTIONARY

LEVEL: low-beginning to low-intermediate

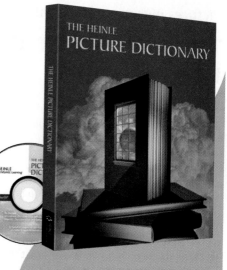

Unlike other dictionaries, *The Heinle Picture Dictionary* presents new vocabulary in contextualized, thematic readings and high-frequency collocations. It also offers immediate practice and reinforcement through "Words in Action." Whether used as a classroom text or a self-study tool, *The Heinle Picture Dictionary* will rapidly move students toward fluency.

- **16 thematic units** focus on everyday themes such as people, food, housing, work, clothes, school, and recreation.

- **4,000 words are taught in context** through color photographs and illustrations, readings, and activities.

- **"Words in Context"** shows how the language is actually used through accessible, contextualized readings at a high-beginning level.

- **"Word Partnerships"** expand students' use and understanding of high-frequency word patterns and collocations.

- **"Words in Action"** gives students opportunities to learn new vocabulary through critical thinking and active learning.

- The **Audio Program** allows students to hear each word pronounced and to hear the "Words in Context" read.

- **Beginning** and **Intermediate Workbooks** feature their own complete listening programs as well as constructive, entertaining activities for solidifying new vocabulary.

- A **comprehensive Lesson Planner** provides three levels of lesson plans featuring hours of vocabulary, grammar, and life skills instructional support for the busy teacher. It also includes an Activity Bank and Classroom Presentation Tool on CD-ROM containing additional activities, worksheets, and templates for use with each unit.

- **Fully searchable Interactive CD-ROM** offers full audio support, voice recording capabilities, and abundant interactive vocabulary practice games and activities.

Codie Award finalist!

COMPONENTS

Student Text (294 pp.)
Beginning Workbook with Audio CDs
Intermediate Workbook with Audio CDs
Audio CD
Lesson Planner with Activity Bank &
    Classroom Presentation Tool CD-ROM
Transparencies
Interactive CD-ROM
Bilingual Editions:
    Brazilian Portuguese; Chinese, Simplified; Chinese, Traditional; Haitian Creole; Japanese; Korean; Spanish
ELT Advantage: *Practical Ideas for the Adult ESL/EFL Classroom* by Rob Jenkins, p. 111

CD-ROM Site License*
* For pricing or to purchase, call Technology Services at 800-423-0563.

See p. 132 for The Heinle Picture Dictionary *ISBN/Price listings*

 For a guided tour, visit**elt**.heinle.com/hpd

Your colleagues say...

"[This book] offers far more challenging and motivating activities than most dictionaries, basic or otherwise, while maintaining an uncluttered, appealing visual impression to the reader."

—Sally Gearhart,
Santa Rosa Junior College,
Santa Rosa, CA

"This dictionary goes beyond other picture dictionaries with only attractive artwork. This one directly contributes to the learners' overall development in the use of the vocabulary in context through short and informative readings and conversations. Congratulations!"

—Bari Ramirez,
Stockard Middle School,
Dallas, TX

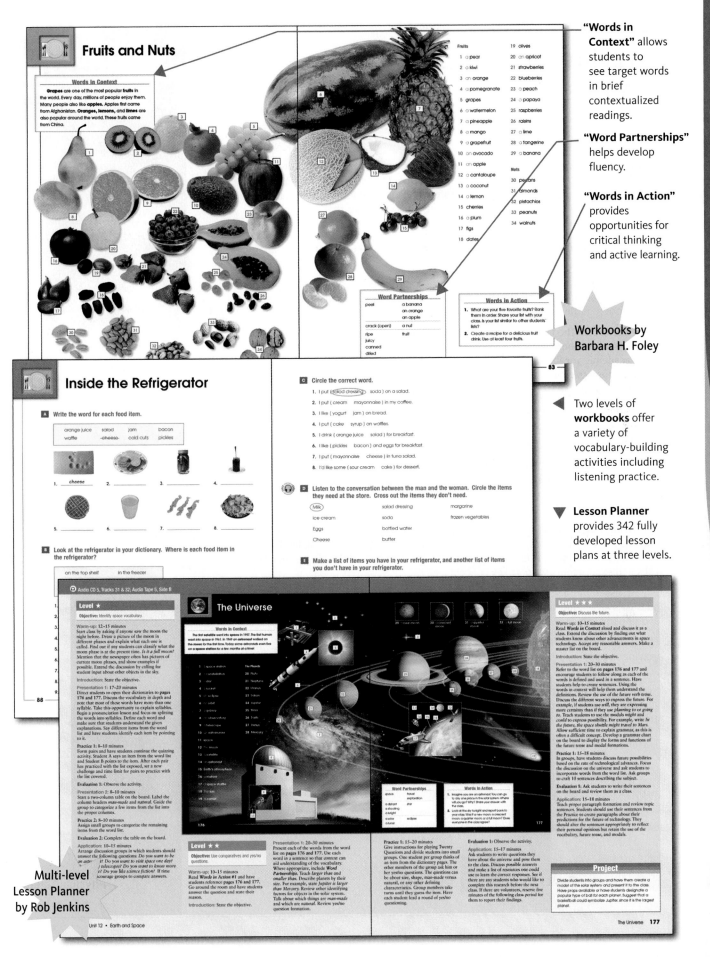

"Words in Context" allows students to see target words in brief contextualized readings.

"Word Partnerships" helps develop fluency.

"Words in Action" provides opportunities for critical thinking and active learning.

Workbooks by Barbara H. Foley

Two levels of **workbooks** offer a variety of vocabulary-building activities including listening practice.

Lesson Planner provides 342 fully developed lesson plans at three levels.

Multi-level Lesson Planner by Rob Jenkins

Give your students a BOOST to success!

GATEWAY TO SCIENCE
Vocabulary and Concepts

Tim Collins

LEVEL: beginning to intermediate

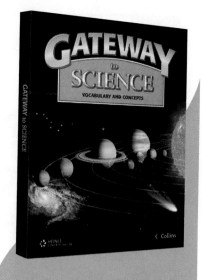

Gateway to Science is a unique program designed to introduce students to content-area knowledge and the skills needed to meet the requirements of science programs as well as national and state assessments. Using picture dictionary and textbook formats, students acquire key vocabulary, concepts, and learning strategies that help boost their success in science!

- **Every lesson follows a distinctive four-page format** that develops the vocabulary and concepts needed for the study of science.

  ✔ **Vocabulary:** The first two pages illustrate topic-based vocabulary in a picture dictionary format. Easy-to-access artwork along with comprehension questions work together to teach science terms in context.

  ✔ **Concepts:** The last two pages teach standards-based concepts related to the lesson vocabulary and topic, and are accompanied by science skills practice, academic vocabulary, comprehension checks, research assignments, and writing activities.

- The **Student Book** features an **English/Spanish glossary** for bilingual classrooms to enhance vocabulary development.

- The **Teacher Edition** provides instructors with teaching suggestions and highly accessible descriptions of science content introduced in every lesson.

- The **Teacher Resource CD-ROMs with Exam***View*® feature customizable test-generating software aligned to state standards. They also include an interactive presentation tool with animated graphic organizers to help students comprehend new vocabulary and key concepts introduced in the student text.

- The **Workbook with Labs** provides expansion activities for each lesson in the student text. Reading comprehension, writing, and listening/speaking skills are reinforced with additional communicative activities and critical thinking exercises. Labs and experiments support key concepts.

- The **Assessment Book** includes two-page quizzes for each lesson that mirror the questions also found in the Exam*View*® test bank, as well as end-of-section tests and an end-of-book test.

- The **Audio Program** features all readings to boost auditory learning and reading fluency.

Science content for ELLs!

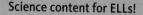

COMPONENTS
Student Text
Teacher Edition
Workbook with Labs
Audio CD
Teacher Resource CD-ROM with Exam*View*® and Classroom Presentation Tool
Assessment Book
ELT Advantage: *Content-based Instruction for Language Learners* by Kathleen M. Bailey, p. 111

See p. 130 for Gateway to Science *ISBN/Price listings*

elt.heinle.com/gateway

Need more science support? See page 18 for the *Footprint Reading Library*.

Gateway to Science *explores four major areas:*

 Science Basics   **Life Science**    **Earth Science**    **Physical Science**

"Focus Question" begins each lesson along with a list of key **Vocabulary**.

"Vocabulary in Context" contextualizes words from the vocabulary list in an informational reading.

"Check Your Understanding" questions assess vocabulary and reading comprehension and provide the opportunity to apply knowledge to **"Critical Thinking"** questions.

Easy-to-follow charts and graphics visually reinforce concepts.

The **"Science Skill"** section focuses on building graphic literacy skills.

The **"Academic Vocabulary"** box introduces vocabulary related to content words across all academic disciplines.

"Word Study" boxes provide useful characteristics of key vocabulary, including word families and words with multiple meanings.

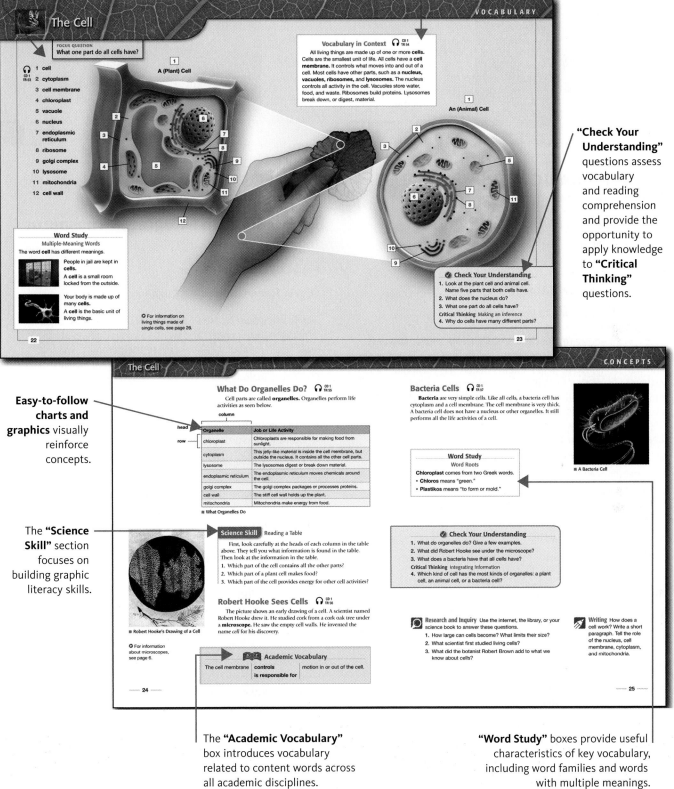

The Cell

VOCABULARY

FOCUS QUESTION
What one part do all cells have?

1 cell
2 cytoplasm
3 cell membrane
4 chloroplast
5 vacuole
6 nucleus
7 endoplasmic reticulum
8 ribosome
9 golgi complex
10 lysosome
11 mitochondria
12 cell wall

A (Plant) Cell

An (Animal) Cell

Vocabulary in Context

All living things are made up of one or more **cells**. Cells are the smallest unit of life. All cells have a **cell membrane**. It controls what moves into and out of a cell. Most cells have other parts, such as a **nucleus**, **vacuoles**, **ribosomes**, and **lysosomes**. The nucleus controls all activity in the cell. Vacuoles store water, food, and waste. Ribosomes build proteins. Lysosomes break down, or digest, material.

Word Study
Multiple-Meaning Words
The word **cell** has different meanings.

People in jail are kept in **cells**.
A **cell** is a small room locked from the outside.

Your body is made up of many **cells**.
A **cell** is the basic unit of living things.

For information on living things made of single cells, see page 26.

Check Your Understanding
1. Look at the plant cell and animal cell. Name five parts that both cells have.
2. What does the nucleus do?
3. What one part do all cells have?
Critical Thinking Making an inference
4. Why do cells have many different parts?

22   23

The Cell

CONCEPTS

What Do Organelles Do?
Cell parts are called **organelles**. Organelles perform life activities as seen below.

column
head
row

Organelle	Job or Life Activity
chloroplast	Chloroplasts are responsible for making food from sunlight.
cytoplasm	This jelly-like material is inside the cell membrane, but outside the nucleus. It contains all the other cell parts.
lysosome	The lysosomes digest or break down material.
endoplasmic reticulum	The endoplasmic reticulum moves chemicals around the cell.
golgi complex	The golgi complex packages or processes proteins.
cell wall	The stiff cell wall holds up the plant.
mitochondria	Mitochondria make energy from food.

What Organelles Do

Science Skill Reading a Table

First, look carefully at the heads of each column in the table above. They tell you what information is found in the table. Then look at the information in the table.
1. Which part of the cell contains all the other parts?
2. Which part of a plant cell makes food?
3. Which part of the cell provides energy for other cell activities?

Robert Hooke Sees Cells
The picture shows an early drawing of a cell. A scientist named Robert Hooke drew it. He studied cork from a cork oak tree under a **microscope**. He saw the empty cell walls. He invented the name *cell* for his discovery.

Robert Hooke's Drawing of a Cell

For information about microscopes, see page 6.

Academic Vocabulary

The cell membrane	controls	motion in or out of the cell.
	is responsible for	

Bacteria Cells
Bacteria are very simple cells. Like all cells, a bacteria cell has cytoplasm and a cell membrane. The cell membrane is very thick. A bacteria cell does not have a nucleus or other organelles. It still performs all the life activities of a cell.

A Bacteria Cell

Word Study
Word Roots

Chloroplast comes from two Greek words.
• **Chloros** means "green."
• **Plastikos** means "to form or mold."

Check Your Understanding
1. What do organelles do? Give a few examples.
2. What did Robert Hooke see under the microscope?
3. What does a bacteria have that all cells have?
Critical Thinking Integrating Information
4. Which kind of cell has the most kinds of organelles: a plant cell, an animal cell, or a bacteria cell?

Research and Inquiry Use the internet, the library, or your science book to answer these questions.
1. How large can cells become? What limits their size?
2. What scientist first studied living cells?
3. What did the botanist Robert Brown add to what we know about cells?

Writing How does a cell work? Write a short paragraph. Tell the role of the nucleus, cell membrane, cytoplasm, and mitochondria.

24   25

35

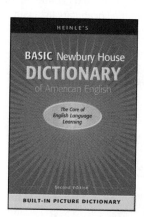

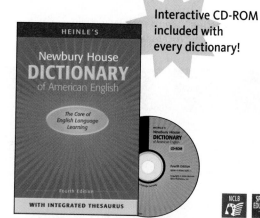

Interactive CD-ROM included with every dictionary!

HEINLE'S BASIC NEWBURY HOUSE DICTIONARY OF AMERICAN ENGLISH with Built-in Picture Dictionary

Second Edition

Philip Rideout, *Chief Editor*

LEVEL: low-beginning to low-intermediate

Ideal for emerging readers and writers, *Heinle's Basic Newbury House Dictionary* focuses on what English language learners need and want to know. To help students build their vocabulary and make the transition from bilingual and picture dictionaries to more comprehensive dictionaries, *Heinle's Basic Newbury House Dictionary* contains:

Learner's Dictionary

- Clear definitions for 15,000+ words using a controlled vocabulary of 2,500 words
- Useful sample sentences to show proper usage
- 800 illustrations to improve comprehension
- Cultural and usage notes
- Extensive appendixes

Built-in Picture Dictionary

- 40-page, full-color picture dictionary highlighting new vocabulary and word families

Built-in Activity Guide

- 12 engaging theme-based lessons developing essential dictionary and vocabulary-building skills

Softcover Dictionary (632 pp.)
Hardcover Dictionary (632 pp.)
Softcover Dictionary with CD-ROM
Hardcover Dictionary with CD-ROM
Dictionary on CD-ROM

HEINLE'S NEWBURY HOUSE DICTIONARY OF AMERICAN ENGLISH with Integrated Thesaurus

Fourth Edition

Philip Rideout, *Chief Editor*

LEVEL: low-intermediate to high-intermediate

Heinle's Newbury House Dictionary focuses on what English language learners need and want to know. To help students build their vocabulary and increase their reading, writing, listening, and speaking skills, *Heinle's Newbury House Dictionary* includes:

Learner's Dictionary

- Clear definitions for 40,000+ frequently used words with up-to-date words and expressions
- Useful sample sentences, illustrations, cultural references, and usage notes
- Extensive appendixes with maps, countries, and more

Integrated Thesaurus

- Includes synonyms, antonyms, and collocations for over 2,500 words to expand vocabulary and writing fluency

Built-in Activity Guide

- 22 engaging theme-based lessons that develop essential dictionary and vocabulary-building skills

Softcover Dictionary with CD-ROM (1232 pp.)
Hardcover Dictionary (1232 pp.)
Hardcover Dictionary with CD-ROM
Dictionary on CD-ROM
CD-ROM Site License*

*For pricing or to purchase, call Technology Services at 800-423-0563.

elt.heinle.com/nhd

For customer support, call **(877) NEED-ESL** or visit **elt.heinle.com** ■ For pricing, ISBNs, and ordering information see pp. 122 – 144

LEVEL GUIDE

	PAGE NUMBER	LITERACY	LOW-BEGINNING	BEGINNING	HIGH-BEGINNING	LOW-INTERMEDIATE	INTERMEDIATE	HIGH-INTERMEDIATE	ADVANCED
LITERACY									
Literacy in Lifeskills: 1, 2	48	•							
Sam and Pat: 1, 2	48	1	2						
CORE PROGRAMS									
Better English Everyday: 1, 2, 3	48			1	1	2	2	3	
Crossroads Café: Photo Stories A, B	48			•	•				
Crossroads Café: Worktexts A, B	48				•	•	•	•	•
Downtown: Basic, 1, 2, 3, 4 NEW BASIC LEVEL!	40		Basic	1	2	3	3	4	
English in Action: 1, 2, 3, 4	44		1	1	2	3	3	4	
In Detail: 1, 2	48							1	2
Intercom 2000, 3/e: 1, 2, 3, 4	48			1	2	3	4		
New Grammar in Action, The: Basic, 1, 2, 3	59		Basic	Basic	1	2	2	3	
Practical English, 2/e: 1, 2, 3	48			1	2	3			
Stand Out, 2/e: Basic, 1, 2, 3, 4, 5 NEW!	38		Basic	1	2	3	3	4	5
Up Close: 1, 2, 3, 4	48			1	2	3	4		
World English: Intro, 1, 2, 3 NEW!	42		Intro	1	1	2	2	3	
World Link: Intro, 1, 2, 3	46			Intro	1	2	3		
World Link Video Course: Intro 1, 2, 3	46			Intro	1	2	3		
World Pass: 1, 2	46							1	2
Writing Practical English, 2/e: 1, 2, 3	48			1	2	3			
WORKPLACE/CITIZENSHIP									
U.S. Citizen, Yes, 3/e NEW!	47			•	•	•			
READING									
Access Reading: 1, 2, 3, 4	48				1	2	3	4	
At Home in Two Lands, 2/e	68				•	•	•		
Far From Home, 3/e	68				•	•	•		
Sam and Pat: 1, 2	48	1	2						
DICTIONARIES									
Collins COBUILD Advanced Dictionary of American English	29								•
Collins COBUILD Basic Dictionary of American English NEW!	25			•	•	•			
Collins COBUILD Intermediate Dictionary of American English	28					•	•	•	
Heinle Picture Dictionary, The	32		•	•	•	•			

Stand Out *works! And now it works even better!*

STAND OUT Basic – 5
Standards-Based English, Second Edition

Rob Jenkins, Staci Johnson

LEVEL: low-beginning to advanced

Built from the standards necessary for adult English learners, the second edition of *Stand Out* gives students the foundation and tools they need to develop confidence and become independent, lifelong learners. Now includes a new advanced level!

- **NEW!** The *Lifeskills* **Video Program** creates engaging opportunities for students to become even more successful learners of English. An online Teacher's Guide supports the video program with lesson plans, video scripts, and student worksheets.

- **NEW! Classroom Presentation Tool** includes art, photos, grammar charts, and audio from the presentation section of each lesson in the Lesson Planner to help make presenting each lesson even easier!

- **NEW! Grammar instruction** is integrated in every lesson, and *Grammar Challenge* workbooks are directly aligned to the student book. Online grammar practice is also available through *Grammar Café*.

- Student Books **integrate language development, life skills, and real-world project activities** in a proven format, utilizing many SCANS competencies and increasing workplace skills.

- **Team Projects** apply unit objectives through motivating task-based activities that group learners of different levels together.

- Ground-breaking **Lesson Planners** take the guesswork out of meeting the standards while offering high-interest, meaningful language activities, and three levels of pacing for each book. Activity Bank CD-ROM includes multi-level worksheets for each lesson.

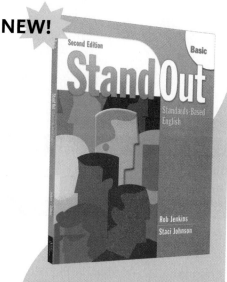

NEW!

Second Edition · **Basic**

Stand Out
Standards-Based English

Rob Jenkins
Staci Johnson

Lifeskills Video Program
for ALL six levels!

SERIES COMPONENTS
Student Texts*
Grammar Challenge Workbooks
Reading & Writing Challenge Workbooks
NEW! Technology Toolkit
NEW! *Lifeskills* Video Program
Audio CDs
Grammar Café, see p. 58
Lesson Planners with Audio CDs and
   Activity Bank CD-ROMs w/audio
NEW! Online Lesson Planners
Classroom Presentation Tools
Assessment CD-ROMs with Exam*View*®
ELT Advantage: *Practical Ideas for the Adult
   ESL/EFL Classroom* by Rob Jenkins, p. 111

*Split Editions available. Ask your Heinle
   representative for details.

*See pp. 140-141 for Stand Out
ISBN/Price listings*

Need more vocabulary support?
See the *Heinle Picture Dictionary* p. 32.

For a guided tour, visit
elt.heinle.com/standout

Ask your Heinle representative
about bundling options with the
Stand Out Lifeskills Video Program!

NEW! Technology Toolkits for each level include:

- Guided Tour CD-ROM
- *Lifeskills* Video on DVD
- Classroom Presentation Tool
- Activity Bank CD-ROM with Audio CD
- Assessment CD-ROM with ExamView® with Audio CD
- *The Heinle Picture Dictionary* Interactive CD-ROM

The Stand Out Approach

Establish a context and purpose.
- ✔ **Warm-up**
- ✔ **Introduction**

Provide students with the building blocks and skills they need.
- ✔ **Presentation**

Provide meaningful tasks.
- ✔ **Practice**

Ensure that students are successful.
- ✔ **Evaluation**

Allow students to use the language.
- ✔ **Application**

Also perfect for self study to promote learner persistence!

Bring your classroom to life!

Lifeskills Video Program

Each level of *Stand Out* features a DVD presenting eight video clips that support and reinforce many of the life skill competencies covered in the series. Each unit consists of the following:

- ▪ A short original dramatic episode that follows Hector, his friends, and his family as they live, work, and study in a community in the United States.

- ▪ A "My Story" segment featuring real-life interviews with students and professionals from around the world.

- ▪ Worksheets with "Before," "While," and "After You Watch" activities.

NEW!

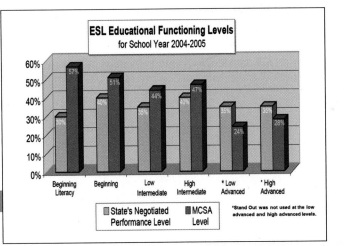

ESL Educational Functioning Levels for School Year 2004-2005 bar chart showing State's Negotiated Performance Level and MCSA Level across Beginning Literacy, Beginning, Low Intermediate, High Intermediate, *Low Advanced, and *High Advanced categories. *Stand Out was not used at the low advanced and high advanced levels.

Stand Out *works!*

"Using the Stand Out *series, we have far exceeded the benchmarks established by the federal government."*

—Helen Sanpei, Principal, McKinley Community School for Adults, Honolulu, HI

And now it works even better!

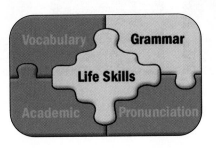

"The major strength of the new edition is the integrated approach of listening, speaking, reading, writing, grammar AND pronunciation practice."

—Heidi Perez, Instructor, Adult Learning Center, Lawrence, MA

Combine the grammar syllabus you want with the standards alignment you need!

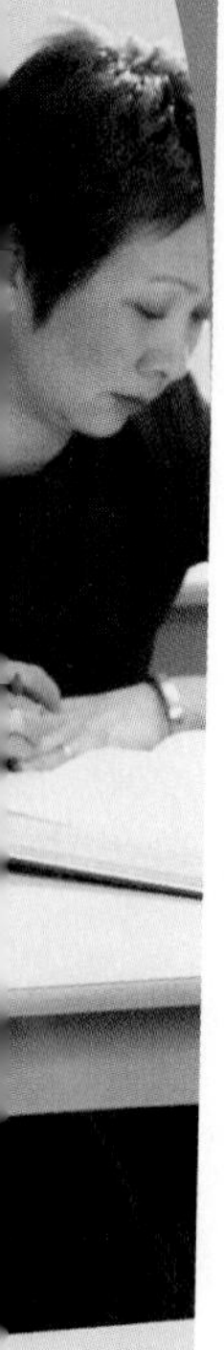

NEW
Basic Level!

DOWNTOWN Basic – 4

English for Work and Life

Edward J. McBride

LEVEL: beginning to high-intermediate

Downtown offers a contextualized, balanced approach that emphasizes the language skills needed in daily life as well as in the workplace. Combining a standards-based and a grammar-based syllabus, *Downtown* gives English learners the comprehensive language skills they need to succeed.

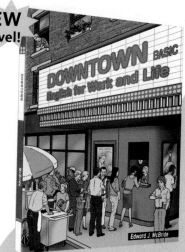

- **NEW! Basic level** gives beginning students the skills they need through level-appropriate learning activities.
- **NEW! Picture Cards** include 100 images which can be used for presentations, classroom activities, games, and more.
- **"Game Time"** offers **lively communicative activities** that allow the students to relax and have fun with the language.
- **Picture dictionary-style chapter openers** introduce vocabulary in context.
- **Theme-based chapters include three lessons,** with the third focusing on the skills and vocabulary necessary for the workplace.
- **The strong grammar syllabus** supports the integrated language learning focus.
- **A humorous serial-style cartoon** in Levels Basic, 1, and 2 and the "Downtown Journal" newspaper in Levels 3 and 4 review instructional content and introduce additional activities at the end of each chapter.
- **Alignment with the CASAS, SCANS, EFF Competencies,** and state standards supports classroom and program goals.
- **Teacher's Editions** include an **Art Bank PowerPoint® Presentation Tool** on CD-ROM which provides colorful and dynamic presentations for classroom use.

"Game Time" activities make learning fun!

SERIES COMPONENTS

Student Texts
Workbooks
Audio CDs
Grammar Café, see p. 58
Teacher's Editions with Art Bank CD-ROM
Assessment CD-ROMs with Exam*View*®
NEW! Picture Cards
Transparencies
ELT Advantage: *Practical Ideas for the Adult ESL/EFL Classroom* by Rob Jenkins, p. 111

See p. 125 for Downtown *ISBN/Price listings*

elt.heinle.com/downtown

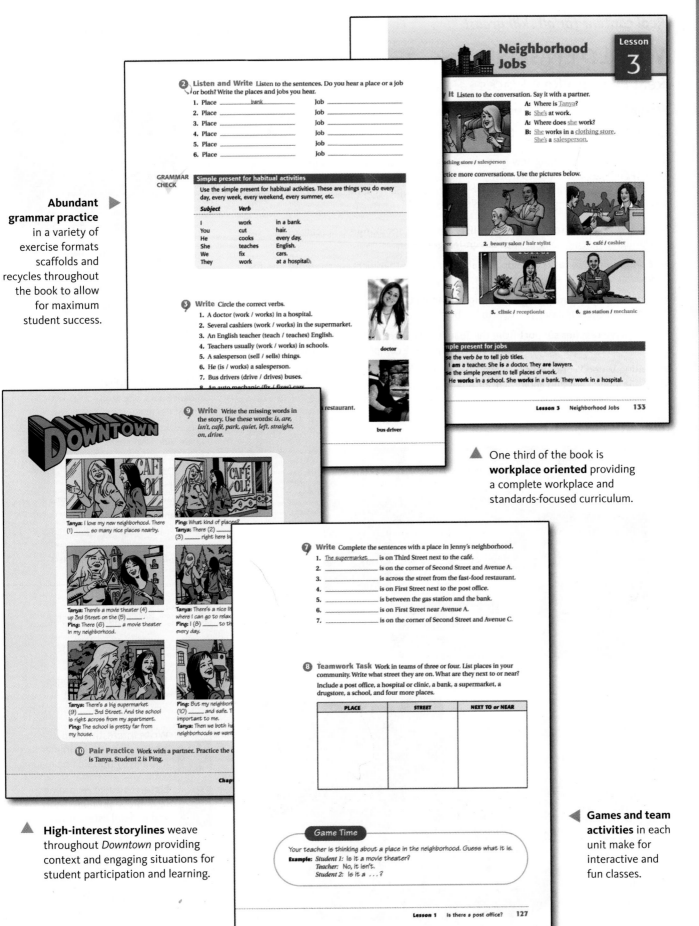

Abundant grammar practice in a variety of exercise formats scaffolds and recycles throughout the book to allow for maximum student success.

2 Listen and Write Listen to the sentences. Do you hear a place or a job or both? Write the places and jobs you hear.

1. Place ....bank....... Job ....
2. Place .... Job ....
3. Place .... Job ....
4. Place .... Job ....
5. Place .... Job ....
6. Place .... Job ....

GRAMMAR CHECK

Simple present for habitual activities

Use the simple present for habitual activities. These are things you do every day, every week, every weekend, every summer, etc.

Subject	Verb	
I	work	in a bank.
You	cut	hair.
He	cooks	every day.
She	teaches	English.
We	fix	cars.
They	work	at a hospital.

3 Write Circle the correct verbs.

1. A doctor (work / works) in a hospital.
2. Several cashiers (work / works) in the supermarket.
3. An English teacher (teach / teaches) English.
4. Teachers usually (work / works) in schools.
5. A salesperson (sell / sells) things.
6. He (is / works) a salesperson.
7. Bus drivers (drive / drives) buses.
8. An auto mechanic (fix / fixes) cars.

doctor

bus driver

Neighborhood Jobs

Lesson 3

... It Listen to the conversation. Say it with a partner.

A: Where is Tanya?
B: She's at work.
A: Where does she work?
B: She works in a clothing store. She's a salesperson.

... thing store / salesperson

... ctice more conversations. Use the pictures below.

2. beauty salon / hair stylist   3. café / cashier

5. clinic / receptionist   6. gas station / mechanic

... mple present for jobs

... se the verb be to tell job titles.
... I am a teacher. She is a doctor. They are lawyers.
... se the simple present to tell places of work.
... He works in a school. She works in a bank. They work in a hospital.

Lesson 3   Neighborhood Jobs   133

One third of the book is **workplace oriented** providing a complete workplace and standards-focused curriculum.

DOWNTOWN

Tanya: I love my new neighborhood. There (1) _____ so many nice places nearby.

Ping: What kind of places?
Tanya: There (2) _____
(3) _____ right here b...

Tanya: There's a movie theater (4) _____ up 3rd Street on the (5) _____.
Ping: There (6) _____ a movie theater in my neighborhood.

Tanya: There's a nice li... where I can go to relax...
Ping: I (8) _____ to th... every day.

Tanya: There's a big supermarket (9) _____ 3rd Street. And the school is right across from my apartment.
Ping: The school is pretty far from my house.

Ping: But my neighbor... (10) _____ and safe. T... important to me.
Tanya: Then we both h... neighborhoods we want...

9 Write Write the missing words in the story. Use these words: is, are, isn't, café, park, quiet, left, straight, on, drive.

... restaurant.

10 Pair Practice Work with a partner. Practice the ... is Tanya. Student 2 is Ping.

Chap...

7 Write Complete the sentences with a place in Jenny's neighborhood.

1. The supermarket is on Third Street next to the café.
2. _____ is on the corner of Second Street and Avenue A.
3. _____ is across the street from the fast-food restaurant.
4. _____ is on First Street next to the post office.
5. _____ is between the gas station and the bank.
6. _____ is on First Street near Avenue A.
7. _____ is on the corner of Second Street and Avenue C.

8 Teamwork Task Work in teams of three or four. List places in your community. Write what street they are on. What are they next to or near?

Include a post office, a hospital or clinic, a bank, a supermarket, a drugstore, a school, and four more places.

PLACE	STREET	NEXT TO or NEAR

Game Time

Your teacher is thinking about a place in the neighborhood. Guess what it is.
Example: *Student 1:* Is it a movie theater?
Teacher: No, it isn't.
Student 2: Is it a ...?

Lesson 1   Is there a post office?   127

High-interest storylines weave throughout *Downtown* providing context and engaging situations for student participation and learning.

Games and team activities in each unit make for interactive and fun classes.

Real content for all skill areas!

WORLD ENGLISH Intro – 3

Real People • Real Places • Real Language

Martin Milner, Kristin L. Johannsen, Rebecca Tarver Chase

LEVEL: low-beginning to high-intermediate

World English is an exciting new four-skills program which uses lively and compelling content, images, and video to teach the language that learners need to succeed in their classrooms and daily lives. *World English* uses real people, real places, and real language to connect English language learners to the world.

- Students develop **reading, writing, listening, and speaking** skills seamlessly through engaging content with integrated grammar.

- **Communicative tasks** develop language strategies that increase students' comfort level in real-world settings.

- Video from **National Geographic Digital Media** on DVD and Student CD-ROM allows teachers to bring the text to life both in the classroom and individually.

- **Extensive teacher support** from the Teacher's Edition, DVD, Assessment CD-ROM with Exam*View®*, and the Teacher Web Site provide complete, time-saving solutions.

- **Online Video Workbooks** for each level contain all National Geographic Digital Media video clips and additional, automatically graded comprehension exercises.

NEW!

Read, Listen, and Watch in ALL skill areas!

SERIES COMPONENTS
Student Books with Student CD-ROM
Student CD-ROMs
Workbooks
Online Video Workbooks
Teacher's Editions
Audio CDs
DVDs
Assessment CD-ROM with Exam*View®*
ELT Advantage: An *Introduction to Teaching ESL/EFL* by Tom Scovel, p. 111

See pp. 143-144 for World English *ISBN/Price listings*

For a guided tour, visit
elt.heinle.com/worldenglish

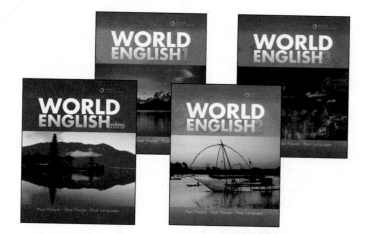

READ

Read engaging passages designed to highlight key grammar and vocabulary.

WRITE

Write interesting and personalized assignments inspired by the exciting readings.

LISTEN

Listen to audio recordings to improve pronunciation and general listening skills.

COMMUNICATE

Communicate with guided activities using the appropriate grammar and vocabulary.

WATCH

Watch exciting, thematically-linked clips from National Geographic Digital Media.

The Student CD-ROM includes:

- ✔ All video clips from the DVD

- ✔ All Listening and Speaking activities from the Audio CD

- ✔ Interactive activities that provide instant feedback

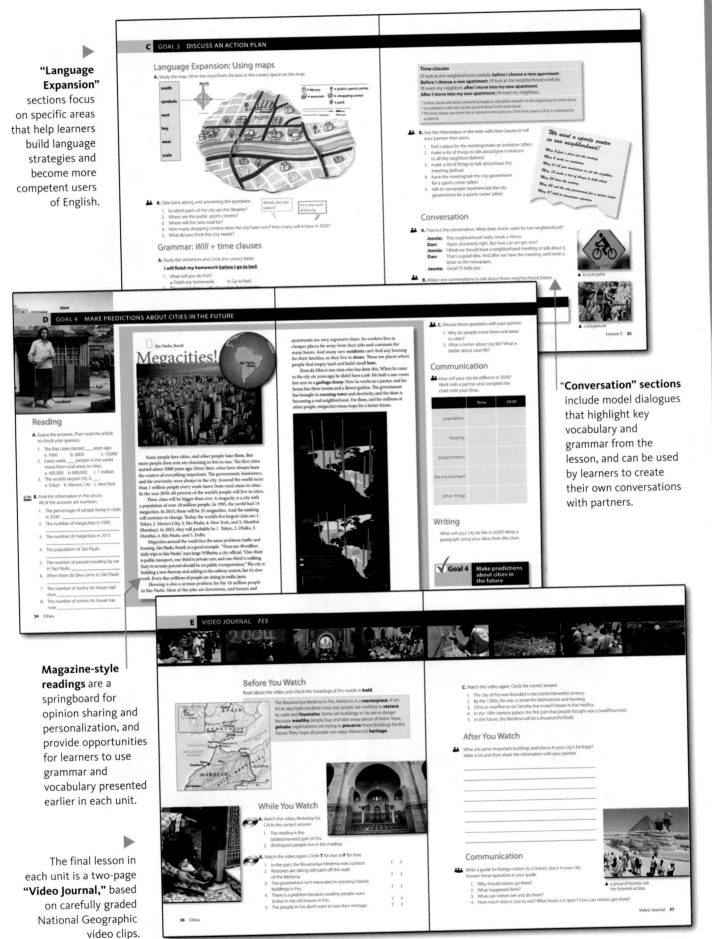

"Language Expansion" sections focus on specific areas that help learners build language strategies and become more competent users of English.

C GOAL 3 DISCUSS AN ACTION PLAN

Language Expansion: Using maps

A. Study the map. Write the word from the box in the correct space on the map.

south
symbols
east
key
west
scale

North

• library   • public sports center
• museum   • shopping center
         • park

B. Take turns asking and answering the questions.

1. In which parts of the city are the libraries?
2. Where are the public sports centers?
3. Where will the new road be?
4. How many shopping centers does the city have now? How many will it have in 2020?
5. What do you think this city needs?

Where's the train station?

It's in the north of the city.

Grammar: Will + time clauses

A. Study the sentences and circle the correct letter.

I will finish my homework before I go to bed.

1. What will you do first?
   a. Finish my homework.   b. Go to bed.

Time clauses

I'll look at the neighborhood carefully **before I choose a new apartment.**
Before I choose a new apartment, I'll look at the neighborhood carefully.
I'll meet my neighbors **after I move into my new apartment.**
After I move into my new apartment, I'll meet my neighbors.

* A time clause tells when something happens. Use before and after at the beginning of a time clause.
* In a sentence with will, use the present tense in the time clause.
* The time clause can come first or second in the sentence. If the time clause is first, it is followed by a comma.

B. Use the information in the note with time clauses to tell your partner their plans.

1. find a place for the meeting/make an invitation (after)
2. make a list of things to talk about/give invitations to all the neighbors (before)
3. make a list of things to talk about/have the meeting (before)
4. have the meeting/ask the city government for a sports center (after)
5. talk to newspaper reporters/ask the city government for a sports center (after)

We need a sports center in our neighborhood!

May 1 find a place for the meeting
May 5 make an invitation
May 8-12 give invitations to all the neighbors
May 15 make a list of things to talk about
May 23 have the meeting
May 24 ask the city government for a sports center
May 27 talk to newspaper reporters

Conversation

A. Practice the conversation. What does Jennie want for her neighborhood?

Jennie: This neighborhood really needs a library.
Dan: You're absolutely right. But how can we get one?
Jennie: I think we should have a neighborhood meeting to talk about it.
Dan: That's a good idea. And after we have the meeting, we'll write a letter to the newspaper.
Jennie: Great! I'll help you.

B. Make new conversations to talk about these neighborhood places.

▲ bicycle paths

▲ a playground

Lesson C 33

"Conversation" sections include model dialogues that highlight key vocabulary and grammar from the lesson, and can be used by learners to create their own conversations with partners.

D GOAL 4 MAKE PREDICTIONS ABOUT CITIES IN THE FUTURE

slum
garbage dump
running water
hut
resident

Reading

A. Guess the answers. Then read the article to check your guesses.

1. The first cities started ___ years ago.
   a. 1000   b. 5000   c. 10,000
2. Every week, ___ people in the world move from rural areas to cities.
   a. 400,000   b. 800,000   c. 1 million
3. The world's largest city is ___.
   a. Tokyo   b. Mexico City   c. New York

B. Find the information in the article. All of the answers are numbers.

1. The percentage of people living in cities in 2030 ___
2. The number of megacities in 1995 ___
3. The number of megacities in 2015 ___
4. The population of São Paulo ___
5. The number of people traveling by car in São Paulo ___
6. When Ilson da Silva came to São Paulo ___
7. The number of rooms his house had then ___
8. The number of rooms his house has now ___

São Paulo, Brazil

Megacities!

São Paulo, Brazil

Some people love cities, and other people hate them. But more people than ever are choosing to live in one. The first cities started about 5000 years ago. Since then, cities have always been the centers of everything important. The government, businesses, and the university were always in the city. Around the world more than 1 million people every week move from rural areas to cities. In the year 2030, 60 percent of the world's people will live in cities.

These cities will be bigger than ever. A megacity is a city with a population of over 10 million people. In 1995, the world had 14 megacities. In 2015, there will be 21 megacities. And the ranking will continue to change. Today, the world's five largest cities are 1. Tokyo, 2. Mexico City, 3. São Paulo, 4. New York, and 5. Mumbai (Bombay). In 2015, they will probably be 1. Tokyo, 2. Dhaka, 3. Mumbai, 4. São Paulo, and 5. Delhi.

Megacities around the world face the same problems: traffic and housing. São Paulo, Brazil, is a good example. "There are 30 million daily trips in São Paulo," says Jorge Wilheim, a city official. "One-third is public transport, one-third is private cars, and one-third is walking. Sixty to seventy percent should be on public transportation." The city is building a new freeway and adding to the subway system, but it's slow work. Every day, millions of people are sitting in traffic jams.

Housing is also a serious problem for the 18 million people in São Paulo. Most of the jobs are downtown, and houses and apartments are very expensive there. So workers live in cheaper places far away from their jobs and commute for many hours. And many new **residents** can't find any housing for their families, so they live in **slums**. These are places where people find empty land and build small **huts**.

Ilson da Silva is one man who has done this. When he came to the city six years ago, he didn't have a job. He lived in a one-room hut next to a **garbage dump**. Now he works as a janitor, and his house has three rooms and a flower garden. The government has brought in **running water** and electricity, and the slum is becoming a real neighborhood. For Ilson, and for millions of other people, megacities mean hope for a better future.

2015

2000

C. Discuss these questions with your partner.

1. Why do people move from rural areas to cities?
2. What is better about city life? What is better about rural life?

Communication

How will your city be different in 2030? Work with a partner and complete the chart with your ideas.

	Now	2030
population		
housing		
transportation		
the environment		
other things		

Writing

What will your city be like in 2030? Write a paragraph using your ideas from the chart.

✓ Goal 4 Make predictions about cities in the future

34 Cities

Magazine-style readings are a springboard for opinion sharing and personalization, and provide opportunities for learners to use grammar and vocabulary presented earlier in each unit.

The final lesson in each unit is a two-page **"Video Journal,"** based on carefully graded National Geographic video clips.

E VIDEO JOURNAL FES

Before You Watch

Read about the video and check the meanings of the words in **bold**.

SPAIN

MOROCCO

ATLANTIC OCEAN

ALGERIA

The Bouananiya Medersa in Fes, Morocco, is a **masterpiece** of art. It's in very bad condition now, but people are working to **restore** its walls and **fountains**. Some old buildings in Fes are in danger because **wealthy** people buy and take away pieces of them. Now, **private** organizations are trying to **preserve** these buildings for the future. They hope all people can enjoy Morocco's **heritage**.

While You Watch

A. Watch the video, Restoring Fes. Circle the correct answer.

1. The medina is the (oldest/newest) part of Fes.
2. (Rich/poor) people live in the medina.

B. Watch the video again. Circle **T** for *true* or **F** for *false*.

1. In the past, the Bouananiya Medersa was a palace. T F
2. Restorers are taking old paint off the walls of the Medersa. T F
3. The government isn't interested in restoring historic buildings in Fes. T F
4. There is a problem because wealthy people want to live in the old houses in Fes. T F
5. The people in Fes don't want to lose their heritage. T F

C. Watch the video again. Circle the correct answer.

1. The city of Fes was founded in the (ninth/eleventh) century.
2. By the 1300s, Fes was a center for (art/science) and learning.
3. (One or two/five or six) families live in each house in the medina.
4. In the 18th-century palace, the first part that people bought was a (wall/fountain).
5. In the future, the Medersa will be a (museum/school).

After You Watch

What are some important buildings and places in your city's heritage? Make a list and then share the information with your partner.

_____
_____
_____
_____
_____
_____

Communication

Write a guide for foreign visitors to a historic place in your city. Answer these questions in your guide.

1. Why should visitors go there?
2. What happened there?
3. What can visitors see and do there?
4. How much does it cost to visit? What hours is it open? How can visitors get there?

▲ a group of tourists visit the Pyramids at Giza

36 Cities

Video Journal 37

Take Action! See, hear, and actively practice the language of everyday life!

ENGLISH IN ACTION 1–4

Barbara H. Foley, Elizabeth R. Neblett

Correlated to EFF, CASAS, SCANS, and State ESL Standards!

LEVEL: low-beginning to high-intermediate

English in Action is a four-level core language series for secondary and adult students that engages learners as workers, family members, and citizens. Students master listening, speaking, reading, writing, and grammar through a variety of lively, classroom-tested, easy-to-use activities.

- **Dictionary:** Colorful pictures introduce vocabulary in a picture dictionary format.
- **"Active Grammar":** Structured exercises and charts present and practice necessary grammar in context.
- **Pronunciation:** Sound discrimination and production activities complement extensive listening opportunities.
- **"Working Together":** Group work, pair work, and cooperative tasks help students explore the language.
- **"The Big Picture":** Lively scenes based on chapter themes integrate listening, vocabulary, and structure.
- **Reading:** Readings from interviews of real people in real communities expand student literacy.
- **"Writing Our Stories":** Authentic models give students an opportunity to write about themselves.
- **"Practicing on Your Own":** Homework exercises provide reinforcement in class or at home.
- **"Looking At...":** Forms, numbers, charts, and a variety of realia provide a closer look at interesting topics.

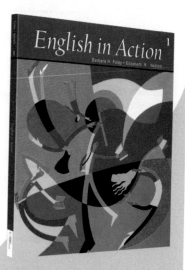

Workbook with Audio CD provides listening practice beyond the textbook!

SERIES COMPONENTS
Student Texts
Workbooks with Audio CD
Audio CDs
Grammar Café, see p. 58
Teacher's Guides
Assessment CD-ROM with Exam*View*®

See p. 126 for English in Action *ISBN/Price listings*

elt.heinle.com/englishinaction

For additional reading practice, see *Access Reading* on p. 48.

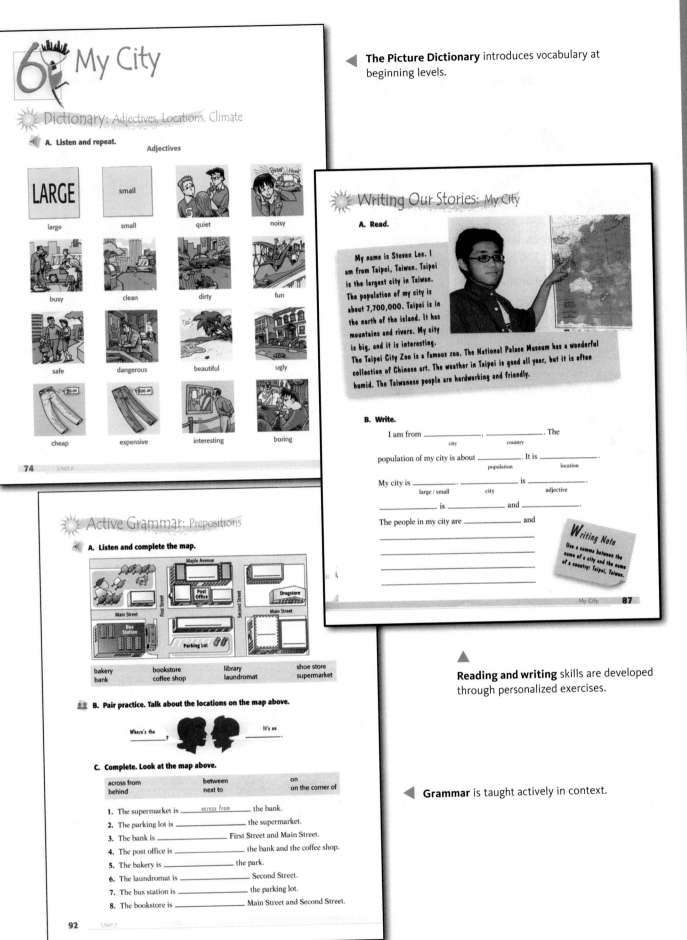

6 My City

Dictionary: Adjectives, Locations, Climate

A. Listen and repeat.

Adjectives

LARGE	small		Better House
large	small	quiet	noisy
busy	clean	dirty	fun
safe	dangerous	beautiful	ugly
cheap	expensive	interesting	boring

74 UNIT 6

The **Picture Dictionary** introduces vocabulary at beginning levels.

Writing Our Stories: My City

A. Read.

My name is Steven Lee. I am from Taipei, Taiwan. Taipei is the largest city in Taiwan. The population of my city is about 7,700,000. Taipei is in the north of the island. It has mountains and rivers. My city is big, and it is interesting.
The Taipei City Zoo is a famous zoo. The National Palace Museum has a wonderful collection of Chinese art. The weather in Taipei is good all year, but it is often humid. The Taiwanese people are hardworking and friendly.

B. Write.

I am from _____ , _____ . The
                city   country

population of my city is about _____ . It is _____ .
                           population   location

My city is _____ . _____ is _____
         large / small   city   adjective

_____ is _____ and _____ .

The people in my city are _____ and

Writing Note
Use a comma between the name of a city and the name of a country: Taipei, Taiwan.

My City 87

▲

Reading and writing skills are developed through personalized exercises.

Active Grammar: Prepositions

A. Listen and complete the map.

Maple Avenue
Post Office
Drugstore
Main Street
Bus Station
Parking Lot
Main Street

bakery	bookstore	library	shoe store
bank	coffee shop	laundromat	supermarket

B. Pair practice. Talk about the locations on the map above.

Where's the _____ ?   It's on _____ .

C. Complete. Look at the map above.

across from	between	on
behind	next to	on the corner of

1. The supermarket is ___across from___ the bank.
2. The parking lot is _____ the supermarket.
3. The bank is _____ First Street and Main Street.
4. The post office is _____ the bank and the coffee shop.
5. The bakery is _____ the park.
6. The laundromat is _____ Second Street.
7. The bus station is _____ the parking lot.
8. The bookstore is _____ Main Street and Second Street.

92 UNIT 7

Grammar is taught actively in context.

45

For a fully-articulated, six-level curriculum, use *World Link* followed by *World Pass*.

WORLD LINK Intro – 3
Developing English Fluency

Susan Stempleski, Nancy Douglas, James R. Morgan with Andy Curtis

LEVEL: beginning to intermediate

Combining dynamic vocabulary with essential grammar and universal topics, *World Link* enables students to communicate confidently and fluently. A complete package of supplementary materials motivates students and empowers teachers to maximize classroom time.

- **Appealing and universal topics** include: Unsolved Mysteries, Modern Family Trends, and Dream Jobs.

- **Unprecedented teacher support** in the Teacher's Edition includes "Lesson Planning Guides" for each unit and "Professional Development Pages" by Andy Curtis.

- **Online components** offer teacher training and resources and student workbooks!

- *World Link Video Course* **offers twelve video units for each level,** designed as World Link support or as a separate stand-alone course, including two distinct formats divided into 2-3 minute clips:

  ✔ **"City Living": original dramatic episodes** about six friends from different countries living, studying, and working in New York City

  ✔ **"Global Viewpoints": real-life interviews** with students and professionals that offer examples of real English language use while presenting viewpoints from a wide variety of cultural backgrounds

Student Texts
Workbooks (Print or Online)
Combo Split Editions (Student Text/Workbook combined)
Teacher's Editions with Presentation Tool CD-ROM
Teacher's Resource Books
Audio CDs
Videos (DVD or VHS)
Video Workbooks (Print or Online)
Video Teacher's Guides
Assessment CD-ROM with Exam*View*® & Audio CD
ELT Advantage: *Pursuing Professional Development* by Andy Curtis, p. 111

***World Link Video Course* Intro – 3**

 For a guided tour, visit **elt.heinle.com/worldlink**

WORLD PASS 1 & 2
Expanding English Fluency

Susan Stempleski, Nancy Douglas, James R. Morgan, Kristin L. Johannsen with Andy Curtis

LEVEL: upper-intermediate to advanced

To help students expand their fluency, *World Pass* focuses on dynamic vocabulary-building, essential grammar, and stimulating activities that emphasize the language they need for real-world communication.

Student Texts
Workbooks (Print or Online)
Combo Split Editions (Student Text / Workbook combined)
Audio CDs
Teacher's Editions
Teacher's Resource Books
CNN® Videos (DVD or VHS)
Assessment CD-ROM with Exam*View*®
ELT Advantage: *Pursuing Professional Development* by Andy Curtis, p. 111

elt.heinle.com/worldpass

U.S. CITIZEN, YES
Preparing for Citizenship, Third Edition

Ronna Magy

LEVEL: beginning to low-intermediate

NEW!

The new edition of *U.S. Citizen, Yes* helps students succeed on the new citizenship test and to become engaged and active citizens.

New to this edition:

■ **Updated readings, vocabulary support,** and **expanded activities** help students learn about U.S. history and government covered in the test.

■ **Guided practice tests** give students the confidence they need to succeed on the Naturalization Test.

■ **Community and Civics Participation Projects** provide ideas for students to learn about and participate in their communities.

■ An **Audio CD** gives students interactive practice for the naturalization interview and the dictation portion of the redesigned exam.

Updated for the new U.S. Citizenship test!

COMPONENTS
Student Text
Audio CD

See p. 142 for U.S. Citizen, Yes ISBN/Price listings

For citizenship flashcards, **visit elt.heinle.com/uscitizenyes**

NEW! Updated Content

1. Before You Read

Barack Obama, Forty-fourth President of the United States

A. Sit in a group of four. Look at the picture above. Talk about the questions. Write your answers in your book.
1. Who is the president of the United States? _____
2. What does the president do? _____
3. Who is the vice president of the United States? _____
4. What does the vice president do? _____
5. What other people advise the president? _____
6. What is the Supreme Court? _____
7. What does the Supreme Court do? _____
8. Who is the chief justice of the Supreme Court? _____
9. What is the political party of the president now? _____

B. Read your answers to your class.

2. Citizenship Reading

A. What do you know about these words? Write your ideas on the lines.

the Executive Branch — the Judicial Branch

B. Read.

U.S. Government: The Executive and Judicial Branches

The Executive Branch The executive branch enforces the laws passed by Congress. The president, vice president, and the Cabinet are the executive branch. The president is in charge of the executive branch.

The Department of Homeland Security (DHS), the Central Intelligence Agency (CIA), the Federal Bureau of Investigation (FBI), the U.S. Citizenship and Immigration Service (USCIS), the Environmental Protection Agency (EPA), and the U.S. Postal Service (USPS) are some of the agencies in the executive branch.

The President and the Vice President The president is the leader of the country. The president is also the leader of the executive branch. The president signs bills into law, enforces the law, prepares budgets, and is the commander in chief of the military. The president may also veto bills. The president lives and works in the White House. The address of the White House is 1600 Pennsylvania Avenue NW, Washington, D.C. The vice president helps the president and is the leader of the Senate.

The president and the vice president are each elected for a term of four years and can serve for two terms. We vote for the president and vice president on Election Day. It is the first Tuesday after the first Monday in November. In January, the president and vice president are inaugurated (sworn into office).

General Information To be president or vice president, a person must be a natural-born citizen of the United States, must be at least 35 years old, and must have lived in the United States for fourteen years. If the president can no longer serve, the vice president becomes the president. If the both the president and the vice president can no longer serve, the Speaker of the House becomes the president. The president and vice president

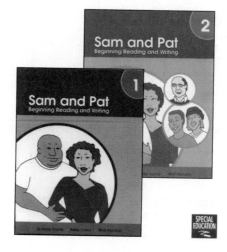

ACCESS READING 1 – 4

Reading in the Real World

Tim Collins

LEVEL: **high-beginning to high-intermediate**

Access Reading helps students learn to access the information and resources they need to become effective workers, community members, and parents. It develops communication, decision-making, interpersonal, and lifelong learning skills through interesting readings and practical application of new knowledge.

- Each unit contains two reading passages based on a topic: health, friends, you and your community, staying informed, our heritage, time, money, and more.

- Essential reading strategies help students improve reading literacy.

- A special *Access Reading* Web site provides additional optional readings and activities.

Student Texts
Audio CDs
Instructor's Manuals

---

elt.heinle.com/accessreading

Ideal with core programs such as
Downtown, p. 40; *Stand Out*, p. 38;
and *English in Action*, p. 44.

SAM AND PAT 1 & 2

Beginning Reading and Writing

Jo Anne Hartel, Betsy Lowry, Whit Hendon

LEVEL: **literacy to low-beginning**

Sam and Pat is a phonics-based series that uses a clear and interesting character-based storyline to teach reading and writing skills at the challenging low-beginning level.

- The intriguing storyline explores a family's daily life experiences at work, school, and home.

- Each lesson focuses on a target sound or sounds.

- "Phonetic Word Grids" corresponding to each lesson give students extra practice in identifying and writing phonetic words.

- Basic phonics-based writing activities enhance vocabulary acquisition and enhance reading skills development.

- Photocopiable flash cards are provided at the back of each text.

Student Texts
Audio CDs

ADDITIONAL ADULT/SECONDARY TITLES

BETTER ENGLISH EVERY DAY 1 – 3
Language for Living

Paul Hamel

LEVEL: beginning to high-intermediate

CROSSROADS CAFÉ

**K. Lynn Savage, Series Director
Anna Cuomo,
Patricia Mooney Gonzalez,
Mary McMullin, Elizabeth Minicz,
Lydia Omari, Kathryn Powell**

LEVEL: beginning to advanced

IN DETAIL 1 & 2
English for Global Communication

Isobel Rainey de Diaz

LEVEL: high-intermediate to advanced

INTERCOM 2000 1 – 4, 3/e

**Anna Uhl Chamot,
Joan Baker Gonzalez,
Isobel Rainey de Diaz,
Richard C. Yorkey**

LEVEL: beginning to intermediate

LITERACY IN LIFESKILLS 1 & 2

Sally Gati

LEVEL: literacy

PRACTICAL ENGLISH 1 – 3, 2/e

Tim Harris, Allan Rowe

LEVEL: beginning to low-intermediate

UP CLOSE 1 – 4
English for Global Communication

**Anna Uhl Chamot,
Isobel Rainey de Diaz,
Joan Baker Gonzalez with
Deborah Gordon and Nina Weinstein**

LEVEL: beginning to intermediate

WRITING PRACTICAL ENGLISH 1 – 3, 2/e

Tim Harris, Allan Rowe

LEVEL: beginning to low-intermediate

LEVEL GUIDE

	PAGE NUMBER	LOW-BEGINNING	BEGINNING	HIGH-BEGINNING	LOW-INTERMEDIATE	INTERMEDIATE	HIGH-INTERMEDIATE	LOW-ADVANCED	ADVANCED
Advanced Grammar Book, The, 2/e	60								•
Applied English Grammar	60					•		•	•
Grammar Café: 1, 2, 3, 4, 5, 6	58		1	1	2	3	4	5	6
Grammar Clips	58		•	•					
Grammar Connection: 1, 2, 3, 4, 5	54		1	2	2	3	4	4	5
Grammar Dimensions, 4/e: 1, 2, 3, 4	50			1	1	2	3	4	4
Grammar Expert: Basic, 1, 2, 3	59		Basic	1	1	2	3		
Grammar in Context, 4/e: Basic, 1, 2, 3	52		Basic	1	2	2	3		
Grammar Links: Basic, 1, 2, 3	56		Basic	1	2	2	3	3	
More Grammar Practice: 1, 2, 3	59			1	2	3	3		
New Grammar in Action, The: Basic, 1, 2, 3	59	Basic	1	1	2	3			
Practice: Grammar	60					•	•	•	•
Problem/Solution	60						•		•
Tense Situations, 2/e	60						•		
Two-Word Verbs in English	60					•	•		•
World English: Intro, 1, 2, 3 NEW!	42	Intro	1	1	2	2	3		
GRAMMAR FOR WRITING									
Read, Write, Edit	78							•	•
Think About Editing	82					•			
Top 10	78			•		•			
Top 20, 2/e	78							•	•
Writing Clearly: An Editing Guide, 2/e	82						•	•	•
Writing Essentials	82					•	•	•	•

The most comprehensive and communicative series available!

GRAMMAR DIMENSIONS 1–4

Form, Meaning, Use, Fourth Edition

Diane Larsen-Freeman, *Series Director*

Book 1: **Victoria Badalamenti, Carolyn Henner-Stanchina**
Book 2: **Ingrid Wisniewska, Heidi Riggenbach, Virginia Samuda**
Book 3: **Stephen Thewlis**
Book 4: **Jan Frodesen, Janet Eyring**

LEVEL: high-beginning to advanced

Through clear and comprehensive grammar explanations, extensive practice exercises, and lively communicative activities, *Grammar Dimensions* helps students develop the skill of "grammaring"—the ability to use structures accurately, meaningfully, and appropriately.

■ **Enhanced College Edition** of *Grammar Dimensions* includes *Grammar Café,* the online grammar solution that increases students' understanding of key concepts and provides 20 hours of FREE extra practice!

■ **Revised Opening Tasks** can be used as a diagnostic or warm-up exercise to explore students' knowledge of each structure's form, meaning, and use.

■ **Updated topics, grammar charts, and grammar exercises** provide detailed grammar practice.

■ The **"Use Your English" pages** offer communicative activities that meaningfully apply grammar to reading, writing, listening, and speaking opportunities.

■ **Internet Activities** explore outside sources of language to expand upon students' communication and language skills.

■ **Workbooks** provide additional exercises to improve grammar, editing activities to increase students' writing skills, and a test-taking section to enhance students' application skills.

■ **Lesson Planners** contain step-by-step teaching instructions with a choice of lesson plans to suit the needs of individual classrooms and teachers.

■ **Assessment CD-ROM with Exam*View*®** allows teachers to create tests and quizzes quickly and easily.

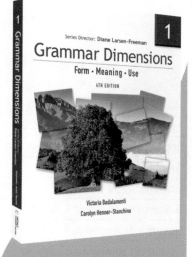

Use grammar accurately, meaningfully, and appropriately!

SERIES COMPONENTS

School Edition
NEW! Enhanced College Edition featuring *Grammar Café*
Split Edition Texts
Workbooks
Audio CDs
Grammar Café, see p. 58
Grammar Clips, see p. 58
Lesson Planners
Assessment CD-ROMs with Exam*View*®
NEW! ELT Advantage: *Teaching Grammar for ESL/EFL* by Diane Larsen-Freeman, p. 111

See p. 131 for Grammar Dimensions ISBN/Price listings

elt.heinle.com/grammardimensions

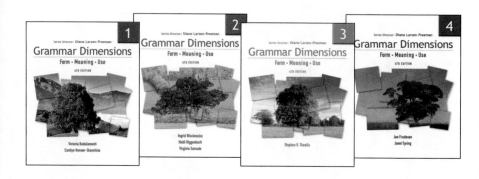

Learning Packages complete the student experience.

● Package the **audio** with the text for only **$1 more.**

● Package the **workbook** with the text for only **$10 more.**

● Package the **audio and the workbook** with the text for only **$11 more.**

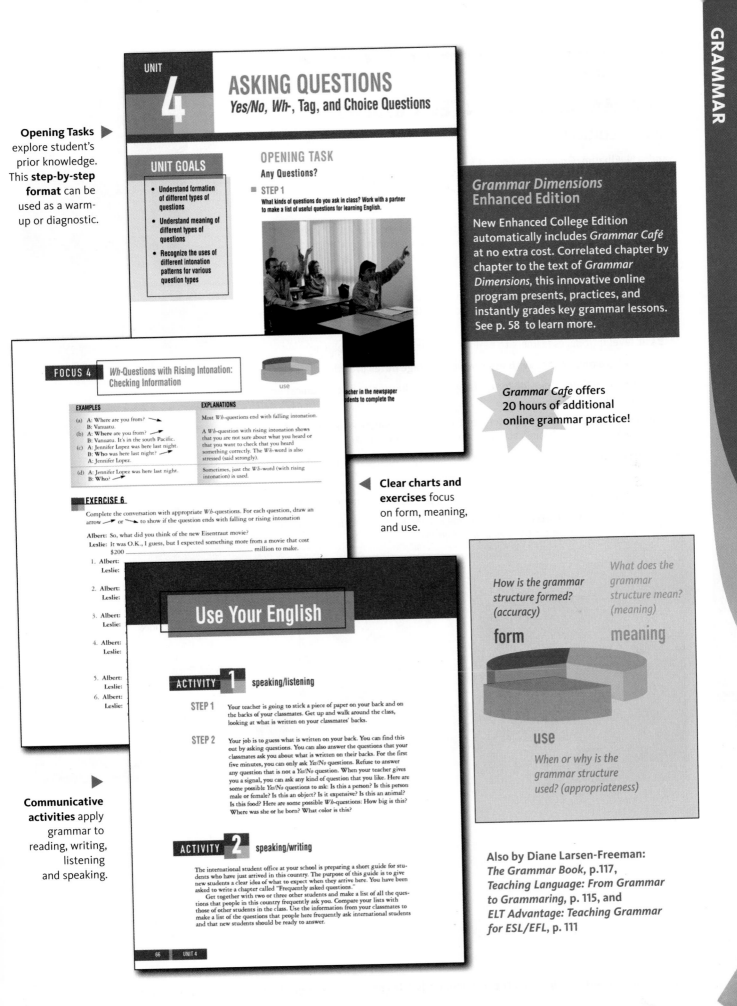

Opening Tasks explore student's prior knowledge. This **step-by-step format** can be used as a warm-up or diagnostic.

UNIT

4

ASKING QUESTIONS
Yes/No, Wh-, Tag, and Choice Questions

UNIT GOALS

- Understand formation of different types of questions
- Understand meaning of different types of questions
- Recognize the uses of different intonation patterns for various question types

OPENING TASK

Any Questions?

■ STEP 1

What kinds of questions do you ask in class? Work with a partner to make a list of useful questions for learning English.

Grammar Dimensions **Enhanced Edition**

New Enhanced College Edition automatically includes *Grammar Café* at no extra cost. Correlated chapter by chapter to the text of *Grammar Dimensions*, this innovative online program presents, practices, and instantly grades key grammar lessons. See p. 58 to learn more.

Grammar Cafe offers 20 hours of additional online grammar practice!

FOCUS 4 | *Wh-*Questions with Rising Intonation: Checking Information

use

EXAMPLES

(a) A: Where are you from?
    B: Vanuatu.
(b) A: **Where** are you from?
    B: Vanuatu. It's in the south Pacific.
(c) A: Jennifer Lopez was here last night.
    B: **Who** was here last night?
    A: Jennifer Lopez.
(d) A: Jennifer Lopez was here last night.
    B: **Who**?

EXPLANATIONS

Most *Wh-*questions end with falling intonation.

A *Wh-*question with rising intonation shows that you are not sure about what you heard or that you want to check that you heard something correctly. The *Wh-*word is also stressed (said strongly).

Sometimes, just the *Wh-*word (with rising intonation) is used.

acher in the newspaper dents to complete the

EXERCISE 6

Complete the conversation with appropriate *Wh-*questions. For each question, draw an arrow ➚ or ➘ to show if the question ends with falling or rising intonation

Albert: So, what did you think of the new Eisentraut movie?
Leslie: It was O.K., I guess, but I expected something more from a movie that cost $200 _____ million to make.

1. Albert:
   Leslie:
2. Albert:
   Leslie:
3. Albert:
   Leslie:
4. Albert:
   Leslie:
5. Albert:
   Leslie:
6. Albert:
   Leslie:

◄ **Clear charts and exercises** focus on form, meaning, and use.

Use Your English

ACTIVITY **1** speaking/listening

STEP 1   Your teacher is going to stick a piece of paper on your back and on the backs of your classmates. Get up and walk around the class, looking at what is written on your classmates' backs.

STEP 2   Your job is to guess what is written on your back. You can find this out by asking questions. You can also answer the questions that your classmates ask you about what is written on their backs. For the first five minutes, you can only ask *Yes/No* questions. Refuse to answer any question that is not a *Yes/No* question. When your teacher gives you a signal, you can ask any kind of question that you like. Here are some possible *Yes/No* questions to ask: Is this a person? Is this person male or female? Is this an object? Is it expensive? Is this an animal? Is this food? Here are some possible *Wh-*questions: How big is this? Where was she or he born? What color is this?

▶ **Communicative activities** apply grammar to reading, writing, listening and speaking.

ACTIVITY **2** speaking/writing

The international student office at your school is preparing a short guide for students who have just arrived in this country. The purpose of this guide is to give new students a clear idea of what to expect when they arrive here. You have been asked to write a chapter called "Frequently asked questions."

Get together with two or three other students and make a list of all the questions that people in this country frequently ask you. Compare your lists with those of other students in the class. Use the information from your classmates to make a list of the questions that people here frequently ask international students and that new students should be ready to answer.

66   UNIT 4

How is the grammar structure formed? (accuracy)

What does the grammar structure mean? (meaning)

form   meaning

use

When or why is the grammar structure used? (appropriateness)

Also by Diane Larsen-Freeman:
The Grammar Book, p.117,
Teaching Language: From Grammar to Grammaring, p. 115, and
ELT Advantage: Teaching Grammar for ESL/EFL, p. 111

Students learn more, remember more, and use grammar more effectively!

GRAMMAR IN CONTEXT Basic – 3
Fourth Edition

Sandra N. Elbaum, *Grammar in Context 1 – 3, 4/e*
Sandra N. Elbaum and Judi P. Pemán, *Grammar in Context Basic*

LEVEL: beginning to high-intermediate

Students learn more, remember more, and use language more effectively when they learn grammar in context. *Grammar in Context* presents grammar in interesting, informative readings and then recycles the language and context throughout every activity.

- **Enhanced College Edition** of *Grammar in Context* comes with *Grammar Café*, a revolutionary online resource that provides 20 FREE hours of interactive grammar practice!

- **Basic level** introduces learners to basic English structure and vocabulary.

- **Updated grammar charts with integrated language notes** provide added clarity.

- **"About You" activities** provide for language personalization and communicative opportunities.

- **Expansion activities** offer opportunities to consolidate language and expand communicative skills through activities both in and out of class.

- **Editing advice** gives pre-writing practice and alerts students to common errors.

- **Split Editions** provide options for shorter courses.

- **Interactive CD-ROM** instructs, illustrates, and practices key grammar points.

- **Instructional Video/DVD** presents teaching suggestions and advice on how to maximize the effectiveness of *Grammar in Context.*

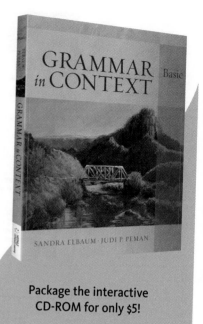

Package the interactive CD-ROM for only $5!

SERIES COMPONENTS
School Edition
NEW! Enhanced College Edition featuring *Grammar Café*
Split Edition Texts
Audio CDs
Grammar Café, see p. 58
Grammar Clips, see p. 58
Teacher's Annotated Editions
Assessment CD-ROMs with Exam*View*®
Interactive Grammar CD-ROM
Instructional Video

See p. 131 for Grammar in Context *ISBN/Price listings*

elt.heinle.com/grammarincontext

Learning Packages complete the student experience.

- Package the **audio** with the text for only **$1 more.**

- Package the **workbook** with the text for only **$10 more.**

- Package the **audio and the workbook** with the text for only **$11 more.**

- Package *Grammar Café*, 20 hours of interactive online grammar practice, for just **$5 more.**

▼ **Contextualized activities** including "About You" activities

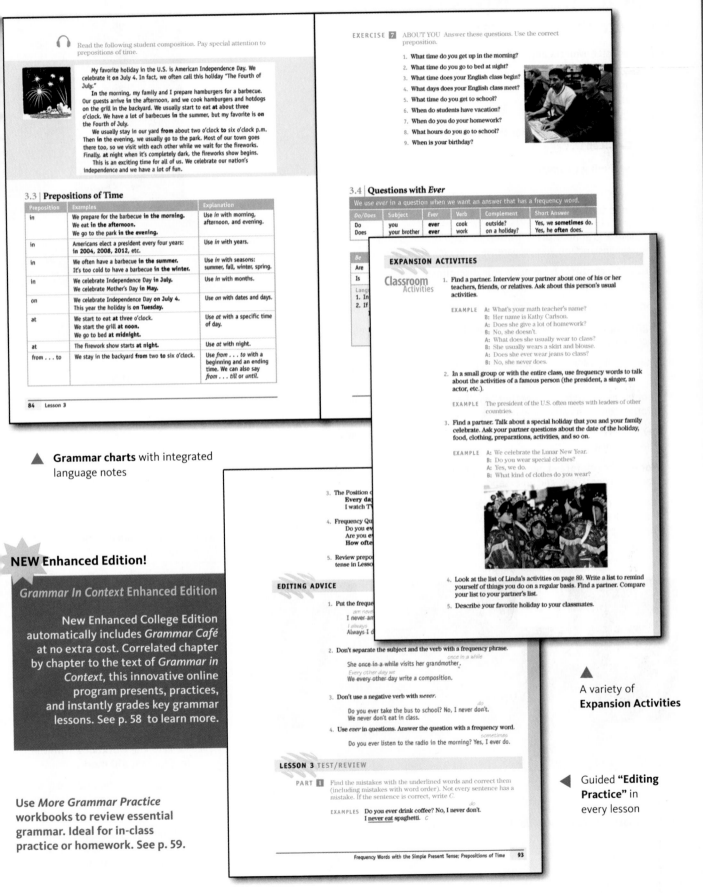

Read the following student composition. Pay special attention to prepositions of time.

My favorite holiday in the U.S. is American Independence Day. We celebrate it **on** July 4. In fact, we often call this holiday "The Fourth of July."

In the morning, my family and I prepare hamburgers for a barbecue. Our guests arrive **in** the afternoon, and we cook hamburgers and hotdogs on the grill in the backyard. We usually start to eat **at** about three o'clock. We have a lot of barbecues **in** the summer, but my favorite is **on** the Fourth of July.

We usually stay in our yard **from** about two o'clock **to** six o'clock p.m. Then **in** the evening, we usually go to the park. Most of our town goes there too, so we visit with each other while we wait for the fireworks. Finally, **at** night when it's completely dark, the fireworks show begins.

This is an exciting time for all of us. We celebrate our nation's independence and we have a lot of fun.

3.3 | Prepositions of Time

Preposition	Examples	Explanation
in	We prepare for the barbecue **in the morning**. We eat **in the afternoon**. We go to the park **in the evening**.	Use *in* with morning, afternoon, and evening.
in	Americans elect a president every four years: **in 2004, 2008, 2012**, etc.	Use *in* with years.
in	We often have a barbecue **in the summer**. It's too cold to have a barbecue **in the winter**.	Use *in* with seasons: summer, fall, winter, spring.
in	We celebrate Independence Day **in July**. We celebrate Mother's Day **in May**.	Use *in* with months.
on	We celebrate Independence Day **on July 4**. This year the holiday is **on Tuesday**.	Use *on* with dates and days.
at	We start to eat **at three o'clock**. We start the grill **at noon**. We go to bed **at midnight**.	Use *at* with a specific time of day.
at	The firework show starts **at night**.	Use *at* with night.
from . . . to	We stay in the backyard **from two to six o'clock**.	Use *from . . . to* with a beginning and an ending time. We can also say *from . . . till* or *until*.

84 Lesson 3

EXERCISE **7** ABOUT YOU Answer these questions. Use the correct preposition.

1. What time do you get up in the morning?
2. What time do you go to bed at night?
3. What time does your English class begin?
4. What days does your English class meet?
5. What time do you get to school?
6. When do students have vacation?
7. When do you do your homework?
8. What hours do you go to school?
9. When is your birthday?

3.4 | Questions with *Ever*

We use *ever* in a question when we want an answer that has a frequency word.

Do/Does	Subject	Ever	Verb	Complement	Short Answer
Do	you	ever	cook	outside?	Yes, we **sometimes** do.
Does	your brother	ever	work	on a holiday?	Yes, he **often** does.

▲ **Grammar charts** with integrated language notes

✦ NEW Enhanced Edition!

Grammar In Context Enhanced Edition

New Enhanced College Edition automatically includes *Grammar Café* at no extra cost. Correlated chapter by chapter to the text of *Grammar in Context*, this innovative online program presents, practices, and instantly grades key grammar lessons. See p. 58 to learn more.

Use *More Grammar Practice* workbooks to review essential grammar. Ideal for in-class practice or homework. See p. 59.

EXPANSION ACTIVITIES

Classroom Activities

1. Find a partner. Interview your partner about one of his or her teachers, friends, or relatives. Ask about this person's usual activities.

   EXAMPLE A: What's your math teacher's name?
   B: Her name is Kathy Carlson.
   A: Does she give a lot of homework?
   B: No, she doesn't.
   A: What does she usually wear to class?
   B: She usually wears a skirt and blouse.
   A: Does she ever wear jeans to class?
   B: No, she never does.

2. In a small group or with the entire class, use frequency words to talk about the activities of a famous person (the president, a singer, an actor, etc.).

   EXAMPLE The president of the U.S. often meets with leaders of other countries.

3. Find a partner. Talk about a special holiday that you and your family celebrate. Ask your partner questions about the date of the holiday, food, clothing, preparations, activities, and so on.

   EXAMPLE A: We celebrate the Lunar New Year.
   B: Do you wear special clothes?
   A: Yes, we do.
   B: What kind of clothes do you wear?

4. Look at the list of Linda's activities on page 80. Write a list to remind yourself of things you do on a regular basis. Find a partner. Compare your list to your partner's list.

5. Describe your favorite holiday to your classmates.

3. The Position of
   Every day
   I watch TV

4. Frequency Qu
   Do you **ever**
   Are you **ever**
   How often

5. Review prepo
   tense in Lesso

EDITING ADVICE

1. Put the freque
   ~~am never~~
   I never am
   ~~I always~~
   Always I d

2. Don't separate the subject and the verb with a frequency phrase.
   She ~~once in a while~~ visits her grandmother. *once in a while*
   ~~Every other day we~~
   We ~~every other day~~ write a composition. *Every other day we*

3. Don't use a negative verb with *never*.
   Do you ever take the bus to school? No, I never ~~don't~~. *do*
   We never ~~don't~~ eat in class.

4. Use *ever* in questions. Answer the question with a frequency word.
   Do you ever listen to the radio in the morning? Yes, I ~~ever~~ do. *sometimes*

▲ A variety of **Expansion Activities**

◀ Guided **"Editing Practice"** in every lesson

LESSON 3 TEST/REVIEW

PART **1** Find the mistakes with the underlined words and correct them (including mistakes with word order). Not every sentence has a mistake. If the sentence is correct, write C.

EXAMPLES Do you ever drink coffee? No, I never ~~don't~~. *do*
I <u>never eat</u> spaghetti. *C*

The level-appropriate grammar your students really need!

GRAMMAR CONNECTION 1–5
Structure Through Content

Marianne Celce-Murcia and M.E. Sokolik, *Series Editors*

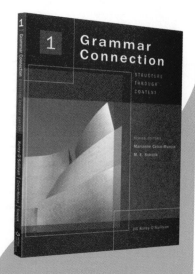

Book 1: **Jill Korey O'Sullivan**
Book 2: **Richard Firsten**
Book 3: **Karen Carlisi**
Book 4: **Sharon Hilles, Noel Houck**
Book 5: **Cathleen D. Cake**

LEVEL: beginning to advanced

At each level, *Grammar Connection* teaches the grammar students really need to know for academic and professional success.

- **Accessible grammar presentation** through readings and conversations offers natural language instruction and prepares learners for academic success.

- **Authentic contexts from academic disciplines** provide essential background for grammar presentation and practice.

- **Concise lessons with clear grammar charts** create an easy-to-follow framework.

- **High-frequency academic vocabulary** is systematically developed in "Content Vocabulary" sections.

- **Multi-skills practice** in reading, writing, listening, and speaking simulates the skills learners need in academic contexts.

- **"Connection: Putting It Together"** synthesizes grammar, vocabulary, and content through communicative activities.

- **Review and Learner Logs** summarize language instruction and enhance learner independence.

- **Workbooks reinforce language** through controlled grammar practice, recycled academic vocabulary, and an extended writing tutorial.

- **Teacher's Annotated Editions** include detailed teaching suggestions as well as a *Classroom Presentation Tool CD-ROM* with Activity Bank Worksheets for interactive grammar presentation and additional communicative practice.

Featuring academic content!

SERIES COMPONENTS
Student Texts
Workbooks
Audio CDs
Grammar Café, see p. 58
Grammar Clips, see pg. 58
Teacher's Annotated Editions with Activity Bank and Classroom Presentation Tool CD-ROMs
Assessment CD-ROM with Exam*View*®

See p. 131 for Grammar Connection ISBN/Price listings

elt.heinle.com/grammarconnection

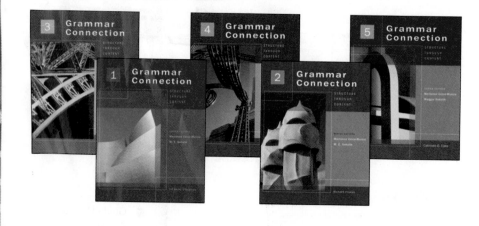

Also by Marianne Celce-Murcia: *The Grammar Book*, p.117.

Learning Packages complete the student experience.

- Package the **audio** with the text for only **$1 more**.

- Package the **workbook** with the text for only **$10 more**.

- Package the **audio and the workbook** with the text for only **$11 more**.

- Package *Grammar Café*, 20 hours of interactive online grammar practice, for just **$5 more**.

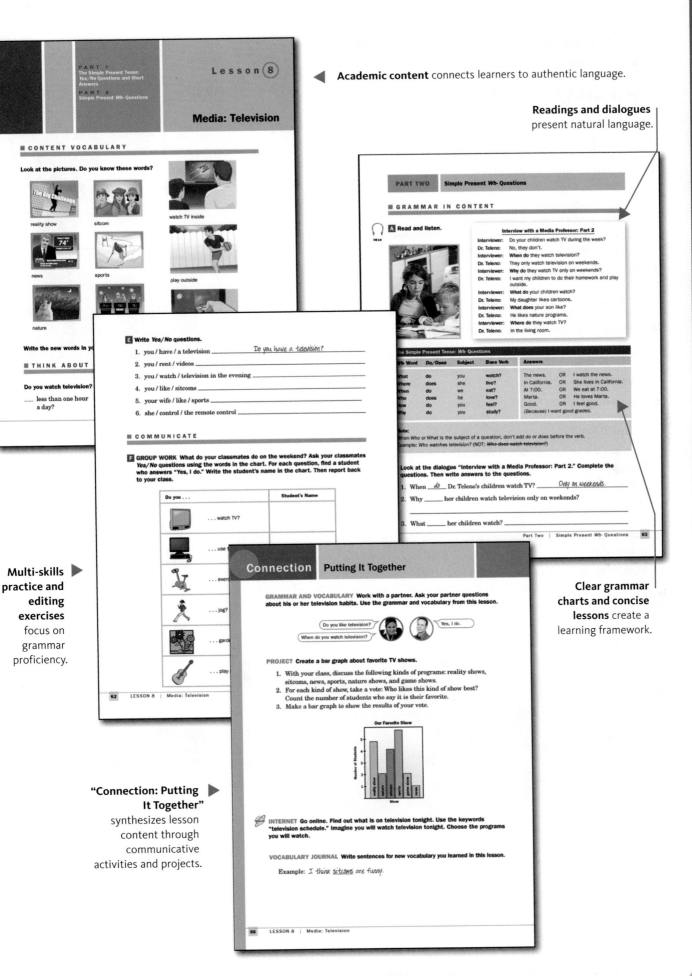

Academic content connects learners to authentic language.

Readings and dialogues present natural language.

PART 1
The Simple Present Tense:
Yes/No Questions and Short
Answers
PART 2
Simple Present Wh- Questions

Lesson 8

Media: Television

■ CONTENT VOCABULARY

Look at the pictures. Do you know these words?

reality show

sitcom

watch TV inside

news

sports

play outside

nature

Write the new words in yo

■ THINK ABOUT

Do you watch television?

____ less than one hour
a day?

PART TWO | Simple Present Wh- Questions

■ GRAMMAR IN CONTENT

A Read and listen.

Interview with a Media Professor: Part 2

Interviewer: Do your children watch TV during the week?
Dr. Teleno: No, they don't.
Interviewer: When do they watch television?
Dr. Teleno: They only watch television on weekends.
Interviewer: Why do they watch TV only on weekends?
Dr. Teleno: I want my children to do their homework and play outside.
Interviewer: What do your children watch?
Dr. Teleno: My daughter likes cartoons.
Interviewer: What does your son like?
Dr. Teleno: He likes nature programs.
Interviewer: Where do they watch TV?
Dr. Teleno: In the living room.

The Simple Present Tense: Wh- Questions

Wh- Word	Do/Does	Subject	Base Verb	Answers		
What	do	you	watch?	The news.	OR	I watch the news.
Where	does	she	live?	In California.	OR	She lives in California.
When	do	we	eat?	At 7:00.	OR	We eat at 7:00.
Who	does	he	love?	Marta.	OR	He loves Marta.
How	do	you	feel?	Good.	OR	I feel good.
Why	do	you	study?	(Because) I want good grades.		

Note:
When Who or What is the subject of a question, don't add do or does before the verb.
Example: Who watches television? (NOT: Who does watch television?)

Look at the dialogue "Interview with a Media Professor: Part 2." Complete the questions. Then write answers to the questions.

1. When __do__ Dr. Teleno's children watch TV? __Only on weekends.__

2. Why _____ her children watch television only on weekends? _____

3. What _____ her children watch? _____

Part Two | Simple Present Wh- Questions   **63**

Clear grammar charts and concise lessons create a learning framework.

E Write Yes/No questions.

1. you / have / a television _____ Do you have a television? ____

2. you / rent / videos _____

3. you / watch / television in the evening _____

4. you / like / sitcoms _____

5. your wife / like / sports _____

6. she / control / the remote control _____

■ COMMUNICATE

F GROUP WORK What do your classmates do on the weekend? Ask your classmates Yes/No questions using the words in the chart. For each question, find a student who answers "Yes, I do." Write the student's name in the chart. Then report back to your class.

Do you . . .	Student's Name
. . . watch TV?	
. . . use t	
. . . exerc	
. . . jog?	
. . . gard	
. . . play	

62   LESSON 8 | Media: Television

Multi-skills practice and editing exercises focus on grammar proficiency.

Connection   **Putting It Together**

GRAMMAR AND VOCABULARY Work with a partner. Ask your partner questions about his or her television habits. Use the grammar and vocabulary from this lesson.

Do you like television?   Yes, I do.

When do you watch television?

PROJECT Create a bar graph about favorite TV shows.

1. With your class, discuss the following kinds of programs: reality shows, sitcoms, news, sports, nature shows, and game shows.
2. For each kind of show, take a vote: Who likes this kind of show best? Count the number of students who say it is their favorite.
3. Make a bar graph to show the results of your vote.

Our Favorite Show

INTERNET Go online. Find out what is on television tonight. Use the keywords "television schedule." Imagine you will watch television tonight. Choose the programs you will watch.

VOCABULARY JOURNAL Write sentences for new vocabulary you learned in this lesson.

Example: I think sitcoms are funny.

66   LESSON 8 | Media: Television

"Connection: Putting It Together" synthesizes lesson content through communicative activities and projects.

A theme-based course combines a focus on form with a communicative approach.

GRAMMAR LINKS Basic – 3

A Theme-based Course for Reference and Practice, Second Edition

M. Kathleen Mahnke, *Series Editor*

Basic: **Linda Butler**
Book 1, 2/e: **Linda Butler, Janet Podnecky**
Book 2, 2/e: **M. Kathleen Mahnke, Elizabeth O'Dowd**
Book 3, 2/e: **Janis van Zante, Debra Daise, Charl Norloff, Randee Falk**

LEVEL: low-beginning to advanced

With engaging universal themes and an emphasis on formal versus informal language, *Grammar Links* integrates concise and manageable grammar presentation with reading, writing, listening, and speaking skills practice.

- **An accessible design** features easy-to-read grammar charts that highlight structures and serve as reference points to revisit throughout the course and for exam preparation.

- **Compelling themes** introduce students to concepts they will encounter in their academic work by contextualizing grammar so that students can truly master English discourse.

- **A strong emphasis on formal versus informal language** helps students make grammatical choices with confidence.

- **Abundant and varied practice exercises and activities** emphasize the four-skills (reading, writing, speaking, and listening). Chapters begin with more controlled activities and move toward more open-ended, communicative activities.

- **Extended reading and listening selections** introduce and illustrate grammar in use.

- **Unit Wrap-ups** provide activities that pull the unit grammar together and enable students to test, further practice, and apply what they have learned.

Package with *Grammar Café* or *Grammar Clips!*

SERIES COMPONENTS
Student Texts
Split Edition Texts
Workbooks
Audio CDs
Grammar Café, see p. 58
Grammar Clips, see p. 58
Online Teaching and Study Centers

See p. 132 for Grammar Links *ISBN/Price listings*

elt.heinle.com/grammarlinks

Learning Packages complete the student experience.

- Package the **audio** with the text for only **$1 more**.

- Package the **workbook** with the text for only **$10 more**.

- Package the **audio and the workbook** with the text for only **$11 more**.

- Package *Grammar Café*, 20 hours of interactive online grammar practice, for just **$5 more**.

"Grammar Hotspot" boxes alert students to troublesome areas of grammar and mistakes to avoid.

"Talking the Talk" boxes address pragmatic concerns related to grammatical choices in written and spoken English.

"Grammar Briefing" charts clearly present English language as structures, functions and meanings, and include usage rules as well as contextualized example sentences.

End-of-unit **"Wrap-up Activities"** enable students to test, further practice, and apply the grammar they have learned.

GRAMMAR HOTSPOT!

1. To form possessive nouns:
   - Add an apostrophe (') to plural nouns that end in -s.
   - Add ' or 's to singular nouns that end in -s.
   - Add 's to all other nouns.

   - With two or more nouns together, add 's or ' only to the second noun.

2. Possessive adjectives and pronouns keep the same form before both singular and plural nouns. They do not have special singular or plural forms.

the **babies'** books
Charles' book OR **Charles's** book
the **baby's** book
the **children's** book
John and Mary's children
the **girls and the boys'** teacher
This is **their** camera.
These are not **their** cameras.
NOT: These are theirs cameras.

TALKING THE TALK

	MOST WRITING AND SPEAKING	VERY FORMAL WRITING
We often use object pronouns after the verb *be*. In very formal writing, we use subject pronouns.	Peter's in the photo. That's **him** in the back.	Peter is in the photograph. That is **he** in the back.

GRAMMAR PRACTICE 2

Pronouns and Possessive Adjectives II

2 Pronouns and Possessive Adjectives: Journey to the Ce...

Complete the story with the correct words from the boxes. Use ea...

they	them	their	✓theirs

Clara and Martin love adventure vacations. Many people take inter...

__theirs__ are especially exciting. Clara and Martin t...
1

vacations on _____ bicycles. They enjoy _____
2

much on these trips. _____ are planning their ne...
4

_____ from Cairo, Egypt, across the desert to the...
5

GRAMMAR BRIEFING 3

Numbers and Measure Words

FORM and FUNCTION

A. Numbers

We use definite numbers (*one, two, three, four, five,* etc.) to count people, places, and things. The patterns are:
- *One* + singular count noun.
- All other numbers + plural noun.

one book, two books, three books

B. Measure Words

Measure words express specific or exact (not general) amounts. Most measure words follow this pattern:

A/ONE/TWO THREE, ETC.	MEASURE WORD	OF	PLURAL COUNT NOUN
a	box		paper clips
a	cup	of	beans
two	pounds		apples

			NONCOUNT NOUN
a	box		paper
a	cup	of	sugar
two	pounds		meat

C. Special Measure Words

Certain nouns have special measure words. These measure words are used only with a small group of nouns.

a **bunch** of grapes, a **bunch** of bananas
a **clove** of garlic
a **head** of lettuce, a **head** of cauliflower
a **loaf** of bread

Unit Four

Wrap-up Activities

1 Travel in the North: EDITING

Correct the errors in this article. There are 15 errors with nouns, pronouns, possessive adjectives, articles, quantifiers, and numbers. (Sometimes there is more than one possible correction.) The first error is corrected for you.

This vehicle travels up to 70 miles a hour. It travels on the ground, but it doesn't have wheels. And it doesn't have a engine! What is it? It's sled.

People used sleds in ancient times. A first sleds were animal skins. Travelers pulled these sleds behind them. But animal skin sleds were slow. Their didn't slide smoothly. So ancient travelers added runners to they. These runners were long pieces of bone or wood. Travelers put the runners under the animal skins. The runners made their sleds travel faster

and more smoothly, but pulling a sled still took several energy. No one didn't like this very much. So people began training animals to pull their sleds. Then sleds became very fast.

Each years in northern countries, many people gather together for special dogsled races. One famous race, the Iditarod, takes place in the early Spring in northern alaska. In this race, teams of dogs and humans travel from Anchorage to Nome— over 1,000 miles of difficult land. There are much challenges: deep snow, unpredictable weather, and wild animals. Dogs often wear boots to protect theirselves from ice. Approximately 75 team compete each year. Some teams don't finish the long trek. But everybody have a great adventure!

See the *Grammar Links* Website for more information about the Iditarod dogsled race.

---

2 Journey to the Bottom of the Sea: SPEAKING/LISTENING

Imagine you are going "camping" at the bottom of the sea! You will live in a "sea bubble" for three days. The bubble has lots of glass on the outside, so you can see all of the interesting fish and plants living in the sea.

Step 1 Read the information in this brochure about your adventure.

FACT SHEET

In your bubble you will have:

* Oxygen—for only three days

* Water—for showers but no clean drinking water

* Sleeping compartment with a shower

* A small bed—no blankets

* A small cooking stove and refigerator—no food

Other information about your bubble:

Heat: Heat from the sun during the day. No heat at night.

Night temperature inside the bubble: 32° Fahrenheit (0°Celsius)

Electricity: turned off at 10:00 every night

Equipment needed to leave bubble and explore: pressurized diving suit, extra oxygen, head lamp

You must take everything you need for three days.

You may take no more than 40 pounds of personal belongings with you in the bubble.

Add new life to your traditional grammar course!

GRAMMAR CAFÉ 1–6

LEVEL: low-beginning to advanced

Grammar Café is a revolutionary online grammar course that presents key grammar lessons on the computer with the help of animated text, graphics, and real-world conversations. The program features a three-step process with presentation, practice, and assessment to meet the needs of students in various courses. Featuring six levels with 20 units per level, *Grammar Café* represents approximately 120 hours of instruction.

Grammar Presentation

A complete grammar lesson includes four parts:

- *Introduction:* presents topic through a practical situation.
- *Dialogue:* uses the grammar as used in context.
- *Lesson:* offers an animated explanation of the structure with voice-over guidance.
- *Chart:* reviews the grammar structure in a summative, printable format.

Learning Activities

- Four activities allow for both form-focused and open-ended grammar practice.
- Most results are instantly graded.
- Open-ended listening and speaking activities are recorded and sent to the instructor for evaluation.

Self-Check Quiz

- Questions confirm that the learner has grasped the grammar concept beyond just the form.
- Results are instantly graded.

POWERED BY

 To watch a demonstration, visit **elt.heinle.com/technology**

Bundle *Grammar Café* with any Heinle writing or grammar text for only $5!

Grammar Clips DVDs cover 26 important grammar points through:

- ✔ Easy-to-understand grammar charts
- ✔ Simple animations
- ✔ Live action video dialogues
- ✔ Quick comprehension checks

Video DVDs
Workbook

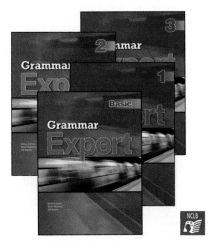

THE NEW GRAMMAR IN ACTION Basic – 3

An Integrated Course in English

Barbara H. Foley, Elizabeth R. Neblett

LEVEL: low-beginning to
high-intermediate

Appropriate for adult and secondary school learners, *The New Grammar in Action* series offers a dynamic approach to teaching grammar. This four-level series presents vocabulary and structures through inviting contexts while integrating listening, speaking, writing, and reading practice. Each unit progresses from controlled exercises to creative, real-world tasks, preparing students for success in English outside of class.

- The "Grammar in Action" section introduces each unit with listening activities and illustrations, setting the context and grammar focus.
- Graphs, charts, and illustrations engage learners in using English in real situations.
- Various exercise types help students of various learning styles and keep classes lively and motivating.
- Assessment Booklet includes pre- and post-tests, as well as tests for each unit.

Student Texts with Audio CD
Audio CDs
Answer Key
Assessment Booklet
Correlation Guide

GRAMMAR EXPERT
Basic – 3

Sarah Bideleux, Gill Mackie,
Series Editors

LEVEL: beginning to high-intermediate

Grammar Expert is a four-level series of grammar reference and practice books. Grammar points are illustrated in an entertaining cartoon featuring Norman, our hard-working hero, who provides a light-hearted start to the unit.

- Concise explanations and clear examples enable students to study grammar points in short chunks to gain a better understanding of the material.
- Grammar exercises within each unit increase in difficulty to provide motivation and to give students graded practice.
- A communication activity and a writing task at the end of each unit help consolidate the grammar points covered in an effective way through realistic situations.
- Five review sections ensure that students have a thorough understanding of all the grammar points covered in the previous units.
- Five review progress tests allow teachers to assess their students' progress.

Student Texts
Assessment CD-ROM with Exam*View*®

MORE GRAMMAR PRACTICE 1 – 3

LEVEL: high-beginning to
high-intermediate

Used alone or in conjunction with your reading, writing, and listening/speaking course books, *More Grammar Practice* helps students learn and review the essential grammar skills to make language learning comprehensive and ongoing.

- Quick lessons are ideal for grammar presentation and review.
- Crystal clear grammar boxes and language notes present target structures.
- Exercises keep students motivated.

Workbooks
Answer Key

APPLIED ENGLISH GRAMMAR

Patricia Byrd, Beverly Benson

LEVEL: high-intermediate to advanced

Authentic academic contexts provide strong grammar instruction and lead students to become more proficient writers.

- Editing skills allow learners to move beyond traditional grammar by applying their knowledge to their own written work.

- Contextualized activities and exercises progress from controlled to communicative.

- Web site provides additional practice and real-life applications.

Student Text

THE ADVANCED GRAMMAR BOOK

Second Edition

Jocelyn Steer, Karen Carlisi, Dawn Schmid

LEVEL: advanced

This best-seller presents grammatical structures through sophisticated and up-to-date contexts. The wide range of communicative activities, simplified charts, and an expanded writing section lead students from grammar recognition to production.

- Students increase their conversational and written competence by analyzing and practicing grammar in context.

- The workbook provides extensive additional exercises for classroom use or self-study.

- Engaging topics such as social changes and alternative medicine suit the interests of both community college and IEP students.

- Expanded Instructor's Manual includes testing materials.

Student Text
Workbook
Instructor's Manual

ADDITIONAL GRAMMAR TITLES

PRACTICE: GRAMMAR

Milada Broukal

LEVEL: intermediate to advanced

PROBLEM/SOLUTION

A Reference for ESL Writers

Patricia Byrd, Beverly Benson

LEVEL: high-intermediate to advanced

TENSE SITUATIONS, 2/e

Pamela Hartmann, Annette Zarian, Patricia Esparaza

LEVEL: high-intermediate

TWO-WORD VERBS IN ENGLISH

J. N. Hook

LEVEL: intermediate to advanced

LEVEL GUIDE

	PAGE NUMBER	LOW-BEGINNING	BEGINNING	HIGH-BEGINNING	LOW-INTERMEDIATE	INTERMEDIATE	HIGH-INTERMEDIATE	ADVANCED
A Good Read: 1, 2, 3 **NEW!**	65			1	2	3		
Access Reading: 1, 2, 3, 4	48			1	2	3	4	
ACTIVE Skills for Reading, 2/e: Intro, 1, 2, 3, 4	64		Intro	1	2	3	4	
Amazing Stories to Tell and Retell: 1, 2, 3	70			1,2	2,3			
American Short Stories, 2/e	70					•		
At Home in Two Lands, 2/e	68					•		
College Reading: 1, 2, 3, 4	67				1	2	3	4
Developing Reading Skills: Beginning, 2/e; Intermediate 1, 2/e; Advanced, 3/e	70		Beg	Beg	Int 1	Int 1	Int 1	A
Expanding Reading Skills, 2/e: Intermediate 2, Advanced	70					Int 2	Int 2	A
Far from Home, 3/e	68			•	•	•		
Footprint Reading Library **NEW!**	18				•	•	•	•
Foundations Reading Library	20	•	•					
Heinle Reading Library, The	16	•	•	•	•	•	•	•
Hot Topics: 1, 2, 3	69				1	2	2	3
Impressions: 1, 2	68					1	2	2
Inside Out/Outside In	70							•
Inside the News	70			•				
Life, Language, & Literature	70							•
Multicultural Workshop, The: 1, 2, 3	70			1	2	2	3	
Read to Succeed: 1, 2	70			1	2			
Reading Advantage, 2/e: 1, 2, 3, 4	70		1	2	3	4	4	
Reading & Vocabulary Development series: 1, 2, 3, 4	65		1	2	2	3	4	
Reading Explorer: 1, 2, 3, 4 **NEW!**	62		1	1	2	3	4	4
Reading for Today series: 1, 2, 3, 4, 5	66		1	2	3	3	4	5
Reading Matters, 2/e: 1, 2, 3, 4	69			1	2	3	4	
Reading the News	69					•	•	•
Reflections, 2/e	70					•		
Rethinking America: 1, 2, 3	68					1	2	3
Sam and Pat: 1, 2	48	1,2						
Steps to Academic Reading series: 1, 2, 3, 4, 5	70		1	2	3	4	5	
Stories Worth Reading: 1, 2	69			1	2			
Tapestry Reading: 1, 2, 3, 4	68			1	2	2	3	4
20th Century American Short Stories: Volumes 1, 2, Anthology	70						•	•
Weaving It Together, 3/e: 1, 2, 3, 4 **NEW!**	74			1	1	2	3	4
World English: Intro, 1, 2, 3 **NEW!**	42	Intro	1	1	2	2	3	
DICTIONARIES								
Collins COBUILD Advanced Dictionary of American English	29							•
Collins COBUILD Basic Dictionary of American English **NEW!**	25		•	•	•			
Collins COBUILD Intermediate Dictionary of American English	28				•	•	•	
Collins COBUILD School Dictionary of American English	27				•	•	•	
Heinle Picture Dictionary, The	32	•	•	•	•			
Heinle's Basic Newbury House Dictionary, 2/e	36	•	•	•	•			
Heinle's Newbury House Dictionary with Integrated Thesaurus, 4/e	36				•	•	•	

Teach reading and vocabulary through the lens of the world!

NEW!

READING EXPLORER 1–4

Nancy Douglas, Paul MacIntyre

LEVEL: beginning to advanced

Reading Explorer is a four-level, content-based reading series featuring video from National Geographic Digital Media to help develop reading and vocabulary skills for all learners. Each unit of *Reading Explorer* contains two reading passages and an optional video activity. Reading passages cover a wide range of real-world topics related to culture, science, social studies, travel, and adventure.

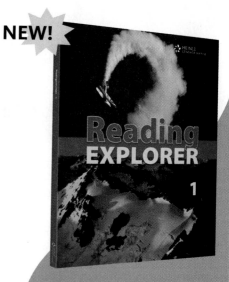

Reading and vocabulary support through print, audio, and video.

Features:

- Motivating **real-world content** supported by stunning visuals help develop learners' understanding of the world.

- **Reading passages** develop visual literacy and incorporate graphic organizers to help learners become better readers of English.

- **"Reading Comprehension"** activities cover essential reading skills and question types commonly found on standardized tests.

- **"Vocabulary Practice"** activities and **"Vocabulary Builder"** boxes present and reinforce high-frequency vocabulary items.

- **Audio CD** contains recordings of all reading selections to help aid in comprehension

- **Video from National Geographic Digital Media** motivates students and aids in visual learning.

SERIES COMPONENTS

Student Texts
Student CD-ROMS
Teacher's Guides
Audio CDs
DVDs (featuring video from
    National Geographic Digital Media)
Assessment CD-ROMs with Exam*View*®
ELT Advantage: *Teaching ESL/EFL Reading*
    by Neil J. Anderson, p. 111

See p. 139 for Reading Explorer *ISBN/Price listings*

For a guided tour, visit
elt.heinle.com/readingexplorer

For additional reading practice and resources, see *Footprint Reading Library*, p. 18.

Bundle the Student Text with the Student CD-ROM!

Student CD-ROM contains:

✔ 12 video clips

✔ 24 reading passages

✔ 48 vocabulary activities with additional self-scoring exercises

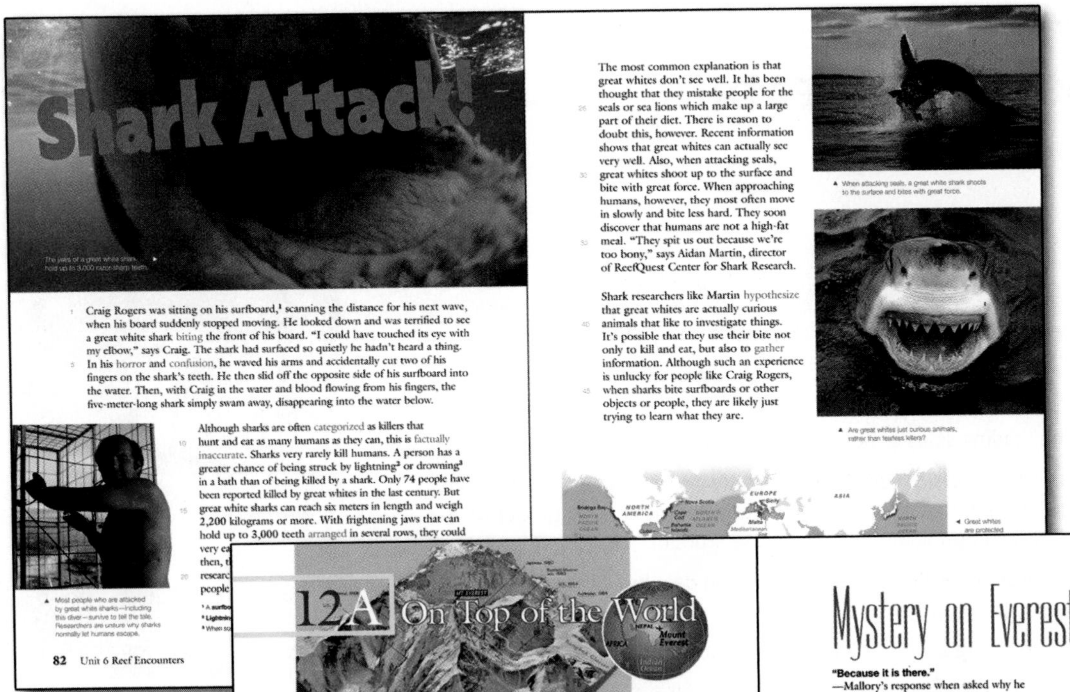

Shark Attack!

The jaws of a great white shark hold up to 3,000 razor-sharp teeth.

Craig Rogers was sitting on his surfboard,[1] scanning the distance for his next wave, when his board suddenly stopped moving. He looked down and was terrified to see a great white shark biting the front of his board. "I could have touched its eye with my elbow," says Craig. The shark had surfaced so quietly he hadn't heard a thing. In his horror and confusion, he waved his arms and accidentally cut two of his fingers on the shark's teeth. He then slid off the opposite side of his surfboard into the water. Then, with Craig in the water and blood flowing from his fingers, the five-meter-long shark simply swam away, disappearing into the water below.

Although sharks are often categorized as killers that hunt and eat as many humans as they can, this is factually inaccurate. Sharks very rarely kill humans. A person has a greater chance of being struck by lightning[2] or drowning[3] in a bath than of being killed by a shark. Only 74 people have been reported killed by great whites in the last century. But great white sharks can reach six meters in length and weigh 2,200 kilograms or more. With frightening jaws that can hold up to 3,000 teeth arranged in several rows, they could very ea... then, t... researc... people...

Most people who are attacked by great white sharks—including this diver—survive to tell the tale. Researchers are unsure why sharks normally let humans escape.

The most common explanation is that great whites don't see well. It has been thought that they mistake people for the seals or sea lions which make up a large part of their diet. There is reason to doubt this, however. Recent information shows that great whites can actually see very well. Also, when attacking seals, great whites shoot up to the surface and bite with great force. When approaching humans, however, they most often move in slowly and bite less hard. They soon discover that humans are not a high-fat meal. "They spit us out because we're too bony," says Aidan Martin, director of ReefQuest Center for Shark Research.

Shark researchers like Martin hypothesize that great whites are actually curious animals that like to investigate things. It's possible that they use their bite not only to kill and eat, but also to gather information. Although such an experience is unlucky for people like Craig Rogers, when sharks bite surfboards or other objects or people, they are likely just trying to learn what they are.

When attacking seals, a great white shark shoots to the surface and bites with great force.

Are great whites just curious animals, rather than fearless killers?

82 Unit 6 Reef Encounters

Units cover a **wide range of real-world topics** including culture, natural science, social issues, the humanities, and travel and adventure.

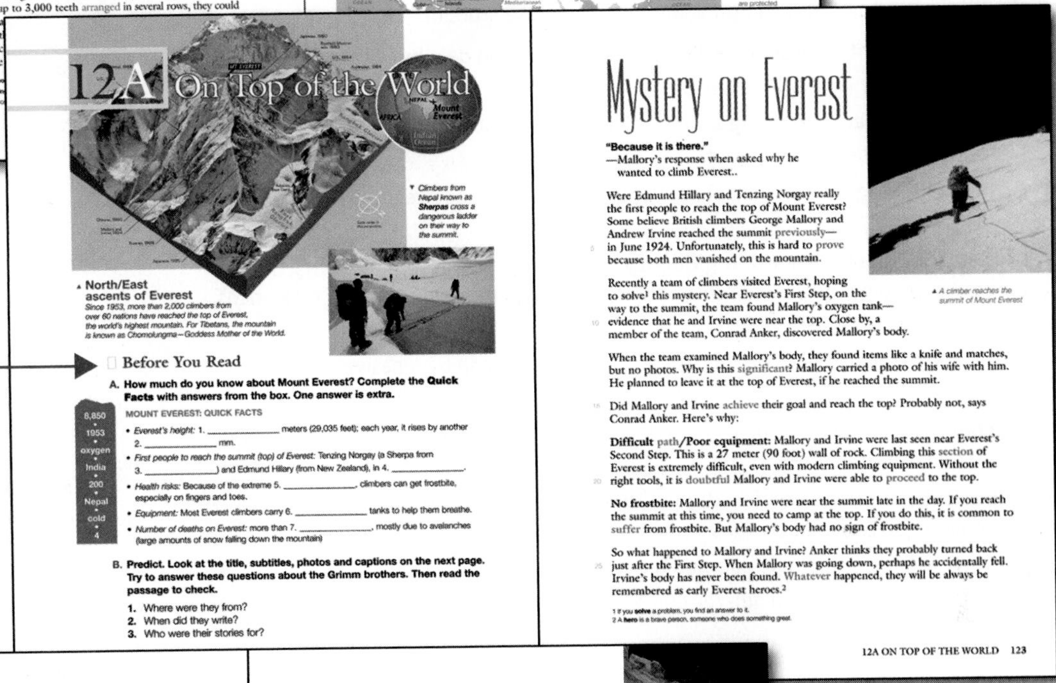

12A On Top of the World

North/East ascents of Everest

Since 1953, more than 2,000 climbers from over 60 nations have reached the top of Everest, the world's highest mountain. For Tibetans, the mountain is known as Chomolungma—Goddess Mother of the World.

Climbers from Nepal known as Sherpas cross a dangerous ladder on their way to the summit.

Before You Read

A. How much do you know about Mount Everest? Complete the Quick Facts with answers from the box. One answer is extra.

8,850 • 1953 • oxygen • India • 200 • Nepal • cold • 4

MOUNT EVEREST: QUICK FACTS

- Everest's height: 1. ________ meters (29,035 feet); each year, it rises by another 2. ________ mm.
- First people to reach the summit (top) of Everest: Tenzing Norgay (a Sherpa from 3. ________) and Edmund Hillary (from New Zealand), in 4. ________.
- Health risks: Because of the extreme 5. ________, climbers can get frostbite, especially on fingers and toes.
- Equipment: Most Everest climbers carry 6. ________ tanks to help them breathe.
- Number of deaths on Everest: more than 7. ________, mostly due to avalanches (large amounts of snow falling down the mountain)

B. Predict. Look at the title, subtitles, photos and captions on the next page. Try to answer these questions about the Grimm brothers. Then read the passage to check.

1. Where were they from?
2. When did they write?
3. Who were their stories for?

Mystery on Everest

"Because it is there."
—Mallory's response when asked why he wanted to climb Everest..

Were Edmund Hillary and Tenzing Norgay really the first people to reach the top of Mount Everest? Some believe British climbers George Mallory and Andrew Irvine reached the summit previously—in June 1924. Unfortunately, this is hard to prove because both men vanished on the mountain.

Recently a team of climbers visited Everest, hoping to solve[1] this mystery. Near Everest's First Step, on the way to the summit, the team found Mallory's oxygen tank—evidence that he and Irvine were near the top. Close by, a member of the team, Conrad Anker, discovered Mallory's body.

A climber reaches the summit of Mount Everest

When the team examined Mallory's body, they found items like a knife and matches, but no photos. Why is this significant? Mallory carried a photo of his wife with him. He planned to leave it at the top of Everest, if he reached the summit.

Did Mallory and Irvine achieve their goal and reach the top? Probably not, says Conrad Anker. Here's why:

Difficult path/Poor equipment: Mallory and Irvine were last seen near Everest's Second Step. This is a 27 meter (90 foot) wall of rock. Climbing this section of Everest is extremely difficult, even with modern climbing equipment. Without the right tools, it is doubtful Mallory and Irvine were able to proceed to the summit.

No frostbite: Mallory and Irvine were near the summit late in the day. If you reach the summit at this time, you need to camp at the top. If you do this, it is common to suffer from frostbite. But Mallory's body had no sign of frostbite.

So what happened to Mallory and Irvine? Anker thinks they probably turned back just after the First Step. When Mallory was going down, perhaps he accidentally fell. Irvine's body has never been found. Whatever happened, they will be always be remembered as early Everest heroes.[2]

1 If you **solve** a problem, you find an answer to it.
2 A **hero** is a brave person, someone who does something great.

12A ON TOP OF THE WORLD 123

"Before You Read" sections focus on content and reading strategies.

"Reading Comprehension" questions ensure student comprehension.

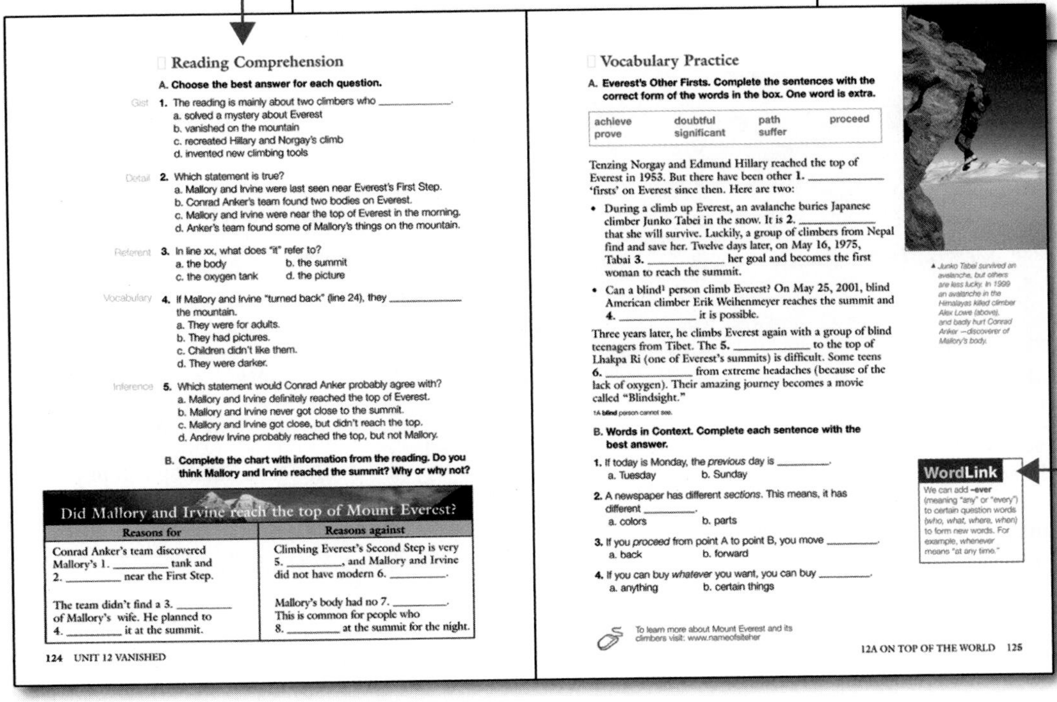

Reading Comprehension

A. Choose the best answer for each question.

Gist 1. The reading is mainly about two climbers who ________.
a. solved a mystery about Everest
b. vanished on the mountain
c. recreated Hillary and Norgay's climb
d. invented new climbing tools

Detail 2. Which statement is true?
a. Mallory and Irvine were last seen near Everest's First Step.
b. Conrad Anker's team found two bodies on Everest.
c. Mallory and Irvine were near the top of Everest in the morning.
d. Anker's team found some of Mallory's things on the mountain.

Referent 3. In line xx, what does "it" refer to?
a. the body b. the summit
c. the oxygen tank d. the picture

Vocabulary 4. If Mallory and Irvine "turned back" (line 24), they ________ the mountain.
a. They were for adults.
b. They had pictures.
c. Children didn't like them.
d. They were darker.

Inference 5. Which statement would Conrad Anker probably agree with?
a. Mallory and Irvine definitely reached the top of Everest.
b. Mallory and Irvine never got close to the summit.
c. Mallory and Irvine got close, but didn't reach the top.
d. Andrew Irvine probably reached the top, but not Mallory.

B. Complete the chart with information from the reading. Do you think Mallory and Irvine reached the summit? Why or why not?

Did Mallory and Irvine reach the top of Mount Everest?	
Reasons for	Reasons against
Conrad Anker's team discovered Mallory's 1. ________ tank and 2. ________ near the First Step.	Climbing Everest's Second Step is very 5. ________, and Mallory and Irvine did not have modern 6. ________.
The team didn't find a 3. ________ of Mallory's wife. He planned to 4. ________ it at the summit.	Mallory's body had no 7. ________. This is common for people who 8. ________ at the summit for the night.

124 UNIT 12 VANISHED

Vocabulary Practice

A. Everest's Other Firsts. Complete the sentences with the correct form of the words in the box. One word is extra.

achieve	doubtful	path	proceed
prove	significant	suffer	

Tenzing Norgay and Edmund Hillary reached the top of Everest in 1953. But there have been other 1. ________ 'firsts' on Everest since then. Here are two:

- During a climb up Everest, an avalanche buries Japanese climber Junko Tabei in the snow. It is 2. ________ that she will survive. Luckily, a group of climbers from Nepal find and save her. Twelve days later, on May 16, 1975, Tabai 3. ________ her goal and becomes the first woman to reach the summit.
- Can a blind[1] person climb Everest? On May 25, 2001, blind American climber Erik Weihenmeyer reaches the summit and 4. ________ it is possible.

Three years later, he climbs Everest again with a group of blind teenagers from Tibet. The 5. ________ to the top of Lhakpa Ri (one of Everest's summits) is difficult. Some teens 6. ________ from extreme headaches (because of the lack of oxygen). Their amazing journey becomes a movie called "Blindsight."

1 A **blind** person cannot see.

Junko Tabei survived an avalanche, but others are less lucky. In 1999 an avalanche in the Himalayas killed climber Alex Lowe (above), and badly hurt Conrad Anker —discoverer of Mallory's body.

B. Words in Context. Complete each sentence with the best answer.

1. If today is Monday, the *previous* day is ________.
a. Tuesday b. Sunday
2. A newspaper has different *sections*. This means, it has different ________.
a. colors b. parts
3. If you *proceed* from point A to point B, you move ________.
a. back b. forward
4. If you can buy *whatever* you want, you can buy ________.
a. anything b. certain things

WordLink
We can add **-ever** (meaning "any" or "every") to certain question words (who, what, where, when) to form new words. For example, whenever means "at any time."

To learn more about Mount Everest and its climbers visit: www.nameofsiteher

12A ON TOP OF THE WORLD 125

"Word Link" boxes provide additional lexical information.

Students develop reading fluency!

ACTIVE SKILLS FOR READING Intro – 4
Second Edition

Neil J. Anderson

LEVEL: beginning to high-intermediate

Build confidence in reading!

ACTIVE Skills for Reading uses thematically organized non-fiction reading passages to teach reading comprehension and vocabulary skills. Written by reading specialist Neil J. Anderson, this innovative series uses an ACTIVE reading methodology to help learners become more confident, independent—and active—readers.

- **Intro level** builds the reading skills of beginning learners.

- **Twelve updated thematic units** in each book carefully develop active reading skills by incorporating pre-reading activities, vocabulary development activities, critical thinking opportunities, and opportunities to increase students' reading fluency.

- **Four Review Units** feature timed readings and focus on developing reading speed and fluency.

- **Enhanced and varied reading selections** include newspaper articles, Web sites, blogs, journals, letters, and more.

- **Critical Thinking sections** encourage students to go beyond reading comprehension to analyze each text and the author's intent.

- **Students increase their reading fluency** by reading passages, graphs, charts and interviews, and by practicing skills such as scanning, predicting, making references, and looking for main ideas.

- **Audio Program** allows students to hear the passages read by a native English speaker.

- **Teacher's Guides** include an introduction to the methodology, a unit walk-through, and detailed lesson notes.

- **Web site** includes Internet search activities to promote extensive reading as well as vocabulary quizzes and activities.

- **Assessment CD-ROM with Exam*View*®** test-generating software allows instructors to create custom tests and quizzes quickly and easily.

SERIES COMPONENTS
Student Texts
Audio CDs
Teacher's Guides
Assessment CD-ROM with Exam*View*®
ELT Advantage: *Teaching ESL/EFL Reading* by Neil J. Anderson, p. 111
Exploring Second Language Reading, p. 114

See p. 122 for Active Skills for Reading *ISBN/Price listings*

elt.heinle.com/asr

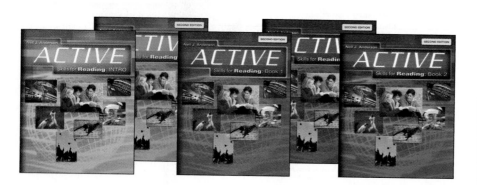

Also see p. 114 for *Exploring Second Language Reading*, Neil J. Anderson's reference guide on teaching reading, or take his online course, ELT Advantage: *Teaching ESL/EFL Reading*, p. 111.

NEW!
See ACTIVE Skills for Communication, pg.84

Author Neil J. Anderson's
ACTIVE Methodology

A = **Activate Prior Knowledge**

C = **Cultivate Vocabulary**

T = **Think About Meaning**

I = **Increase Reading Fluency**

V = **Verify Strategies**

E = **Evaluate Progress**

Increase reading, vocabulary, and dictionary skills!

NEW!

READING & VOCABULARY DEVELOPMENT SERIES 1–4

Patricia Ackert, Linda Lee

LEVEL: beginning to high-intermediate

Through intriguing readings and carefully designed activities, this best-selling series helps students develop reading skills and systematically increase their active vocabulary. Learners develop useful and relevant vocabulary while exploring and expanding critical thinking skills.

- **Five thematic reading selections per unit** recycle vocabulary, sentence structure, and content knowledge.

- **Carefully designed pre-reading work and post-reading comprehension activities** build students' reading and critical thinking skills.

- A **variety of exercises and games** as well as dictionary activities and collocations recycle key vocabulary found throughout the readings.

- **CNN® video clips** and activities expand vocabulary and provide authentic input.

- **Assessment CD-ROM with Exam***View*® test-generating software allows instructors to create custom tests and quizzes quickly and easily.

Student Texts
Audio CDs
Answer Key and Video Transcripts
Assessment CD-ROM with Exam*View*®
CNN® Videos (DVD or VHS)

---

elt.heinle.com/readingandvocabulary

A GOOD READ 1–3

Developing Strategies for Effective Reading

Carlos Islam, Carrie Steenburgh

LEVEL: high-beginning to intermediate

A Good Read is a three-level reading strategies course intended for young adult and adult learners. The series promotes fluent and effective reading through specially-written texts, extensive coverage of reading strategies, and an explicit focus on lexical development.

- Texts cover a wide range of topics and text types, exposing learners to different types of reading.

- Comprehensive range of reading strategies developed through clear, easy-to-read explanations and explicit practice.

- Lexical phrases, such as collocations, phrasal verbs, and verb phrases, are highlighted to improve student's vocabulary and reading fluency.

Student Texts
Audio CDs
Teacher's Guides

---

elt.heinle.com/agoodread

Engaging themes and intensive practice build reading proficiency!

READING FOR TODAY SERIES 1–5

Lorraine C. Smith, Nancy Nici Mare

LEVEL: beginning to advanced

These best-selling, academic skills texts systematically develop students' reading and vocabulary skills through engaging themes and intensive practice. Students learn successful reading strategies and are further prompted to build proficiency in their writing, listening, and speaking skills.

■ **Readings** on topics of general interest and academic content engage readers and provide a real context for building vocabulary.

■ **Focus on critical reading skills** allows students to practice skimming, scanning, finding the main idea, using context clues, drawing conclusions, and more.

■ **InfoTrac® College Edition online library** gives students FREE 4-month access* to an online library of over 10 million articles for further exploration. (*Available with books 4 & 5)

■ **CNN® video clips and activities** expand the theme of each unit and provide authentic input.

■ **Internet activities** encourage students to use the Web.

■ **Assessment CD-ROM with Exam**_View_® test-generating software allows instructors to create custom tests and quizzes.

■ **Audio CDs** contain the readings.

■ **Instructor's Manuals** include general teaching suggestions, answer keys, video scripts, and assessment.

Best-selling series!

SERIES COMPONENTS
Student Texts
Audio CDs
Instructor's Manuals with Answer Key
CNN® Videos (VHS)
Assessment CD-ROM with Exam_View_®

See p. 139 for Reading for Today series ISBN/Price listings

elt.heinle.com/readingfortoday

For customer support, call **(877) NEED-ESL** or visit **elt.heinle.com** ■ For pricing, ISBNs, and ordering information see pp. 122 – 144

Prepares students for the rigorous reading demands of college-level courses!

COLLEGE READING 1 – 4

Patricia Byrd, Joy M. Reid, Cynthia Schuemann, *Series Editors*

Book 1: **Cheryl Benz with Myra M. Medina**
Book 2: **Linda Robinson Fellag**
Book 3: **John D. Avery, Linda Robinson Fellag**
Book 4: **Cheryl Benz, Cynthia Schuemann**

LEVEL: low-intermediate to advanced

College Reading, part of the *English for Academic Success* series, focuses on the development of the reading skills students need to be successful in college. Authentic academic readings and carefully selected topics help students build general background knowledge which will be valuable in their future college studies.

- ■ **Authentic reading selections** from college and high school texts represent a range of disciplines with high enrollment patterns at U.S. colleges.

- ■ **Practical exercises and activities** improve reading skills and enhance the teaching-learning process.

- ■ **Content and academic skills** are developed through the inclusion of appropriate academic tasks and through strategies that help students understand and handle what is expected of them in college classes.

- ■ **The Academic Word List** is thoroughly integrated, drawing student attention to high-frequency academic words found across disciplines.

- ■ **Chapter objectives are tied to the series' competencies** which were derived from a review of educator-generated course expectations.

- ■ **Review and assessment,** provided at the end of each chapter, revisits objects and vocabulary, and provides a practice text.

- ■ Extensive **online instructor and student support.**

- Class-tested
- Competency-based
- Adjunct approved

SERIES COMPONENTS
Student Texts
Online Instructor and Student Resources

See pp. 123-124 for College Reading *ISBN/Price listings*

elt.heinle.com/collegereading

Other titles in the *English for Academic Success* series include:

College Writing 1 – 4, p. 79
College Oral Communication 1 – 4, p. 85
College Vocabulary 1 – 4, p. 98

For professional development or in-service training on teaching academic English, see:

Essentials of Teaching Academic Reading series, p. 117

TAPESTRY READING 1–4

Rebecca Oxford, *Series Editor*
M.E. Sokolik, *Reading Editor*

Book 1: **Virginia Guleff,**
          M. E. Sokolik, Carol Lowther
Book 2: **Michael Ryall**
Book 3: **Linda Robinson Fellag**
Book 4: **M. E. Sokolik**

LEVEL: high-beginning to advanced

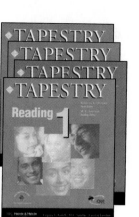

Thought-provoking reading selections and integrated learning strategies help students become proficient in English and prepared for academic challenges.

- Academic skills and language strategies give students the knowledge and skills to become successful, independent learners.
- "Setting Goals" and "Self-Assessment" sections help students monitor their own progress.

Student Texts
CNN® Videos (VHS)
Instructor's Manuals

For a well-integrated curriculum, see *Tapestry Writing*, p. 80 and *Tapestry Listening & Speaking*, p. 90.

RETHINKING AMERICA 1–3

M. E. Sokolik

LEVEL: intermediate to advanced

Intriguing cultural readings and CNN® videos help students truly understand American life.

- Fascinating reading selections illuminate U.S. life and challenge students to get below the surface of a variety of cultural topics.
- Pairs of authentic readings offer different perspectives on a single topic and encourage critical thinking.
- Numerous activities build vocabulary and reading skills.
- An almanac at the end of each book provides maps, historical timelines, and a wealth of cultural facts and figures.
- CNN® video clips for each unit stimulate writing activities.

Student Texts
CNN® Videos (VHS)
Instructor's Manual

FAR FROM HOME
Third Edition

AT HOME IN TWO LANDS
Reading and Word Study
Second Edition

William P. Pickett

LEVEL: high-beginning to intermediate

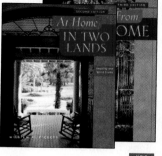

Far From Home and *At Home in Two Lands* work together to introduce high frequency, low-level vocabulary in high-interest readings featuring different cultural backgrounds.

- Updated readings and enhanced content covering contemporary topics
- Systematic presentation of high-frequency vocabulary in cross-cultural and everyday situations
- Mini-dictionary entries and word family exercises for vocabulary development
- Current topics for written and oral presentations
- Thematically-linked Internet tasks for practice in research and Web skills

Student Texts
Audio CDs
Assessment CD-ROM with ExamView®

IMPRESSIONS 1 & 2
America Through Academic Readings

Cheryl Benz, Stephen Benz

LEVEL: intermediate to advanced

Through academic readings, *Impressions* helps students explore American culture and develop the reading, vocabulary, and critical thinking skills necessary to be successful learners.

- Authentic academic readings focus on American culture and values to help students achieve cultural literacy.
- High-frequency vocabulary chosen from the Academic Word List helps students become proficient readers across all academic disciplines.
- Excerpts from real student essays function as models for student writing.
- Reading-Response Journal activities enable students to become interactive readers.
- Writing topics increase critical thinking and mirror the writing assignments students face in academic classes.

Student Texts

HOT TOPICS 1 – 3

Cheryl Pavlik

LEVEL: low-intermediate
to advanced

Hot Topics is guaranteed to engage readers, stimulate thinking, and provoke conversation while supporting reading skills development.

- Each unit features three readings on a related controversial topic, the last one more challenging than the previous two.

- Students increase reading fluency through pre-reading questions, skimming and scanning activities, use of context clues, vocabulary analysis, and development of critical thinking skills.

- Open-ended questions at the end of each unit allow students to voice their opinions and defend their viewpoints through discussion or in writing.

Student Texts
Audio CDs
CNN® Videos (DVD)
Instructor's Manual
Assessment CD-ROM with Exam*View*®

READING THE NEWS

Pete Sharma

LEVEL: intermediate to advanced

With *Reading the News*, students not only improve their ability to read newspapers in English—they gain practice that will help prepare them for TOEFL®, TOEIC®, and IELTS® exams. Authentic articles on contemporary issues from the *International Herald Tribune* encourage students to read English outside the classroom.

- Helps prepare students for exams through exercises that practice TOEFL®, TOEIC® and IELTS® exam tasks

- Presents a wide variety of high-interest articles grouped thematically by newspaper section

- Targets the reading, listening, vocabulary and other essential language skills learners need most for functional literacy in reading newspapers in English

- Includes "Special Focus on the Newspaper" sections offering strategies for analyzing an article's content and viewpoint

Student Text
Instructor's Manual
Audio CDs

STORIES WORTH READING 1 & 2

Skills Worth Learning

Betsy Cassriel, Gail Reynolds

LEVEL: high-beginning to
low-intermediate

Stories Worth Reading uses up-to-date, multicultural readings taken from news, feature articles, and authentic literature to engage low-level readers.

- Two readings per unit explore the topic and develop vocabulary skills.

- Fun application activities encourage students to use their new vocabulary.

- Writing models support students as they produce their own writing samples.

- Research activities teach library and Internet search skills to help students find information on their own.

- Instructor's Manual offers many supplemental activities and photocopiable templates for expansion.

Student Texts
Audio CDs
Instructor's Manual
CNN® Video (DVD)
Assessment CD-ROM with Exam*View*®

READING MATTERS 1 – 4

An Interactive Approach to Reading, Second Edition

Books 1 – 2: **Mary Lee Wholey**
Books 3 – 4: **Mary Lee Wholey and Nadia Henein**

LEVEL: high-beginning to
high-intermediate

Through stimulating vocabulary-rich readings and a communicative, integrated-skills approach *Reading Matters* helps students develop fluency and accuracy in academic reading.

- Paired reading selections are organized thematically and enable students to compare and contrast points of view.

- Abundant practice exercises and reading activities help students master different texts and vocabulary.

Student Texts
Online Instructor and Student Resources

INSIDE OUT/OUTSIDE IN

Exploring American Literature

Victoria Holder, Dorothy Lindsay, Lyn Motai, Deborah vanDommelen, Karen Wiederholt

LEVEL: advanced

With a focus on literary analysis, this anthology of short stories and poems helps students develop reading skills and encourages them to read literary works for enjoyment.

- Selections, by a diverse set of authors such as Ernest Hemingway, Toni Cade Bambara, Li-Yong Lee, and Bernard Malumund, range from traditional to more contemporary works.

- Activities on basic comprehension, literary analysis, and analytical writing help prepare students for future academic success.

- Important cultural, historical, or geographical background is provided for each selection.

- Charts, sketches, diagrams, and role plays tap into students' different learning styles.

Student Text
Online Teaching Center

elt.heinle.com/insideout

20TH CENTURY AMERICAN SHORT STORIES

Revised Edition

Jean A. McConochie

LEVEL: high-intermediate to advanced

These classic texts introduce students to American literature through a rich selection of contemporary authors.

- Unabridged, unsimplified stories are by Sandra Cisneros, Ernest Hemingway, Toshio Mori, Richard Wright, John Updike, Raymond Carver, Grace Paley, and more.

- A strong connection between reading and writing is promoted.

- Volumes 1 and 2 include pre- and post-reading support such as biographical information, glossary, and new discussion and writing activities.

- Anthology combines only the readings and introductory material from both volumes.

Volumes 1 & 2
Anthology

ADDITIONAL READING TITLES

AMERICAN SHORT STORIES
Exercises in Reading and Writing, Second Edition

Greg Costa

LEVEL: intermediate

AMAZING STORIES TO TELL AND RETELL 1 – 3

Lynda Berish, Sandra Thibaudeau

LEVEL: high-beginning to low-intermediate

DEVELOPING READING SKILLS 1 – 3
EXPANDING READING SKILLS 1 & 2

Linda Markstein, Louise Hirasawa

LEVEL: beginning to advanced

INSIDE THE NEWS
A Reading Text for Students of English

Connie Shoemaker, Susan Polycarpou

LEVEL: high-beginning

LIFE, LANGUAGE, & LITERATURE

Linda Robinson Fellag

LEVEL: advanced

THE MULTICULTURAL WORKSHOP 1 – 3
A Reading and Writing Program

Linda Lonon Blanton, Linda Lee

LEVEL: high-beginning to high-intermediate

READ TO SUCCEED 1 & 2
Academic Reading Right from the Start

Roberto Robledo, Dolores Howard

LEVEL: high-beginning to low-intermediate

READING ADVANTAGE 1 – 4
Second Edition

Casey Malarcher

LEVEL: beginning to high-intermediate

REFLECTIONS, 2/e

John Dennis, Suzanne Griffin

LEVEL: intermediate

STEPS TO ACADEMIC READING SERIES

Book 1: **Steps and Plateaus**
Jean Zukowski/Faust
Book 2: **Out of the Ordinary**
Jean Zukowski/Faust
Book 3: **Across the Board**
Jean Zukowski/Faust
Book 4: **In Context**
Jean Zukowski/Faust,
Susan S. Johnston,
Elizabeth E. Templin
Book 5: **Between the Lines**
Jean Zukowski/Faust,
Susan S. Johnston

LEVEL: beginning to high-intermediate

LEVEL GUIDE

	PAGE NUMBER	LOW-BEGINNING	BEGINNING	HIGH-BEGINNING	LOW-INTERMEDIATE	INTERMEDIATE	HIGH-INTERMEDIATE	LOW-ADVANCED	ADVANCED
Basic Composition for ESL, 3/e	82			•					
Blueprints: 1, 2	80					1	1	2	2
Catalyst: 1, 2	77				1	2	2		
College Writing: 1, 2, 3, 4	79				1	2	3	4	4
Composition Practice, 3/e: 1, 2, 3, 4	80		1		2	3	4		
Destinations: 1, 2 NEW!	77				1	1	2		
Developing Composition Skills, 2/e	81						•		
Discoveries in Academic Writing	82						•	•	•
Great Writing series, 3/e: 1, 2, 3, 4, 5 NEW!	72			1,2	2,3	4	5	5	5
Idea Exchange: 1, 2	82					1	2		
Independent Writing, 2/e	82								•
Key Concepts: Reading and Writing Across the Disciplines: 1, 2 NEW!	76						•	•	•
Looking Ahead: 1, 2, 3, 4	82					1	2	3	4
One Step at a Time: 1, 2	82				1	2			
Past, Present, & Future, 4/e	82					•			
Read, Write, Edit	78						•	•	
Refining Composition Skills, 5/e	81						•		•
Sourcework	82							•	•
Starting Lines	82		•						
Tapestry Writing: 1, 2, 3, 4	80			1	2	2	3	3,4	4
Think About Editing	82					•			
Tools for Writing	82					•			
Top 10	78				•	•			
Top 20, 2/e	78						•	•	•
Weaving It Together, 3/e: 1, 2, 3, 4 NEW!	74		1	1	2	3	4		
Write from the Start, 2/e	82			•					
Write Ideas	82		•						
Write in the Middle, 2/e	82					•			
Write Path, The	82								
Writing Clearly: An Editing Guide, 2/e	82						•	•	•
Writing Essentials	82					•	•	•	•
Writing Workout	82			•					
Writing Workshop	84							•	•
World English: Intro, 1, 2, 3 NEW!	42	Intro	1	1	2	2	3		

DICTIONARIES

	PAGE NUMBER	LOW-BEGINNING	BEGINNING	HIGH-BEGINNING	LOW-INTERMEDIATE	INTERMEDIATE	HIGH-INTERMEDIATE	LOW-ADVANCED	ADVANCED
Collins COBUILD Advanced Dictionary of American English	29							•	•
Collins COBUILD Basic Dictionary of American English NEW!	25		•	•	•				
Collins COBUILD Intermediate Dictionary of American English	28					•	•	•	
Collins COBUILD School Dictionary of American English	27					•	•	•	
Heinle Picture Dictionary, The	32	•	•	•	•				
Heinle's Basic Newbury House Dictionary, 2/e	36	•	•	•	•				
Heinle's Newbury House Dictionary with Integrated Thesaurus, 4/e	36					•	•	•	

Great Writing *bridges the gap from ESL writers to mainstream writers!*

THE GREAT WRITING SERIES

Great Writing 1: *Great Sentences for Great Paragraphs*
Keith S. Folse, April Muchmore-Vokoun, Elena Vestri Solomon

Great Writing 2: *Great Paragraphs*
Keith S. Folse, April Muchmore-Vokoun, Elena Vestri Solomon

Great Writing 3: *From Great Paragraphs to Great Essays*
Keith S. Folse, Elena Vestri Solomon, David Clabeaux

Great Writing 4: *Great Essays*
Keith S. Folse, April Muchmore-Vokoun, Elena Vestri Solomon

Great Writing 5: *Greater Essays*
Keith S. Folse, Tison Pugh

LEVEL: high-beginning to advanced

The *Great Writing* series uses clear explanations and extensive practical activities to help students write great sentences, paragraphs, and essays. Each book contains a wide variety of writing models in carefully selected rhetorical styles that provide practice in working with the writing process to develop a final piece of writing.

- **NEW! "Building Better Vocabulary"** features teach students how to accurately and effectively use written English.

- **NEW! "Timed Writing"** activities prepare students for success on standardized tests like the TOEFL®.

- **NEW! Assessment CD-ROM with Exam*View*®** allows teachers to create tests and quizzes easily.

- **NEW! Classroom Presentation Tool** makes instruction clearer and learning simpler.

- **Guided, structured activities** help students to quickly master writing tasks.

- **Student writing models** help students focus on specific writing skills and multiple rhetorical structures.

- **Brief Writer's Handbook with Activities** located at the back of the student book is a quick-reference resource for effective writing suggestions.

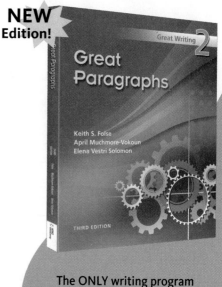

NEW Edition!

The ONLY writing program by Keith Folse!

SERIES COMPONENTS
Student Texts
Assessment CD-ROM with Exam*View*®
Classroom Presentation Tool CD-ROM

See p. 132 for The Great Writing Series *ISBN/Price listings*

For Instructor's resources, visit
elt.heinle.com/greatwriting

New four-color design!

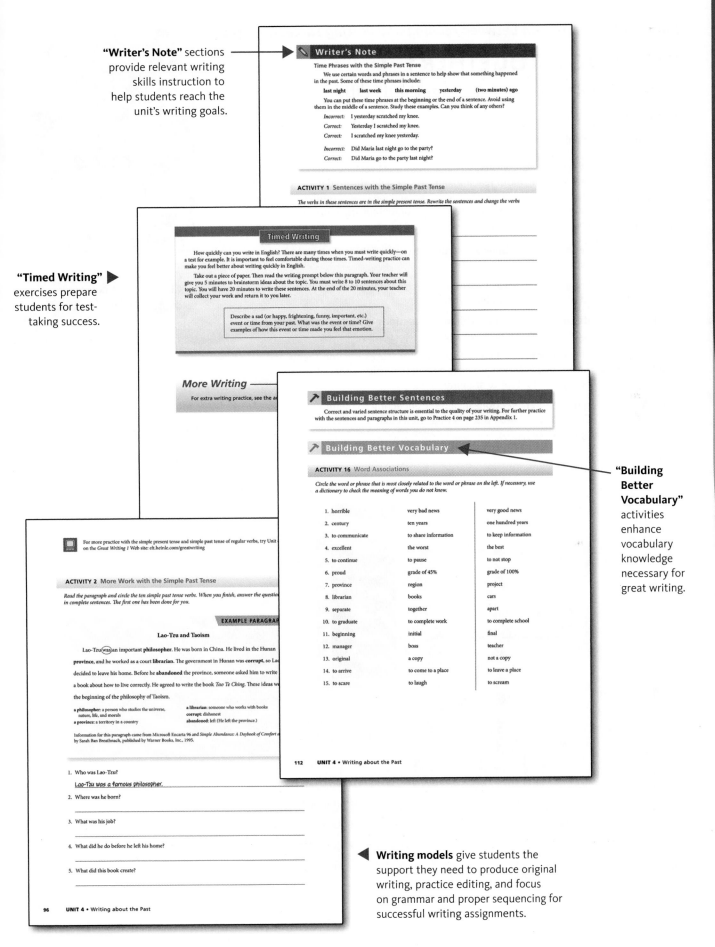

"Writer's Note" sections provide relevant writing skills instruction to help students reach the unit's writing goals.

"Timed Writing" exercises prepare students for test-taking success.

"Building Better Vocabulary" activities enhance vocabulary knowledge necessary for great writing.

Writing models give students the support they need to produce original writing, practice editing, and focus on grammar and proper sequencing for successful writing assignments.

Writer's Note

Time Phrases with the Simple Past Tense

We use certain words and phrases in a sentence to help show that something happened in the past. Some of these time phrases include:

last night   **last week**   **this morning**   **yesterday**   **(two minutes) ago**

You can put these time phrases at the beginning or the end of a sentence. Avoid using them in the middle of a sentence. Study these examples. Can you think of any others?

Incorrect: I yesterday scratched my knee.

Correct: Yesterday I scratched my knee.

Correct: I scratched my knee yesterday.

Incorrect: Did Maria last night go to the party?

Correct: Did Maria go to the party last night?

ACTIVITY 1 Sentences with the Simple Past Tense

The verbs in these sentences are in the simple present tense. Rewrite the sentences and change the verbs

Timed Writing

How quickly can you write in English? There are many times when you must write quickly—on a test for example. It is important to feel comfortable during those times. Timed-writing practice can make you feel better about writing quickly in English.

Take out a piece of paper. Then read the writing prompt below this paragraph. Your teacher will give you 5 minutes to brainstorm ideas about the topic. You must write 8 to 10 sentences about this topic. You will have 20 minutes to write these sentences. At the end of the 20 minutes, your teacher will collect your work and return it to you later.

Describe a sad (or happy, frightening, funny, important, etc.) event or time from your past. What was the event or time? Give examples of how this event or time made you feel that emotion.

More Writing

For extra writing practice, see the a

Building Better Sentences

Correct and varied sentence structure is essential to the quality of your writing. For further practice with the sentences and paragraphs in this unit, go to Practice 4 on page 235 in Appendix 1.

Building Better Vocabulary

ACTIVITY 16 Word Associations

Circle the word or phrase that is most closely related to the word or phrase on the left. If necessary, use a dictionary to check the meaning of words you do not know.

1. horrible	very bad news	very good news
2. century	ten years	one hundred years
3. to communicate	to share information	to keep information
4. excellent	the worst	the best
5. to continue	to pause	to not stop
6. proud	grade of 45%	grade of 100%
7. province	region	project
8. librarian	books	cars
9. separate	together	apart
10. to graduate	to complete work	to complete school
11. beginning	initial	final
12. manager	boss	teacher
13. original	a copy	not a copy
14. to arrive	to come to a place	to leave a place
15. to scare	to laugh	to scream

112   UNIT 4 • Writing about the Past

For more practice with the simple present tense and simple past tense of regular verbs, try Unit on the *Great Writing 1* Web site: elt.heinle.com/greatwriting

ACTIVITY 2 More Work with the Simple Past Tense

Read the paragraph and circle the ten simple past tense verbs. When you finish, answer the questio in complete sentences. The first one has been done for you.

EXAMPLE PARAGRAP

Lao-Tzu and Taoism

Lao-Tzu (was) an important **philosopher**. He was born in China. He lived in the Hunan **province**, and he worked as a court **librarian**. The government in Hunan was **corrupt**, so Lao decided to leave his home. Before he **abandoned** the province, someone asked him to write a book about how to live correctly. He agreed to write the book *Tao Te Ching*. These ideas w the beginning of the philosophy of Taoism.

a philosopher: a person who studies the universe, nature, life, and morals
a province: a territory in a country

a librarian: someone who works with books
corrupt: dishonest
abandoned: left (He left the province.)

Information for this paragraph came from *Microsoft Encarta 96* and *Simple Abundance: A Daybook of Comfort a* by Sarah Ban Breathnach, published by Warner Books, Inc., 1995.

1. Who was Lao-Tzu?

   Lao-Tzu was a famous philosopher.

2. Where was he born?

3. What was his job?

4. What did he do before he left his home?

5. What did this book create?

96   UNIT 4 • Writing about the Past

Building the connection between reading and writing success!

WEAVING IT TOGETHER 1–4
Connecting Reading and Writing, Third Edition

Milada Broukal

LEVEL: beginning to high-intermediate

NEW for 2010!

The new edition of *Weaving It Together* connects high-interest readings with clear writing activities. Learners build both reading and writing skills through understanding relevant readings and confidently expressing concepts and ideas in carefully structured writing exercises. By connecting these two necessary competencies, learners seamlessly develop both language and academic skills.

- **NEW! New and enhanced vocabulary instruction** teaches students how to build vocabulary and words in different contexts.

- **NEW! Updated reading passages** on intriguing topics stimulate students to write creatively and act as models for student writing.

- **NEW! Revised discussion and critical thinking questions include more** exercises that challenge students to become better readers.

- **NEW! "What Do You Think?"** section in each unit introduces the unit theme and **"What Do You Think Now?"** section provides a comprehension check at the end of each unit, connecting the content to students' lives.

- **NEW! "Weaving it Together" sections** include "Connecting to the Internet" activities and "Timed Writing" prompts, offering a full-circle connection of the unit theme to reading and writing.

Clear and comprehensive reading and writing instruction.

SERIES COMPONENTS
Student Texts
Audio CDs
Instructor's Manuals
Assessment CD-ROM with Exam*View*®

See p. 143 for Weaving it Together *ISBN/Price listings*

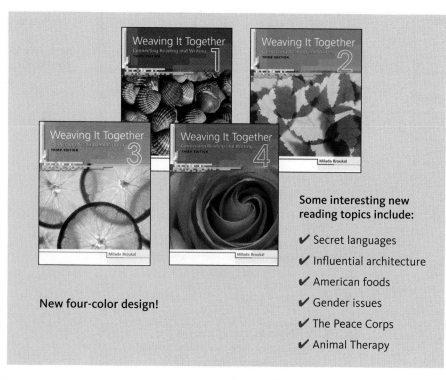

New four-color design!

Some interesting new reading topics include:

- ✔ Secret languages
- ✔ Influential architecture
- ✔ American foods
- ✔ Gender issues
- ✔ The Peace Corps
- ✔ Animal Therapy

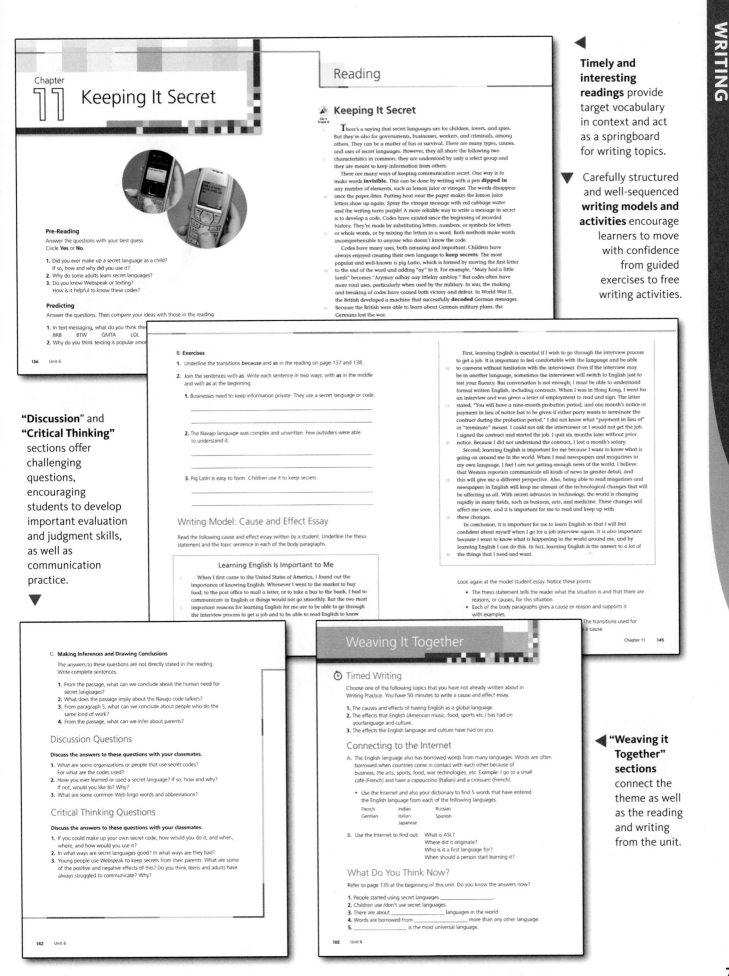

Chapter 11 — Keeping It Secret

Pre-Reading

Answer the questions with your best guess.
Circle **Yes** or **No**.

1. Did you ever make up a secret language as a child?
   If so, how and why did you use it?
2. Why do some adults learn secret languages?
3. Do you know Webspeak or texting?
   How is it helpful to know these codes?

Predicting

Answer the questions. Then compare your ideas with those in the reading.

1. In text messaging, what do you think thes...
   BRB   BTW   GMTA   LOL
2. Why do you think texting is popular amon...

136 Unit 6

Reading

Keeping It Secret

There's a saying that secret languages are for children, lovers, and spies. But they're also for governments, businesses, workers, and criminals, among others. They can be a matter of fun or survival. There are many types, causes, and uses of secret languages. However, they all share the following two characteristics in common: they are understood by only a select group and they are meant to keep information from others.

There are many ways of keeping communication secret. One way is to make words **invisible**. This can be done by writing with a pen **dipped in** any number of elements, such as lemon juice or vinegar. The words disappear once the paper dries. Putting heat near the paper makes the lemon juice letters show up again. Spray the vinegar message with red cabbage water and the writing turns purple! A more reliable way to write a message in secret is to develop a code. Codes have existed since the beginning of recorded history. They're made by substituting letters, numbers, or symbols for letters or whole words, or by mixing the letters in a word. Both methods make words incomprehensible to anyone who doesn't know the code.

Codes have many uses, both amusing and important. Children have always enjoyed creating their own language to **keep secrets**. The most popular and well-known is pig Latin, which is formed by moving the first letter to the end of the word and adding "ay" to it. For example, "Mary had a little lamb" becomes "Arymay adhay aay ittlelay amblay." But codes often have more vital uses, particularly when used by the military. In war, the making and breaking of codes have caused both victory and defeat. In World War II, the British developed a machine that successfully **decoded** German messages. Because the British were able to learn about German military plans, the Germans lost the war.

Timely and interesting readings provide target vocabulary in context and act as a springboard for writing topics.

▼ Carefully structured and well-sequenced **writing models and activities** encourage learners to move with confidence from guided exercises to free writing activities.

B. Exercises

1. Underline the transitions *because* and *as* in the reading on page 137 and 138.

2. Join the sentences with *as*. Write each sentence in two ways: with *as* in the middle and with *as* at the beginning.

   1. Businesses need to keep information private. They use a secret language or code.

   _____

   _____

   2. The Navajo language was complex and unwritten. Few outsiders were able to understand it.

   _____

   _____

   3. Pig Latin is easy to form. Children use it to keep secrets.

   _____

   _____

Writing Model: Cause and Effect Essay

Read the following cause and effect essay written by a student. Underline the thesis statement and the topic sentence in each of the body paragraphs.

Learning English Is Important to Me

When I first came to the United States of America, I found out the importance of knowing English. Whenever I went to the market to buy food, to the post office to mail a letter, or to take a bus to the bank, I had to communicate in English or things would not go smoothly. But the two most important reasons for learning English for me are to be able to go through the interview process to get a job and to be able to read English to know

First, learning English is essential if I wish to go through the interview process to get a job. It is important to feel comfortable with the language and be able to converse without hesitation with the interviewer. Even if the interview may be in another language, sometimes the interviewer will switch to English just to test your fluency. But conversation is not enough; I must be able to understand formal written English, including contracts. When I was in Hong Kong, I went for an interview and was given a letter of employment to read and sign. The letter stated, "You will have a nine-month probation period, and one month's notice or payment in lieu of notice has to be given if either party wants to terminate the contract during the probation period." I did not know what "payment in lieu of" or "terminate" meant. I could not ask the interviewer or I would not get the job. I signed the contract and started the job. I quit six months later without prior notice. Because I did not understand the contract, I lost a month's salary.

Second, learning English is important for me because I want to know what is going on around me in the world. When I read newspapers and magazines in my own language, I feel I am not getting enough news of the world. I believe that Western reporters communicate all kinds of news in greater detail, and this will give me a different perspective. Also, being able to read magazines and newspapers in English will keep me abreast of the technological changes that will be affecting us all. With recent advances in technology, the world is changing rapidly in many fields, such as business, arts, and medicine. These changes will affect me soon, and it is important for me to read and keep up with these changes.

In conclusion, it is important for me to learn English so that I will feel confident about myself when I go for a job interview again. It is also important because I want to know what is happening in the world around me, and by learning English I can do this. In fact, learning English is the answer to a lot of the things that I need and want.

Look again at the model student essay. Notice these points:

- The thesis statement tells the reader what the situation is and that there are reasons, or causes, for this situation.
- Each of the body paragraphs gives a cause or reason and supports it with examples.
- ... The transitions used for ... s a cause.

Chapter 11   145

C. Making Inferences and Drawing Conclusions

The answers to these questions are not directly stated in the reading. Write complete sentences.

1. From the passage, what can we conclude about the human need for secret languages?
2. What does the passage imply about the Navajo code talkers?
3. From paragraph 5, what can we conclude about people who do the same kind of work?
4. From the passage, what can we infer about parents?

Discussion Questions

Discuss the answers to these questions with your classmates.

1. What are some organizations or people that use secret codes? For what are the codes used?
2. Have you ever learned or used a secret language? If so, how and why? If not, would you like to? Why?
3. What are some common Web lingo words and abbreviations?

Critical Thinking Questions

Discuss the answers to these questions with your classmates.

1. If you could make up your own secret code, how would you do it, and when, where, and how would you use it?
2. In what ways are secret languages good? In what ways are they bad?
3. Young people use Webspeak to keep secrets from their parents. What are some of the positive and negative effects of this? Do you think teens and adults have always struggled to communicate? Why?

142   Unit 6

"Discussion" and "Critical Thinking" sections offer challenging questions, encouraging students to develop important evaluation and judgment skills, as well as communication practice. ▼

Weaving It Together

Timed Writing

Choose one of the following topics that you have not already written about in Writing Practice. You have 50 minutes to write a cause and effect essay.

1. The causes and effects of having English as a global language.
2. The effects that English (American music, food, sports etc.) has had on your language and culture.
3. The effects the English language and culture have had on you.

Connecting to the Internet

A. The English language also has borrowed words from many languages. Words are often borrowed when countries come in contact with each other because of business, the arts, sports, food, war technologies, etc. Example: I go to a small café (French) and have a cappuccino (Italian) and a croissant (French).

- Use the Internet and also your dictionary to find 5 words that have entered the English language from each of the following languages.

   French   Indian   Russian
   German   Italian   Spanish
               Japanese

B. Use the Internet to find out: What is ASL?
                                   Where did it originate?
                                   Who is it a first language for?
                                   When should a person start learning it?

What Do You Think Now?

Refer to page 135 at the beginning of this unit. Do you know the answers now?

1. People started using secret languages _____
2. Children use /don't use secret languages.
3. There are about _____ languages in the world.
4. Words are borrowed from _____ more than any other language.
5. _____ is the most universal language.

162   Unit 6

◀ **"Weaving it Together" sections** connect the theme as well as the reading and writing from the unit.

KEY CONCEPTS 1 & 2

Reading and Writing Across the Disciplines

Barbara Smith-Palinkas, Kelly Croghan-Ford

LEVEL: intermediate to advanced

Key Concepts helps students master the academic content, academic vocabulary, and academic reading and writing skills they need to succeed at college.

- **Authentic readings from real college textbooks** help students build on their knowledge of academic subjects.

- **Reading passages act as models** for the rhetorical styles students produce in their writing assignments.

- **Practice of each step in the writing process** guides students in perfecting their writing.

- **Academic Word List and discipline-specific vocabulary** is introduced and practiced to build students' academic vocabulary knowledge.

- **Vocabulary building exercises** help students discern differences in meaning by focusing on word forms, context, and usage.

- **Integrated grammar activities** improve students writing at the sentence level.

NEW!

KEY CONCEPTS **1**

HEINLE CENGAGE Learning

KEY CONCEPTS **2**

READING AND WRITING ACROSS THE DISCIPLINES

Barbara Smith-Palinkas
Kelly Croghan-Ford

The complete
academic success solution!

SERIES COMPONENTS
Student Texts

See p. 136 for Key Concepts: Reading and Writing Across the Disciplines *ISBN/Price listings*

elt.heinle.com/keyconceptsrw

For an integrated approach, see

Key Concepts 1 & 2: Listening, Note Taking, and Speaking Across the Disciplines, p. 88.

KEY CONCEPTS **1**

KEY CONCEPTS **2**

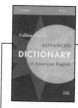

ADVANCED
DICTIONARY
of American English

Need more vocabulary support?
See *Collins COBUILD Advanced Dictionary of American English*, p. 29.

NEW!

DESTINATIONS 1 & 2
Writing for Academic Success

Nancy Herzfeld-Pipkin

LEVEL: low-intermediate to high-intermediate

Destinations prepares students for academic achievement. Step-by-step writing explanations and tasks centered on content area readings help students develop and refine academic writing at the sentence, paragraph, and essay level.

- **A variety of writing activities** coach students in effective sentence and paragraph (Book 1) and paragraph and essay development (Book 2).

- **Clear charts and exercises** focus on sentence level writing and editing skills.

- **Structured writing activities and models** at the paragraph and essay level help students master English composition skills, including the skill of summarizing.

- **Authentic and adapted readings in academic content areas** prepare students for the next step in their education.

- *Destinations: Grammar for Academic Success* **workbooks** provide complete grammar activities that support the writing and content focus of the texts.

- **Assessment CD-ROM with Exam*View*®** test-generating software allows instructors to create quizzes and tests easily for both the writing and grammar texts.

Student Texts
Grammar Workbooks
Instructor's Manuals: Writing and Grammar
Assessment CD-ROMs with Exam*View*®

elt.heinle.com/destinations

CATALYST 1 & 2
Writing from Reading

Steve Jones, *Series Editor*

Book 1: **Steve Jones, Suzanne Kalbach**
Book 2: **Marianne Brems**

LEVEL: low-intermediate to intermediate

Connecting students' everyday experiences to different academic disciplines, *Catalyst* uses a variety of readings as a springboard for writing.

- **Compelling readings** on topics such as personalities, the meaning of art, the history of architecture, and the role of sports engage students and act as a catalyst for writing.

- **A balanced approach to writing** guides students through the writing process and teaches them the mechanics of good writing.

- **Grammar explanations and exercises** woven throughout each chapter help students express their ideas more clearly.

- **Vocabulary exercises** introduce high-frequency words students need in their daily lives plus words from the Academic Word List students will encounter in college.

- **Assessment CD-ROM with Exam*View*®** test-generating software allows instructors to create quizzes and tests quickly and easily.

Student Texts
Audio CDs

elt.heinle.com/catalyst

TOP 10

TOP 20, Second Edition
Great Grammar for Great Writing

Top 10: **Keith S. Folse, Elena Vestri Solomon, Donna M. Tortorella**
Top 20, 2/e: **Keith S. Folse, Elena Vestri Solomon, Barbara Smith-Palinkas**

LEVEL: **low-intermediate to advanced**

Top 10 and *Top 20* help students master the essential grammar they need to produce great writing. They can be used as stand-alone coursebooks or to supplement any writing series, such as the *Great Writing* series (p. 72).

Top 10 focuses on correcting the ten most common grammatical errors beginning writers make.

- **Straightforward grammar explanations** allow students to understand how structures are used in writing.

- **Guided activities** encourage students to learn about typical grammar errors, identify them, and then correct them.

- Strong emphasis on **editing exercises** teaches the self-editing skills students need to develop to be successful writers.

Top 20 reviews the twenty most troublesome grammar points students struggle with in their writing.

- **Authentic academic writing models** help contextualize grammar exercises.

- A **variety of exercises** show students how to find and correct common grammatical errors.

- New chapter on how to **edit essays** enhances learner independence.

- **Improved grammar explanations** help students to bridge the gap between their writing and native-speaker writing.

Student Texts
Online Teaching and Study Centers

elt.heinle.com/top20

READ, WRITE, EDIT
Grammar for College Writers

Patricia Porter, Deborah vanDommelen

LEVEL: **low-advanced to advanced**

Read, Write, Edit focuses on grammar structure and editing strategies to help students learn the necessary skills to express themselves accurately and effectively in college writing. Readings from a variety of academic genres and disciplines expose students to writing and grammar concepts as they appear in context.

- Grammar structures are presented in a clear, visual format through charts offering usage tips and examples of common problems.

- A variety of activities support grammar learning through listening and doing: dictation, board work, individual work, peer discussion, and group presentation.

- Each reading is supported by pre-reading guides, comprehension checks, and writing prompts.

- Editing skills are practiced on readings from the book, from students' own writing, and work from their peers.

Student Text

elt.heinle.com/readwriteedit

Help students prepare for the rigorous writing demands of college-level courses!

COLLEGE WRITING 1 – 4

Patricia Byrd, Joy M. Reid, Cynthia Schuemann, *Series Editors*

Book 1: **Karen E. Walsh**
Book 2: **Eileen Cotter**
Book 3: **Gabriella Nuttall**
Book 4: **Li-Lee Tunceren, Sharon Cavusgil**

LEVEL: low-intermediate to advanced

College Writing, part of the *English for Academic Success* series, prepares students for academic written work by teaching them the language, content, and rhetoric needed for success in college courses. The texts build student confidence by presenting step-by-step, easy-to-learn processes for effective writing.

- **Authentic writing assignments** are drawn from actual college courses across the curriculum. Students are motivated to study, knowing they will likely receive such assignments in the future.

- **Authentic Writing Models** provide specific examples of writing so that students can compare writing styles, discuss writing strategies, and understand instructor expectations.

- **"Power Grammar" boxes** introduce the grammar structures students need for fluency and accuracy in academic written English.

- **"Spotlight on Writing Skills"** draws student's attention to particular writing points that will be emphasized in the writing assignment and apply to successful academic writing.

- **Self-editing and peer response exercises** using response sheets from the appendix are included in all writing assignments.

- Extensive **online instructor and student support.**

- Class-tested
- Competency-based
- Adjunct approved

SERIES COMPONENTS
Student Texts
Online Instructor and Student Resources

See p. 124 for College Writing *ISBN/Price listings*

---

elt.heinle.com/collegewriting

Other titles in the *English for Academic Success* series include:
   College Reading 1 – 4, p. 67
   College Oral Communication 1 – 4, p. 85
   College Vocabulary 1 – 4, p. 98

For professional development or in-service training on teaching academic English, see:

   Essentials of Teaching Academic Writing, p. 117

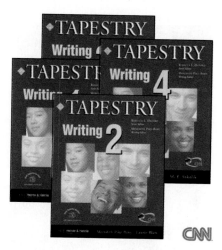

TAPESTRY WRITING 1–4

Rebecca Oxford, *Series Editor*
Meredith Pike-Baky, *Writing Editor*

Book 1: **Meredith Pike-Baky**
Book 2: **Meredith Pike-Baky,**
Laurie Blass
Book 3: **Marie Hutchison Weidauer**
Book 4: **M.E. Sokolik**

LEVEL: high-beginning to advanced

Academic writing activities, integrated learning strategies, CNN® videos, and a Web site effectively provide students with the tools they need to be successful, independent learners.

- Writing and reading selections prepare students for the assignments they will do in college.

- "Academic Power Strategies," give students the knowledge and skills to become successful, independent learners.

- "Language Learning Strategies" help students learn to write well.

- CNN® video clips provide an exciting springboard for writing activities.

- "Setting Goals" and "Self-Assessment" sections help students monitor their own progress.

Students Texts
CNN® Videos
Instructor's Manuals

elt.heinle.com/tapestry

For a well-integrated curriculum, see
Tapestry Reading, **p. 68 and**
Tapestry Listening & Speaking, **p. 90.**

BLUEPRINTS 1 & 2

Composition Skills for
Academic Writing

**Keith S. Folse, M. Kathleen Mahnke,
Elena Vestri Solomon,
Lorraine Williams**

LEVEL: intermediate to advanced

The *Blueprints 1 & 2* academic writing series offers a unique combination of instruction in the rhetorical processes as well as paraphrasing, summarizing, and synthesizing. This multi-layered approach helps students develop good writing habits and avoid the pitfalls of plagiarism. Students receive ample opportunities to write at the sentence, paragraph, and essay levels.

- A focus on academic writing beyond the ESL classroom motivates students to practice their new skills on the types of writing faced in academic settings.

- A combination of author-generated, student-generated, and authentic readings gives students a wide variety of writing models covering diverse academic topics such as DNA tests, computer programs, and literary analysis.

- Grammar points that are particularly useful to writers at the intermediate and advanced levels are explained and practiced in every unit.

Student Texts
Online Teaching and Study Centers

elt.heinle.com/blueprints

COMPOSITION PRACTICE 1–4

Third Edition

Linda Lonon Blanton

**LEVEL: high-beginning to
high-intermediate**

This classic, step-by-step approach emphasizes the fundamentals of great composition writing.

- Books 1 & 2 focus on developing strong skills for descriptive and narrative writing on familiar, everyday topics.

- Books 3 & 4 develop expository and argumentation writing skills, and build students' analytic abilities as they write for a broader, more academic audience.

- Pre-reading activities and post-reading caption writing exercises support the readings and introduce the grammatical and rhetorical focus in Books 1 & 2.

- Richly detailed sequential illustrations, maps, photos, and graphs help students with comprehension of vocabulary and idioms in both readings and model compositions.

- Varied exercises on comprehension, vocabulary, grammar, semantic organization, and writing techniques prepare students to write successful compositions.

- Online activities encourage students to use the Internet as a resource for their writing.

Student Texts

For customer support, call **(877) NEED-ESL** or visit **elt.heinle.com** ■ For pricing, ISBNs, and ordering information see pp. 122 – 144

Students build writing skills in the rhetorical modes!

DEVELOPING COMPOSITION SKILLS
Rhetoric and Grammar, Second Edition

Mary K. Ruetten

LEVEL: intermediate

REFINING COMPOSITION SKILLS
Rhetoric and Grammar, Fifth Edition

Regina L. Smalley, Mary K. Ruetten, Joann Rishel Kozyrev

LEVEL: high-intermediate to advanced

This best-selling series combines extensive development and practice in the rhetorical modes while integrating instruction with readings, grammar, and critical thinking skills.

- *Developing Composition Skills* focuses students on narrating, describing, analyzing, comparing and contrasting, classifying, and evaluating at the **paragraph level** and offers a complete introduction to the essay as a bridge to essay-level writing.

- In addition to thoroughly presenting and reviewing writing modes taught at the lower level, *Refining Composition Skills* **develops essay writing skills** needed for college: example, comparison and contrast, classification, process analysis, cause and effect, and argument.

- **Updated multicultural readings** act as a springboard for student writing.

- **CNN® video clips** provide writing prompts for each chapter.

- **Internet activities** encourage students to use the Internet for research, motivation, and inspiration.

- **"Getting Started"** section includes goals, writing assignments, and video activities.

Practice in rhetorical modes from paragraphs to essays!

CNN

SERIES COMPONENTS
Student Texts
Instructor's Manuals
CNN® Videos

See p. 125 for Developing Composition Skills *ISBN/Price listings*

See p. 139 for Refining Composition Skills *ISBN/Price listings*

Writers master the essay!

Your colleagues say...

I have found Developing Composition Skills *enormously helpful in my writing classes. A number of my peers are also fond of this book. You can definitely see the improvement in student writing over the semester while using this text."*

—*Erin Lofthouse,*
City College of San Francisco, CA

I have used Refining Composition Skills *in my teaching for 15 years and have found it an excellent tool in the teaching of composition. For me, its greatest strengths are the example compositions, the exercises, the grammar explanations, and the appendixes."*

—*Lynn T. Bunker,*
University of Houston, TX

Writers perfect the paragraph!

WRITING CLEARLY
An Editing Guide, Second Edition

Janet Lane, Ellen Lange

LEVEL: high-intermediate to advanced

Writing Clearly: An Editing Guide helps students recognize and remedy the fifteen most common ESL writing errors.

■ Explanations, selected grammar rules, strategies, and exercises help students correct their own writing.

■ Exercises progress from error identification, to production of correct sentences, to error analysis.

■ CNN® video clips further stimulate writing activities.

Student Text
Instructor's Manual
CNN® Video

SOURCEWORK
Academic Writing from Sources

Nancy E. Dollahite, Julie Haun

LEVEL: low-advanced to advanced

Sourcework helps students work from outside sources and guides them through the process of writing their first academic research paper.

■ Students learn how to take notes from readings, analyze information, outline structures, create thesis statements, write and refine drafts, and more.

■ University-level readings give students the content they need to write sophisticated pieces.

Student Text
Online Teaching and Study Centers

ADDITIONAL WRITING TITLES

BASIC COMPOSITION FOR ESL
An Expository Workbook, Third Edition

Jann Huizenga, Gladys Berro Francis, Courtenay Meade Snellings

LEVEL: high-beginning

DISCOVERIES IN ACADEMIC WRITING

Barbara Harris Leonhard

LEVEL: high-intermediate to advanced

IDEA EXCHANGE 1 & 2
From Speaking to Writing

Linda Lonon Blanton

LEVEL: intermediate to high-intermediate

INDEPENDENT WRITING
Second Edition

Judith L. Paiva, Teresa D. O'Donnell

LEVEL: advanced

LOOKING AHEAD 1 – 4

Patricia Byrd, Joy M. Reid,
Series Editors

Book 1: **Sharon Cavusgil**
Book 2: **Linda Robinson Fellag**
Book 3: **Elizabeth Byleen**
Book 4: **Christine A. Holten, Judith Marasco**

LEVEL: intermediate to advanced

ONE STEP AT A TIME 1 & 2
Computer Assisted Writing with Grammar

Judith García

LEVEL: low-intermediate to intermediate

PAST, PRESENT, & FUTURE
A Reading and Writing Course, 4/e

Joan Young Gregg, Joan Russell

LEVEL: intermediate

STARTING LINES
Beginning Writing

David Blot, David M. Davidson

LEVEL: beginning

THINK ABOUT EDITING
A Grammar Editing Guide for ESL Writers

Allen Ascher

LEVEL: intermediate

TOOLS FOR WRITING
A Structured Process for Intermediate Students

Linda Robinson Fellag, Laura T. Le Dréan

LEVEL: intermediate

WRITE FROM THE START
Second Edition

David M. Davidson, David Blot

LEVEL: high-beginning

WRITE IDEAS
A Beginning Writing Text

Connie Shoemaker, Susan Polycarpou

LEVEL: beginning

WRITE IN THE MIDDLE:
A Guide to Writing for the ESL Student, 2/e

Connie Shoemaker, Doug Larson

LEVEL: intermediate

THE WRITE PATH
Basics of Paragraph Writing

Kelly Kennedy-Isern

LEVEL: intermediate

WRITING ESSENTIALS
Exercises to Improve Spelling, Sentence Structure, Punctuation, and Writing

Paige Wilson, Teresa Ferster Glazier

LEVEL: intermediate to advanced

WRITING WORKOUT
A Program for New Students of English

Jann Huizenga, Maria Thomas-Ruzic

LEVEL: high-beginning

WRITING WORKSHOP
Promoting College Success

Linda Lonon Blanton, Linda Lee

LEVEL: low-advanced to advanced

LEVEL GUIDE

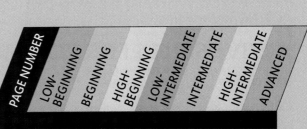

LISTENING AND SPEAKING

	PAGE NUMBER	LOW-BEGINNING	BEGINNING	HIGH-BEGINNING	LOW-INTERMEDIATE	INTERMEDIATE	HIGH-INTERMEDIATE	ADVANCED
ACTIVE Skills for Communication: Intro, 1, 2 **NEW!**	84		Intro	Intro	1	1, 2	2	
All Clear: 1, 2, 3	90			1	1	2	2	3
Can't Stop Talking, 2/e	96				•			
College Oral Communication: 1, 2, 3, 4	85				1	2	3	4
Communicating Effectively in English, 2/e	93					•	•	
Communication Strategies: 1, 2, 3, 4 **NEW!**	92				1	2	3	4
Culturally Speaking, 2/e **NEW!**	93					•		
Expressions: Intro, 1, 2, 3	96		Intro	1	2	3		
From College to Careers: Listening in the Real World	92						•	•
Getting Together	96					•		
Heart of the Matter, The	96					•	•	
Key Concepts: Listening, Note Taking, and Speaking Across the Disciplines: 1, 2	88					1	2	
Let's Start Talking	96			•				
Listen In, 2/e: 1, 2, 3	94			1	2	3		
Listen, Speak, Present	96							•
Listen to Me!, 3/e **NEW!**	86	•						
Listening Advantage: 1, 2, 3, 4 **NEW!**	91	1	2	3	4			
Listening and Notetaking series, 3/e: 1, 2, 3	91					1	2	2,3
Non-Stop Discussion Workbook, The, 2/e	96					•	•	•
Now Hear This!, 3/e **NEW!**	86			•	•			
On Speaking Terms: 1, 2 **NEW!**	87			1	2			
Say It Naturally, 2/e: 1, 2	96			1	1	1,2	2	2
So to Speak: 1, 2	94	1	2					
Step Up: 1, 2	89					1	2	
Talk It! series, 2/e: 1, 2, 3	89					1	2	3
Tapestry Listening & Speaking: 1, 2, 3, 4	90			1	2	2	3	4
World English: Intro, 1, 2, 3 **NEW!**	42	Intro	1	1	2	2	3	

PRONUNCIATION

	PAGE NUMBER	LOW-BEGINNING	BEGINNING	HIGH-BEGINNING	LOW-INTERMEDIATE	INTERMEDIATE	HIGH-INTERMEDIATE	ADVANCED
Pronouncing American English, 2/e	96					•	•	•
Sound Bites	96			•	•			
Sounds Great: 1, 2	96				1	2		
Speak Up, 2/e: 1, 2	96	1	2					
Targeting Pronunciation, 2/e	96					•	•	•
Well Said series 3/e: Intro, 1 **NEW!**	95					•	•	•

DICTIONARIES

	PAGE NUMBER	LOW-BEGINNING	BEGINNING	HIGH-BEGINNING	LOW-INTERMEDIATE	INTERMEDIATE	HIGH-INTERMEDIATE	ADVANCED
Collins COBUILD Advanced Dictionary of American English	29							•
Collins COBUILD Basic Dictionary of American English **NEW!**	25		•	•	•			
Collins COBUILD Intermediate Dictionary of American English	28					•	•	•
Collins COBUILD School Dictionary of American English	27					•	•	•
Heinle Picture Dictionary, The	32	•	•	•	•			
Heinle's Basic Newbury House Dictionary, 2/e	36	•	•	•	•			
Heinle's Newbury House Dictionary with Integrated Thesaurus, 4/e	36					•	•	•

Develop communication skills using Neil J. Anderson's ACTIVE methodology!

ACTIVE SKILLS FOR COMMUNICATION
Intro – 2

Curtis Kelly, Chuck Sandy, Neil J. Anderson, *Series Consultant*

LEVEL: beginning to high-intermediate

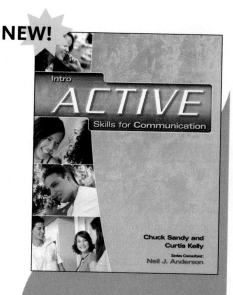

NEW!

Build confidence in communicating!

ACTIVE Skills for Communication is an exciting new three-level series that develops learners' speaking and listening skills. Written by ELT specialists Curtis Kelly and Chuck Sandy, with series consultant Neil J. Anderson, the series uses the ACTIVE approach to help learners become more fluent, confident—and active—speakers of English. Each unit contains easy-to-follow, step-by-step activities that lead toward a major speaking task. The tasks are based on real-life situations and are designed to increase self-confidence and foster positive attitudes towards learning English.

- **Fluency strategies** help learners develop effective conversation management skills.

- **Critical thinking** activities encourage learners to think deeply about how they express themselves in English.

- **Useful expressions** help learners interact more freely in personalized speaking activities.

- **Presentation tips** assist learners in developing confidence and effective presentation skills.

- **Spoken English** sections show learners how native speakers of English really talk.

- **Workbooks** provide learners with reinforcement and extension activities for vocabulary, grammar, conversation strategies, and critical thinking.

- **Teacher's Editions** include notes, answer keys, teaching suggestions, additional activities, and photocopiable activity pages for each unit, unit assessments and tests, and audio scripts.

SERIES COMPONENTS
Student Texts
Workbooks
Audio CDs
Classroom Audio CDs
Teacher's Editions

See p. 122 for Active Skills for Communication *ISBN/Price listings*

elt.heinle.com/asc

See page 64 for Neil J. Anderson's best-selling *ACTIVE Skills for Reading* series!

Author Neil J. Anderson's
ACTIVE Methodology

A = **Activate Prior Knowledge**

C = **Cultivate Vocabulary**

T = **Think About Meaning**

I = **Increase Reading Fluency**

V = **Verify Strategies**

E = **Evaluate Progress**

Activities covered in the three levels of ACTIVE Skills for Communication *include:*

- Interviewing other learners to make a class album
- Designing a style makeover
- Discussing ways to improve school life
- Participating in a job interview
- Buying, selling, and bargaining for goods

- Discussing moral dilemmas
- Making a personal action plan
- Creating a new business concept
- Participating in a mini-debate
- Acting in a TV trailer
- Planning the ideal town
- Organizing a dream vacation

Prepares students for the rigorous demands
of college-level courses!

COLLEGE ORAL COMMUNICATION 1–4

Patricia Byrd, Joy M. Reid, Cynthia Schuemann, *Series Editors*

Book 1: **Marsha Chan**
Book 2: **Ann E. Roemer**
Book 3: **Cheryl L. Delk**
Book 4: **Steve Jones**

LEVEL: low-intermediate to advanced

College Oral Communication, part of the *English for Academic Success* series, helps meet the academic needs of students by teaching them how to comprehend the spoken English used by instructors and students in college classrooms. Engaging activities provide ample practice of academic listening and academic speaking.

■ **Authentic classroom interactions and lectures** provide opportunities for students to learn how to listen to lectures, take notes, then use their notes for other academic tasks such as tests or small group discussions.

■ **Academic speaking tasks** reflect the types of tasks expected of college students, such as participating in class, engaging in formal and informal small group discussions on lecture content, and presenting oral summaries.

■ **The Academic Word List is integrated throughout** to help students develop techniques for learning and using new academic vocabulary in order to recognize the words when they hear and use them in spoken English.

■ Extensive **online instructor and student support.**

- Class-tested
- Competency-based
- Adjunct approved

SERIES COMPONENTS
Student Texts
Audio CDs
Online Instructor and Student Resources

See p. 123 for College Oral Communication *ISBN/Price listings*

elt.heinle.com/collegeoral

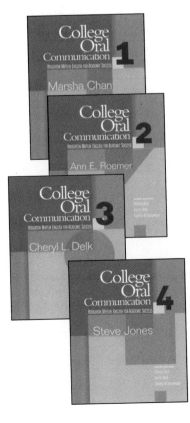

Other titles in the *English for Academic Success* series include:

College Reading 1 – 4, p. 67
College Writing 1 – 4, p. 79
College Vocabulary 1 – 4, p. 98

For professional development or in-service training on teaching academic English, see:

Essentials of Teaching Academic Oral Communication, p. 117

A completely updated and revised edition of the best-selling listening series!

LISTEN TO ME!
Third Edition

Barbara H. Foley

LEVEL: beginning

NOW HEAR THIS!
Third Edition

Barbara H. Foley

LEVEL: high-beginning to low-intermediate

Using real-life themes, high-interest narratives, and natural speech, *Listen to Me!* and *Now Hear This!* teach the listening and speaking skills relevant to students' lives.

- ▪ **NEW! New and updated topics** on money, jobs, communication, and families make learning more interesting and relevant.

- ▪ **Listening comprehension and listening discrimination** activities foster better listening strategies.

- ▪ **Integrated pronunciation and grammar exercises** improve students' speaking skills.

- ▪ **Group speaking activities** personalize the language and allow students to use the skills they have learned.

Listen to Me!

- ▪ **NEW! Examples of natural speech** in the listening exercises expose students to real spoken English.

- ▪ **NEW! "Listening and Pronunciation Note" boxes** highlight the listening skills being taught and help students maximize their learning.

Now Hear This!

- ▪ **NEW! "Person on the Street" sections** present short responses from college students and adults exposing students to real spoken English.

- ▪ **NEW! Note-taking activities** introduce students to a variety of note-taking formats, including writing numbers, completing check lists, and recording reasons or details.

NEW!

Students learn the essential communication skills!

SERIES COMPONENTS
Student Texts
Audio CDs

See p. 137 for Listen to Me! *ISBN/Price listings*

See p. 138 for Now Hear This! *ISBN/Price listings*

elt.heinle.com/listentome

elt.heinle.com/nowhearthis

ON SPEAKING TERMS

Real Language for Real Life

Book 1: **Eliana Santana Williamson**
Book 2: **Eliana Santana Williamson, Yvonne Cramner**

LEVEL: high-beginning to low-intermediate

A two-level, corpus-informed listening and speaking series that focuses on functional, real-life situations to prepare students for social and academic life.

- Uses **corpus-informed** spoken English to provide authentic examples of formal and informal speech, giving lower-level students natural and relevant language models.

- **Speaking strategies** (such as hesitation and reaction) are designed to help students become better speakers and converse with more confidence.

- Integrated **Grammar lessons** teach the grammar necessary for students to communicate effectively and naturally in conversations.

- **Listening exercises** teach listening strategies and skills, rather than simply testing them.

- The Audio CD contains listening activities and **conversations that model student tasks.**

NEW!

On Speaking Terms 1
REAL LANGUAGE FOR REAL LIFE
Eliana Santana Williamson

On Speaking Terms 2
REAL LANGUAGE FOR REAL LIFE
Eliana Santana Williamson
Yvonne Cramner

Corpus-informed instruction for relevant communication skills!

Your colleagues say...

"I like the fact that On Speaking Terms focuses on authentic spoken language and frequently 'chunks' of useful language. I think the authors have chosen basic and important topics... the concious recycling of materials really helps students learn and retain the material."

"The dialogues present natural situations in class that give students phrases, timing, ways of interrupting and beginning tasks... even cultured information."

SERIES COMPONENTS

Student Texts
Audio CDs
Instructor Web Site
   Instructor Notes
   Answer Key
   Audio Script
Student Web Site

See p. 138 for On Speaking Terms *ISBN/Price listings*

elt.heinle.com/onspeakingterms

KEY CONCEPTS 1 & 2

Listening, Note Taking, and Speaking Across the Disciplines

Elena Vestri Solomon, John Shelley

LEVEL: intermediate to high-intermediate

Key Concepts exposes students to the material they will encounter in college—including discipline-based lectures, academic vocabulary, and structured speaking activities. Students gain valuable academic knowledge and essential note-taking skills necessary for success in college.

- ■ **Content-based lessons** introduce students to key concepts from major academic disciplines such as humanities, communications, biological sciences, social sciences, history, and business.

- ■ **Vocabulary from the Academic Word List** (20 words per chapter) is introduced and extensively practiced to ensure mastery of the academic terms most commonly used in higher education.

- ■ **Listening, note-taking, and group-work activities** provide opportunities for students to practice vital skills needed to achieve at the college level.

- ■ **Varied listening tasks and formats**, such as short dialogues and university lectures, help students to listen for and understand academic English.

Students learn the essential communication skills!

SERIES COMPONENTS
Student Texts
Audio CDs
Online Instructor and Student Resources

See p. 136 for Key Concepts: Listening, Note Taking, and Speaking Across the Disciplines *ISBN/Price listings*

elt.heinle.com/keyconcepts

For an integrated approach, see

Key Concepts 1 & 2: Reading and Writing Across the Disciplines, p. 76.

**Need more vocabulary support?
See Collins COBUILD Advanced
Dictionary of American English, p. 29.**

TALK IT! SERIES 1–3

Listening, Speaking, and Pronunciation, Second Edition

The *Talk It!* series helps intermediate through advanced students learn to communicate fluently and accurately by integrating listening, speaking, and pronunciation practice. Themes range from high-interest conversational topics such as talking to a landlord or professor in the lower-level text, to academic themes like unusual science and alternative medicine in the higher-level texts.

- **The sounds, rhythms, and intonations of English** are taught through pronunciation lessons which hone in on trouble areas for ESL students.

- **Listening passages in each chapter** include pre- and post-listening activities and feature interviews, radio documentaries, and dialogues in a variety of accents and styles.

1. TALK IT UP!, Second Edition

Joann Rishel Kozyrev

LEVEL: intermediate

2. TALK IT THROUGH!

Joann Rishel Kozyrev, Marni Baker Stein

LEVEL: high-intermediate

3. TALK IT OVER!, Second Edition

Joann Rishel Kozyrev

LEVEL: advanced

Student Texts
Audio CDs
Online Instructor and Student Resources

elt.heinle.com/talkit

STEP UP 1 & 2

Listening, Speaking, and Critical Thinking

Margaret Teske, Peggy Marcy

LEVEL: intermediate to high-intermediate

Step Up uses high-interest topics and unique stepped learning objectives to guide students in developing language fluency and confidence.

- **Speaking Strategies** help students build essential academic skills such as analyzing, synthesizing, and evaluating information.

- **"Speaking for TOEFL® Success" exercises** help students gain confidence from timed speaking in small groups, then talk individually using computers and headphones.

- **Extensive opportunities for discussion and debate** get students to apply speaking and listening strategies to practical situations that involve critical thinking.

- **Unit-end projects** prompt students to synthesize oral communication strategies—inside and outside of the classroom—through surveys, research, and other interactive activities.

- Additional resources include **online support** for instructors and students and an assessment **Audio CD.**

Student Texts
Audio CDs
Online Instructor and Student Resources

elt.heinle.com/stepup

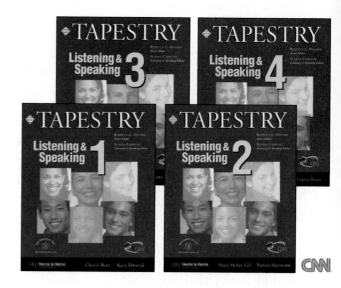

ALL CLEAR 1–3
Listening and Speaking

Helen Kalkstein Fragiadakis

LEVEL: high-beginning to advanced

All Clear teaches students to recognize and produce the high-frequency idioms, phrases, and contemporary expressions needed in a range of conversational situations. A variety of listening, speaking, and pronunciation activities work with language in realistic contexts, integrating development of all language skills.

- **Dialogues** set up the lesson theme and serve as springboards for learning idioms and other expressions.

- **Listening skills** are developed through pre-, while-, and post-listening activities related to each unit's introductory dialogue.

- **"Your Turn" speaking activities** encourage learners to use the newly acquired idioms and expressions interactively.

- **Numerous listening and speaking activities** help build fluency through the integration of reading, writing, and grammar skills.

- Special attention is given to the **grammar related to expressions** in order to help develop fluency and accuracy.

- For each lesson, there is a **pronunciation section** at the back of the book that uses the language and theme of that lesson to practice specific pronunciation points.

Student Texts
Audio CDs
Assessment CD-ROM with Exam*View*®

---

elt.heinle.com/allclear

TAPESTRY LISTENING & SPEAKING 1–4

Rebecca Oxford, *Series Editor*
Susana Christie, *Listening & Speaking Editor*

Book 1: **Cheryl Benz, Kara Dworak**
Book 2: **Pamela Hartmann, Mary McVey Gill**
Book 3: **Karen Carlisi, Susana Christie**
Book 4: **Helen Kalkstein Fragiadakis, Virginia Maurer**

LEVEL: high-beginning to advanced

Useful and engaging listening and speaking activities, learning strategies, CNN® videos, and a Web site effectively provide students with the tools they need to be successful, independent learners.

- **Authentic listening selections** from news broadcasts, interviews, debates, and more, prepare students for understanding college assignments.

- **A variety of speaking activities** such as role plays, debates, and presentations provide opportunities to use vocabulary, and language functions.

- **"Academic Power Strategies,"** such as finding a mentor or forming a study group, give students the knowledge and skills to become successful, independent learners.

- **"Language Learning Strategies"** help students maximize their listening and speaking skills.

- **CNN® video clips** expand the topics and further develop listening and speaking skills.

Student Texts
Audio CDs
CNN® Videos (VHS)
Instructor's Manuals

---

elt.heinle.com/tapestry

For a well-integrated curriculum, see *Tapestry Reading,* **p. 68 and** *Tapestry Writing,* **p. 80.**

NEW!

Great for TOEFL® prep!

LISTENING AND NOTETAKING SERIES 1–3

This groundbreaking listening and notetaking series includes videotaped lectures that simulate the academic lecture experience.

1. INTERMEDIATE LISTENING COMPREHENSION,
Third Edition

Patricia A. Dunkel, Phyllis L. Lim

LEVEL: intermediate

This text is designed to familiarize students with the major rhetorical patterns of formal, spoken English.

2. NOTEWORTHY, Third Edition

Phyllis L. Lim, William Smalzer

LEVEL: high-intermediate to advanced

Noteworthy develops students' listening and notetaking skills, provides insights into U.S. life and culture, and builds cross-disciplinary vocabulary.

3. ADVANCED LISTENING COMPREHENSION,
Third Edition

Patricia A. Dunkel, Frank Pialorsi

LEVEL: advanced

Lectures and readings on topics of universal interest provide stimulating content-based material for developing comprehension, notetaking, and academic study skills.

Student Texts
Audio CDs
Videos (DVD or VHS)
ELT Advantage: *Developing ESL/EFL Listening Comprehension*
    by Patricia A. Dunkel, p. 111

elt.heinle.com/notetaking

LISTENING ADVANTAGE 1–4

Tom Kenny, Tamami Wada

LEVEL: beginning to intermediate

This new four-level, strategies-based course is designed to improve listening skills through the use of activities and topics that are meaningful to students' lives.

- **Wide range of realistic listening types** includes social conversations, transactional dialogues, broadcasts, and announcements.
- **Self-study Audio CD** with accompanying exercises provides additional homework/language lab practice.
- **Regular progress tests** familiarize students with common standardized test formats.
- **Easy-to-teach unit format** and a clearly written teacher's guide make lesson preparation quick and simple.
- **"Language Focus" sections** raise students' awareness of key grammatical and functional patterns featured in the main listening passages.
- **"Pronunciation" and "Conversation Strategy" sections** in every unit help students understand the most important features of spoken English.

Student Texts with Audio CD
Teacher's Guides
Classroom Audio CDs

elt.heinle.com/listeningadvantage

NEW!

COMMUNICATION STRATEGIES 1 – 4

Books 1 & 2: **David Paul**
Book 3:   **Jun Liu, Tracy Davis, Susanne Rizzo**
Book 4:   **Jun Liu, Kathryn Harper**

LEVEL: intermediate to advanced

Communication Strategies covers the vocabulary, patterns, and collocations that English language learners need to communicate actively.

■ **Communication strategies, vocabulary, and useful expressions** are taught and practiced in pair and small-group activities.

■ **Collocations and language patterns** are integrated together, with an alphabetical listing at the back of the book for reference.

■ All new **language is recycled** thoroughly.

■ **Extra practice material** is provided to the teacher in the "Further Activities" section in each unit.

■ A page for "Consolidation and Recycling" at the end of each unit ensures sufficient **review of language points**.

Student Texts
Teacher's Books
Audio CDs

Practice for the TOEFL® speaking section!

FROM COLLEGE TO CAREERS

Listening in the Real World

Angel Bishop Petty, Robert Engel

LEVEL: high-intermediate to advanced

Using authentic and spontaneous speech samples from native English speakers, *From College to Careers* helps students develop the listening comprehension skills to understand natural English in the classroom and the real world.

■ **Audio clips expose students to the challenging aspects of natural speech** such as pauses, hesitations, fillers, false starts, repetition, corrections, repairs, backtracking, non-standard grammar, and varying speech rates.

■ **Pre-listening activities** focus students on using their knowledge and experience to discuss topics related to what they are about to hear.

■ **Vocabulary exercises** encourage students to practice key words, phrases, and expressions that will appear in the audio segment.

■ **Listening comprehension checks** prompt students to listen for main ideas, details, and sequencing.

■ **Guided discussion** helps students improve their critical-thinking skills through relating the recording's content to current events and cultural perspectives.

■ **Further study activities** require students to complete individual or group research tasks outside of class, such as going to the library or conducting an interview with a native speaker.

Student Text
Audio CD
Online Teaching and Study Centers

---

elt.heinle.com/collegetocareers

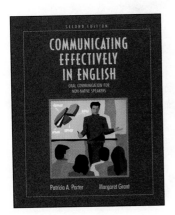

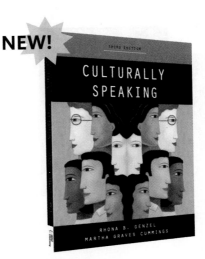

NEW!

COMMUNICATING EFFECTIVELY IN ENGLISH

Oral Communication for
Non-Native Speakers,
Second Edition

Patricia Porter, Margaret Grant

LEVEL: high-intermediate to advanced

This student-centered text presents a highly interactive, experiential format for developing stronger speaking and listening skills in a variety of contexts.

- Small-group and large-group communication

- Interview, discussion, and public speaking skills

- Progression from informative to persuasive speeches

- Emphasizes the process of developing a speech

Student Text
Instructor's Manual

CULTURALLY SPEAKING

Third Edition

Rhona B. Genzel, Martha Graves Cummings

LEVEL: intermediate

Culturally Speaking builds useful, comfortable, communication skills in a new culture through an interactive exploration of everyday experiences. Students share their own cultural thoughts and traditions and compare them with contemporary American customs and everyday situations.

- New and updated content on current topics such as safety and law, values, and the American Dream **engage students** and **promote discussion.**

- Fun **Quick Custom Quizzes** help students compare their cultural experiences with life in the United States.

- **Web Research** activities encourage students to explore other cultures through the Internet.

- **Model "dialogues" on Audio CD** provide students with culturally accurate conversational examples.

- **Case Studies** encourage students to talk critically about what to do in challenging cultural situations.

- **Integrated Skills** activities at the end of each chapter review content while improving reading, writing, listening and speaking skills.

- **Chapter Summary** activities review the skills and content taught in the chapter and teach students how to summarize the main points of the lesson.

Student Text
Audio CD

LISTEN IN 1–3
Second Edition

David Nunan

LEVEL: high-beginning to intermediate

High-interest tasks support the development of receptive and productive skills while including critical listening and learning strategies.

- **Real-life listening practice** uses listening passages based on authentic sources.

- **Starter Unit provides an overview** of each book's listening skills and strategies.

- **"In Focus" section** offers opportunity for cultural comparison and personalization in each unit.

- **Language boxes highlight key expressions** related to each unit's topics and goals.

- **Student Audio CD is included in every Student Book** for risk-free practice outside the classroom.

- Exam*View*® CD-ROM Assessment Package allows teachers to **customize mid-term and final listening tests.**

Student Texts
Teacher's Edition
Classroom Audio CDs
Assessment CD-ROMs with Exam*View*®
ELT Advantage: *An Introduction to Task-Based Teaching* by David Nunan, p. 111

SO TO SPEAK 1 & 2
Integrating Speaking, Listening, and Pronunciation

Megan Webster, Judy DeFilippo

LEVEL: beginning to high-beginning

So to Speak develops students' ability to communicate fluently by integrating listening, speaking, and pronunciation practice.

- The audio program features interesting, accessible topics that provide relevant practice for **daily conversations.**

- **Communicative approach,** featuring cooperative learning strategies and engaging activities such as role-plays and socio-dramas, fosters meaningful conversation.

- "Language Focus" sections provides ample practice of **vocabulary, idioms,** and **expressions.**

- "Pronunciation Focus" emphasizes suprasegmentals, such as syllable and word stress, to improve intelligibility, and offers practice in challenging **high-frequency phonemes.**

- "Listening Focus" addresses strategies for improving listening skills, including **gist, main ideas,** and **inference.**

Student Texts
Audio CDs
Online Teaching Center

---

elt.heinle.com/sotospeak

A lively approach to improving pronunciation and speaking skills!

NEW Third Edition!

WELL SAID SERIES Intro, 1
Pronunciation for Clear Communication

Linda Grant

LEVEL: low-intermediate to advanced

The *Well Said* series offers a lively communicative approach to building and improving pronunciation and speaking skills through strategies development and abundant confidence-building activities.

- **Focus on the high priority features** of stress, rhythm, and intonation helps students improve overall speech intelligibility.

- **Emphasis on pair and small group activities** help students practice their pronunciation and listening skills in motivating, interactive settings.

- **Different formats** such as poems, speeches, and text messages offer varying cultural points while providing contextualized pronunciation practice.

- **Learner-centered activities** progress from controlled practice to relevant, natural communicative contexts.

- **A comprehensive audio program** exposes students to different accents, yet provides a clear North American English model for speaking practices such as read-alongs.

- **"You Choose!" boxes** that suggest where to effectively integrate consonant and vowel supplements into the chapters according to class or individual needs.

What's NEW in the third edition of *Well Said?*

- **TOEFL® iBT exercises** link pronunciation practice to specific Speaking Tasks on the TOEFL® iBT.

- **Updated authentic** speech samples, readings, questionnaires, surveys, and interviews provide students with practical situations, helping them take their studies beyond the classroom to interact with native speakers.

- **Corpus-informed exercises** allow students to practice the features of speech in natural, high frequency chunks.

Well Said Intro also includes:

- **"Practice" and "Helpful Hints" sections** include visual, auditory, and kinesthetic approaches for reinforcing learning and building self-monitoring skills.

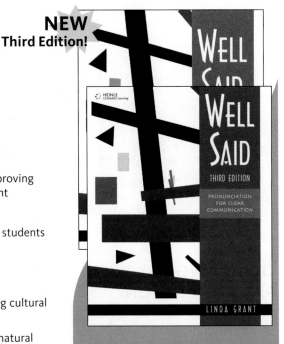

Builds student confidence
in speaking and pronunciation!

SERIES COMPONENTS
Student Texts
Audio CDs
Instructor's Manuals

See p. 143 for Well Said *series ISBN/Price listings*

elt.heinle.com/wellsaid

What your colleagues say about the third edition:

"*This is what pronunciation teachers dream of: to have a text to use that doesn't need supplementation. I think* Well Said *is really ahead of the game in this regard."*

— Anne Delaney,
University of California, San Diego

"*The exercises in* Well Said *bring student problems to the forefront, whether I notice a problem a student is having or a student bursts out with 'I didn't know that! I always said it this way.' When I'm using* Well Said, *I get a significant number of moments during the semester when a student's light bulb comes on!"*

—Steven M. Cunningham,
Valencia Community College, FL

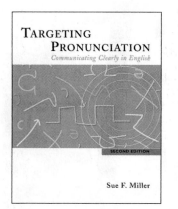

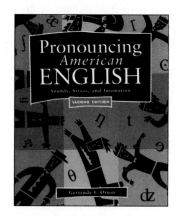

TARGETING PRONUNCIATION

Communicating Clearly in English, Second Edition

Sue F. Miller

LEVEL: intermediate to advanced

Targeting Pronunciation uses an interactive approach and clear explanations to help students communicate effectively in English.

- Diagnostic package is helpful for evaluating individual speech needs, setting priorities, and providing student feedback.

- Self-quizzes at the end of each chapter reinforce students' understanding of chapter material.

- An improved chapter organization makes it easier for instructors to teach pronunciation in a progressive, logical sequence.

- A variety of listening and speaking exercises increase student confidence in mastering English speech rhythm and intonation.

- "Talk Times" communicative activities—planned in the classroom and executed outside the class—facilitate the transfer of pronunciation targets to real-life situations.

Student Text
Audio CDs
Online Teaching and Study Centers

---

elt.heinle.com/targetingpron

PRONOUNCING AMERICAN ENGLISH

Sounds, Stress, and Intonation, Second Edition

Gertrude F. Orion

LEVEL: intermediate to advanced

This second edition provides extensive activities to help college-bound students develop clear speech and appropriate intonation.

- Vowels, consonants, stress, and intonation

- Recognition and production activities

- Paired communicative practice

- Sounds in isolation, sentences, dialogues, and rhymes

- Text/Tape Package: text and all listenings on 8 audio tapes

---

Student Text
Answer Key/Instructor's Manual
Audio CDs

ADDITIONAL LISTENING, SPEAKING & PRONUNCIATION TITLES

EXPRESSIONS Intro – 3
Meaningful English Communication

David Nunan, Ken Beatty

LEVEL: beginning to intermediate

GETTING TOGETHER
An ESL Conversation Book

Susan Stempleski, Alison Rice, Julia Falsetti

LEVEL: intermediate

THE HEART OF THE MATTER

Marjorie Vai

LEVEL: intermediate to high-intermediate

LET'S START TALKING
CAN'T STOP TALKING, 2/e
THE NON-STOP DISCUSSION WORKBOOK, 2/e

George M. Rooks

LEVEL: high-beginning to advanced

LISTEN, SPEAK, PRESENT
A Step-by-Step Presenter's Workbook

Martha Graves Cummings

LEVEL: advanced

SAY IT NATURALLY 1 & 2
Verbal Strategies for Authentic Communication, 2/e

Allie Patricia Wall

LEVEL: high-beginning to advanced

SOUND BITES
Pronunciation Activities

Joann Rishel Kozyrev

LEVEL: high-beginning to low-intermediate

SOUNDS GREAT 1 & 2
Pronunciation for Speakers of English

Beverly Beisbier

LEVEL: low-intermediate to intermediate

SPEAK UP 1 & 2, 2/e

Cheryl Pavlik, Anna Stumpfhauser de Hernandez

LEVEL: beginning to high-beginning

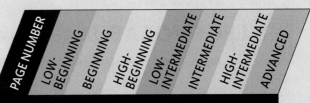

LEVEL GUIDE

	PAGE NUMBER	LOW-BEGINNING	BEGINNING	HIGH-BEGINNING	LOW-INTERMEDIATE	INTERMEDIATE	HIGH-INTERMEDIATE	ADVANCED
IDIOMS								
Academic Spelling Power	100				●			
Academic Word Power: 1, 2, 3, 4	99					1,2	3,4	
Against All Odds	100						●	●
All Clear: 1, 2, 3	90			1	2	2	3	3
Big Picture, The	100						●	
VOCABULARY								
American Business Vocabulary	108					●		
American Vocabulary Program: 1, 2, 3	99				1	2	3	
College Vocabulary: 1, 2, 3, 4	98				1	2	3	4
Developing Vocabulary Skills, 2/e	100							●
Essential Academic Vocabulary	100						●	●
Practice: Vocabulary	100						●	●
Walk, Amble, Stroll: 1, 2	99			1	2	2		
DICTIONARIES								
Collins COBUILD Advanced Dictionary of American English	29							●
Collins COBUILD Basic Dictionary of American English NEW!	25		●	●	●			
Collins COBUILD Intermediate Dictionary of American English	28				●	●	●	
Collins COBUILD School Dictionary of American English	27				●	●	●	
Collins COBUILD English/Español Glossary	30			●	●	●		
Heinle Picture Dictionary, The	32	●	●	●	●			
Heinle's Basic Newbury House Dictionary, 2/e	36	●	●	●	●			
Heinle's Newbury House Dictionary with Integrated Thesaurus, 4/e	36				●	●	●	

Prepares students for the rigorous demands of college-level courses!

COLLEGE VOCABULARY 1 – 4

Patricia Byrd, Joy M. Reid, Cynthia Schuemann, *Series Editors*

Book 1: **Julie Howard**
Book 2: **Chaudron Gille**
Book 3: **Keith S. Folse, Marcella Farina**
Book 4: **John D. Bunting**

LEVEL: low-intermediate to advanced

College Vocabulary, part of the *English for Academic Success* series, helps students develop the ability to understand and use the most common words in academic texts, as chosen from the Academic Word List. Use alone in a vocabulary class or as supplements in reading, writing, or oral communication classes.

▪ Vocabulary is presented and practiced within contexts that represent **real usage.**

▪ **Varied, sequenced exercises** ensure that students use new words frequently.

▪ **Review sections** provide practice with the targeted vocabulary.

▪ Extensive **online instructor and student support.**

- Class-tested
- Competency-based
- Adjunct approved

SERIES COMPONENTS
Student Texts
Online Instructor and Student Resources

See p. 124 for College Vocabulary
ISBN/Price listings

elt.heinle.com/collegevocab

Build vocabulary through reading!

Use the *Reading and Vocabulary Development* series and help your students increase their active vocabulary.

Book 1: from 300 to 800 words
Book 2: from 800 to 1,300 words
Book 3: from 1,300 to 2,000 words
Book 4: from 2,000 to 2,500 words

For more information on this best-selling series, see p. 65.

Other titles in the *English for Academic Success* series include:

College Reading 1 – 4, p. 67
College Writing 1 – 4, p. 79
College Oral Communication 1 – 4, p. 85

For professional development or in-service training on teaching academic English, see:

Essentials of Teaching Academic Vocabulary, p. 117

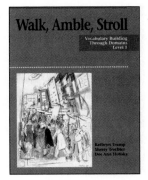

ACADEMIC WORD POWER 1–4

Donna Obenda, Series Editor

Book 1: **Lisa Hollinger**
Book 2: **Celia Thompson**
Book 3: **Pat Bull**
Book 4: **Barbara Jones**

LEVEL: intermediate to
high-intermediate

Each book in *Academic Word Power 1 – 4* focuses on 140 word families from the Academic Word List, ensuring students learn the vocabulary they need most for success in college-level courses.

- Contextualized vocabulary in every lesson begins with a reading that includes all of the focus words followed by vocabulary development, practice, and strategies for learning academic vocabulary.

- Interactive speaking activities link focus words with past experience and knowledge to aid retention.

Student Texts
Online Teaching and Study Centers

AMERICAN VOCABULARY PROGRAM 1–3

John Flower, Michael Berman, Ron Martínez, Mark Powell

LEVEL: low-intermediate to
high-intermediate

The *American Vocabulary Program* provides essential vocabulary practice of all types of lexical items: words, word partnerships, and fixed expressions.

- Over 1,000 words and phrases are taught at each level.

- Vocabulary learning is systematic, efficient, and fun.

- The series is ideal for classroom use or self-study.

- Exercises cover a comprehensive selection of subject and language.

Student Texts

WALK, AMBLE, STROLL 1 & 2

Vocabulary Building
Through Domains

Dee Ann Holisky, Kathy Trump, Sherry Trechter

LEVEL: high-beginning to intermediate

Walk, Amble, Stroll teaches students vocabulary and vocabulary learning strategies through the use of semantic fields or domains.

- A meaning system is taught to help students acquire new words.

- Strategies for continued learning are provided.

- Review units in Instructor's Manual offer further consolidation and practice.

Student Texts
Instructor's Manual/Answer Key

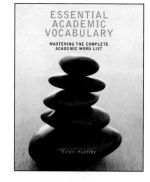

DEVELOPING VOCABULARY SKILLS

Second Edition

Dennis Keen

LEVEL: advanced

This vocabulary text teaches students to analyze, understand, and remember vocabulary by developing word attack strategies.

- Readings, collaborative exercises, and contextualized activities present vocabulary.
- Suffixes, prefixes, and roots are grouped into manageable units according to meaning.
- Contextual exercises demonstrate language in use.

Student Text
Answer Key/Instructor's Manual

ESSENTIAL ACADEMIC VOCABULARY

Mastering the Complete Academic Word List

Helen Huntley

LEVEL: high-intermediate to advanced

Essential Academic Vocabulary prepares students for academic success by helping them preview, learn, and practice vocabulary from the Academic Word List in context.

- New vocabulary and word forms are introduced and contextualized through readings chosen from actual college textbooks.
- Exercises and activities give students ample practice using academic vocabulary in college writing and speaking.

Student Text
Online Teaching and Study Centers

elt.heinle.com/essentialvocab

ADDITIONAL VOCABULARY TITLES

ACADEMIC SPELLING POWER

Julie Howard

LEVEL: low-intermediate

AGAINST ALL ODDS
Speaking Naturally with Idioms

Marie Hutchison Eichler

LEVEL: high-intermediate to advanced

THE BIG PICTURE
Idioms as Metaphors

Kevin King

LEVEL: high-intermediate

PRACTICE: VOCABULARY

Milada Broukal

LEVEL: intermediate to advanced

LEVEL GUIDE

	PAGE NUMBER	HIGH-BEGINNING	INTERMEDIATE	HIGH-INTERMEDIATE	ADVANCED
TEST PREPARATION					
Complete Guide to the TOEFL® Test: iBT Edition, The	102		•	•	•
Complete Guide to the TOEIC® Test, 3/e	104		•	•	•
Heinle TOEFL® Test Assistant series, The	104		•	•	•
IELTS express: Intermediate, Upper-Intermediate	104		I	UI	
IELTS Practice Tests	104		•	•	•
Introductory Guide to the TOEIC® Test	104	•	•		
Online Tutorial for the TOEFL® iBT **NEW!**	103		•	•	•
COLLEGE PREPARATION					
Bridge to College Success	104				•
Linkages	104			•	

TOEFL® and TOEIC® are registered trademarks of Educational Testing Service (ETS). These products are not endorsed or approved by ETS.

The total package for test-taking success!

THE COMPLETE GUIDE TO THE TOEFL® TEST

iBT Edition

Bruce Rogers

LEVEL: intermediate to advanced

Written by trusted test preparation author Bruce Rogers, *The Complete Guide to the TOEFL® Test, iBT Edition* offers instruction and practice that closely mirrors the actual TOEFL® test. This text will help students master the skills necessary to achieve the best possible score on the TOEFL® iBT, preparing them to succeed in an academic environment.

- The text provides **test-taking strategies** at the beginning of each section, **extensive practice** with all exercise types found on the TOEFL® iBT, a **separate section on essay writing**, additional exercises addressing the most common errors made on the TOEFL® test, and **two full practice tests**.

- **Practice for the new Speaking section** of the TOEFL® test provides oral prompts as well as actual examples of test-takers completing this part of the exam.

- **An interactive CD-ROM provides electronic practice** through a tutorial, practice with all exercise types found on the TOEFL® iBT, a test bank of TOEFL®-type questions, and **two complete TOEFL® tests.**

- The **Audio Program** provides listening activities for practice on the listening portion of the TOEFL® iBT.

For success on all sections of the TOEFL®!

COMPONENTS

Student Text/CD-ROM Package
Answer Key/Audio Script
Audio CDs
Interactive CD-ROM
Online Tutorial for the TOEFL® iBT

See p. 124 for The Complete Guide to the TOEFL® Test *ISBN/Price listings*

elt.heinle.com/toefl

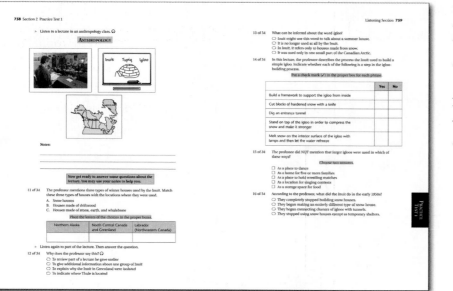

▲ Complete practice tests prepare students for success on the TOEFL® iBT!

For 40 hours of additional practice with instant feedback for the TOEFL® iBT, see the *Online Tutorial for the TOEFL® iBT!*

Prepare for the TOEFL® iBT—online! **NEW!**

ONLINE TUTORIAL FOR THE TOEFL® iBT

LEVEL: intermediate to advanced

Online Tutorial for the TOEFL® iBT combines innovative technology with a unique learning pedagogy to prepare students for TOEFL® exam success.

- An electronic diagnostic test individually assesses each student and creates a **customized learning path** that allows them to focus their study.

- The tutorial includes over 10 hours of study for all four parts of the TOEFL® exam—**reading, listening, speaking, and writing.**

- **Speaking practice** identifies errors in pronunciation, fluency, word stress, and linkage, providing immediate feedback using Carnegie Speech technology—a leader in speech recognition technology. (www.carnegiespeech.com)

- Students independently identify areas needing improvement through **self-assessment activities** in each section.

- **Two practice tests** that simulate versions of the TOEFL® exam follow the preparation for each section of the exam.

- **NEW! Now available in three configurations:** The Complete Edition, Listening and Speaking Only, and Reading and Writing Only. All versions include Practice Tests!

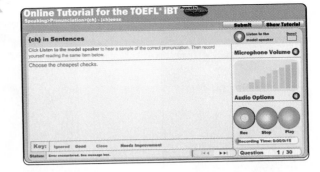

▲ Analyzes student speech using advanced **speech recognition technology**

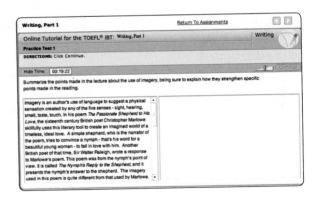

▲ Practice exercises based on each students' **Customized Learning Plan**

Online Tutorial for the TOEFL® iBT *is powered by...*

About MyELT

MyELT is an Internet-based learning management system designed just for English language teachers and students. Instructors use *MyELT* to assign Heinle online learning content, track student grades, create student progress reports, and more. Students use *MyELT* to complete the online activities, monitor their own learning progress, and review as necessary.

About Carnegie Speech

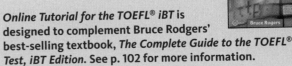
Improving Spoken English

Carnegie Speech's technology pinpoints errors in the sounds, grammar, rhythm, pitch and fluency of the student's speech and provides individualized instruction that maximizes improvement and minimizes training time.

Simulates TOEFL® iBT test-taking experience

Online Tutorial for the TOEFL® iBT is designed to complement Bruce Rodgers' best-selling textbook, *The Complete Guide to the TOEFL® Test, iBT Edition.* See p. 102 for more information.

LINKAGES

A Content-Based Integrated Skills Program

Patrice Connerton, Frances Reid

LEVEL: high-intermediate

Linkages is a content-based, integrated skills text that bridges the gap between language learning and the acquisition of academic knowledge.

- **Content-based readings** in business, U.S. history, sociology, and literature
- **Thematic organization** that allows for recycling of vocabulary, syntax, and discourse style
- **Authentic readings** that are carefully adapted
- **Cognitive skills:** analysis, classification, evaluation, and reaction

Student Text
Instructor's Manual/Tapescript
Audio (Tapes)
Video (VHS)

BRIDGE TO COLLEGE SUCCESS

Intensive Academic Preparation for Advanced Students

Heather Robertson

LEVEL: advanced

Bridge to College Success challenges students to complete authentic academic assignments in the context of content-based instruction in the U.S. social and educational systems.

- Authentic full-chapter **reading selections focusing on introductory college subjects**
- **Vocabulary development, test-taking, and study skills** that prepare students for college
- **Strategy-based**
- Questions for analysis **encourage independent thinking**

Student Text
Audio (Tapes)
Video (VHS)

ADDITIONAL TEST PREPARATION TITLES

THE COMPLETE GUIDE TO THE TOEIC® TEST
iBT Edition

Bruce Rogers
LEVEL: intermediate to advanced

THE HEINLE TOEFL® TEST ASSISTANT SERIES

Milada Broukal, Kathleen Flynn
LEVEL: intermediate to advanced

INTRODUCTORY GUIDE TO THE TOEIC® TEST

Bruce Rogers
LEVEL: high-beginning to intermediate

IELTS EXPRESS SERIES

Richard Hallows, Martin Lisboa, Mark Unwin
LEVEL: intermediate to upper-intermediate

IELTS PRACTICE TESTS

Mark Harrison, Russell Whitehead
LEVEL: intermediate to advanced

LEVEL GUIDE

	PAGE NUMBER	BEGINNING	HIGH-BEGINNING	LOW-INTERMEDIATE	INTERMEDIATE	HIGH-INTERMEDIATE	ADVANCED
American Business Vocabulary	108				•		
Best Practice: Elementary, Pre-Intermediate, Intermediate, Upper-Intermediate	108	Elem	Elem	P-Int	Int	U-Int	
Business Concepts for English Practice, 2/e	108					•	•
Business Language Practice	108				•	•	
Financial English	108				•	•	
Language of Meetings, The	108				•	•	
Management and Marketing	108				•	•	•
New Business Matters	108					•	
Presenting in English	108				•	•	
Professional English series							
English for Professional Success	106				•		
English for Health Sciences	106				•		
English for Business	106				•		
English for the Humanities	106				•		
English for Science and Engineering	106				•		
Working Week, The	108				•		

A new approach in ESP instruction!

PROFESSIONAL ENGLISH SERIES

Kristin L. Johannsen, Martin Milner, Josephine O'Brien, Hector Sanchez, Ivor Williams

LEVEL: intermediate

The five-volume *Professional English* series is designed for both pre-work students and those already working. Teachers and learners will find a variety of practice opportunities in problem solving, critical thinking, and professional communication.

- **An integrated four-skills** approach breaks with the traditional practice of reading/vocabulary ESP instruction.

- **Two-page lessons** provide a variety of interesting work situations.

- **Grammar Reference** allows for review and self-study of the essential grammar required at the intermediate level.

- **An international English Audio Program** with a variety of American, British, and non-native accents develops the listening skills required by today's global community.

- **A comprehensive Teacher's Resource Book** includes photocopiable tests, teaching notes, answer keys, and photocopiable activities to extend reading, writing, communication, and grammar skills.

Perfect for professional development and corporate communications!

COMPONENTS
Student Texts with Audio CD
Teacher's Resource Books

See p. 139 for Professional English *series ISBN/Price listings*

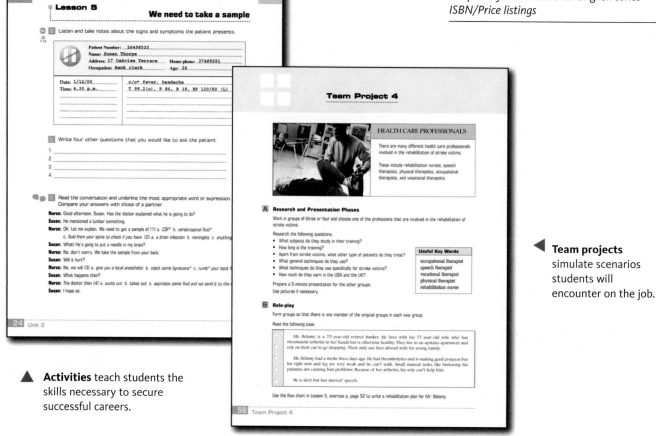

▲ **Activities** teach students the skills necessary to secure successful careers.

▲ **Team projects** simulate scenarios students will encounter on the job.

(Sample pages from *English for Health Sciences*)

■■ Professional
■■ English

ENGLISH FOR PROFESSIONAL SUCCESS

English for Professional Success is especially designed for university students who want to use their English for international communication in professional contexts like:

■ Professional development

■ Job-hunting

■ Relocating

■ On-the-job skills

■ The language of the workplace

ENGLISH FOR HEALTH SCIENCES

English for Health Sciences is written for university students who want to use their English for international communication in Health Science fields. Health Science majors can practice English language skills in the following job-related scenarios:

■ Diagnosing

■ Patient treatment

■ Critical patient care

■ Rehabilitation and long-term treatment

■ Patient referrals

ENGLISH FOR BUSINESS

English for Business provides students with the language and life skills necessary to pursue business-related career goals. Through language practice based in real-world situations, this integrated skills approach builds confidence and motivates students towards successful careers with lessons focusing on the following topics:

■ Job-hunting

■ Creating a resume

■ Interview techniques

■ The language of sales, marketing, and finance

■ Corporate culture

ENGLISH FOR THE HUMANITIES

English for the Humanities is an integrated skills book designed to provide 40 hours of teaching and practice material for university students specializing in a liberal arts program or studying for a degree in the social sciences. Students can practice English language skills in these areas:

■ Philosophy

■ Language

■ Art

■ History

■ Social Science

ENGLISH FOR SCIENCE AND ENGINEERING

English for Science and Engineering is an integrated skills book designed to provide 40 hours of teaching and practice material for university students and professionals specializing or working in any of the fields of exact science or engineering. Science and/or engineering majors can practice their English language skills in the following job-related scenarios:

■ Research and development

■ Design and testing

■ Construction and manufacturing production

■ Quality control and inspection, operation and maintenance

■ Management

THE WORKING WEEK
Spoken Business English with
a Lexical Approach

Anne Watson-Delestrée, Jimmie Hill

LEVEL: intermediate

The Working Week is a business text that
emphasizes speaking, listening, and
problem solving in different work
situations.

Student Text
Instructor's Manual
Audio (Tape)

THE LANGUAGE OF
MEETINGS

Malcolm Goodale

LEVEL: intermediate to
high-intermediate

The Language of Meetings is a lively,
comprehensive course that provides all
the necessary language to ensure full
and effective participation in a
business meeting.

Student Text

NEW BUSINESS
MATTERS
Business English with
a Lexical Approach

**Mark Powell, Ron Martínez,
Rosi Jillett, Charles Mercer**

LEVEL: high-intermediate

New Business Matters is a stimulating
language course for students of business
English. Its unique lexical syllabus
precisely identifies what business
students need to learn in order to
increase their fluency in English.

Coursebook
Workbook
Teacher's Book
Audio CDs
Assessment CD-ROM with Exam*View*®
CNN® Video

elt.heinle.com/nbm

PRESENTING IN
ENGLISH
How to Give Successful
Presentations

Mark Powell

LEVEL: intermediate to
high-intermediate

Presenting in English provides the
language and skills needed to give truly
effective presentations, in English.

Student Text
Audio (Tape) (American English)

BEST PRACTICE 1 – 4
Business English in a Global Context

**Bill Mascull, Jeremy Comfort,
David Kerridge**

LEVEL: elementary to
upper-intermediate

Best Practice is a four-level business
English course designed for both pre-
work and in-work students.

Student Texts
Workbooks
Teacher's Resource Books
Audio CDs
Assessment CD-ROM with Exam*View*®

elt.heinle.com/bestpractice

ADDITIONAL ENGLISH FOR BUSINESS
& SPECIFIC PURPOSES TITLES

AMERICAN BUSINESS
VOCABULARY

John Flower, Ron Martínez
LEVEL: intermediate

BUSINESS CONCEPTS FOR
ENGLISH PRACTICE, 2/e

**Marianne McDougal Arden,
Barbara Tolley Dowling**
LEVEL: high-intermediate to advanced

BUSINESS LANGUAGE
PRACTICE

John Morrison Milne
LEVEL: intermediate to
high-intermediate

FINANCIAL ENGLISH
with Mini-Dictionary of Finance

Ian MacKenzie
LEVEL: intermediate to
high-intermediate

MANAGEMENT AND
MARKETING
with Mini-Dictionary
of 1,000 Common Terms

Ian MacKenzie
LEVEL: intermediate to advanced

PAGE GUIDE

ELT advantage

Ongoing Professional Development for English Language Teachers

ELT ADVANTAGE

2009 SIIA //CODiE// FINALIST

Keep pace with the latest instructional methods and industry best practices. Explore *ELT Advantage*, an entire suite of professional development courses, workshops, and virtual seminars that help teachers increase their expertise in English language instruction.

Developed by world-renowned English language teachers and authors, the *ELT Advantage* professional development offerings include:

✔ **Online courses** covering new and emerging English language teaching methods

✔ **TESOL virtual, online seminars** hosted by pioneers in the English language teaching profession

✔ **Training sites** that help you teach with Heinle's best-selling textbook series

✔ **Correlated courses** to Heinle programs to ensure efficient implementation

To learn more and view a demo, visit elt.heinle.com/ELTAdvantage.

Online Courses for Teachers

New courses added frequently

▪ 6-week courses, two lessons per week

▪ Practical assignments for each lesson

▪ Moderated discussion board

▪ Lessons can be completed in 90 minutes or less—anytime, anywhere

▪ Post-program assessment

TESOL® Certificate of Completion for approved courses

University Credits available

▲ Watch virtual, online seminars focusing on key issues related to ESL and EFL.

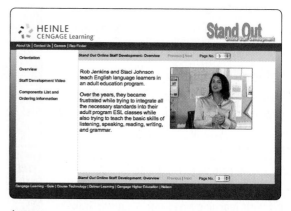

▲ Secure teacher training sites demonstrate for you and your colleagues how to teach with our award-winning programs.

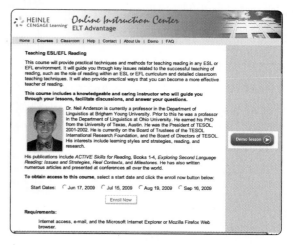

▲ Select from specialized courses, watch author video segments, and access innovative content.

See p. 125 for course ISBN/Price listings.

Choose from a growing selection of Online courses, including:

Assessing Language Ability in Young Adults and Adults
Andrew D. Cohen

Communicative Teaching for the ESL/EFL Classroom
Kevin Keating

Content-Based Instruction for Language Learners
Kathleen M. Bailey

Developing ESL/EFL Listening Comprehension
Patricia A. Dunkel

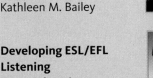
An Introduction to Corpora in English Language Teaching
Michael McCarthy, Anne O'Keeffe, and Steve Walsh

An Introduction to Language Assessment in the K-12 Classroom
Natalie Kuhlman

An Introduction to Task-Based Teaching
David Nunan

An Introduction to Teaching English to Young Learners
Annie Hughes

An Introduction to Teaching ESL/EFL
Tom Scovel

Language Learning Technologies for K-12 Teachers
Joyce Nutta

Making the Most of Learner's Dictionaries
Michela Clari

Practical Ideas for the Adult ESL/EFL Classroom
Rob Jenkins

Pursuing Professional Development
Andy Curtis

Teaching ESL/EFL Reading
Neil J. Anderson

Teaching Grammar for ESL/EFL **NEW!**
Diane Larsen-Freeman

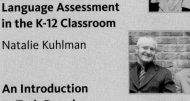
Teaching Lexically
Hugh Dellar and Andrew Walkley

Teaching ESL/EFL Vocabulary **NEW!**
I.S.P. Nation

What your colleagues are saying about ELT Advantage...

"Honestly, this was an absolutely wonderful experience! ... The assignments were well thought out and the lessons insightful. It was a perfect mix of current theory and methodology."

—Martha Yeager Tobar, Cerritos College, California

"One of the best things about this program is the wealth of hands-on activities and ideas provided in each course. ... the lessons are chock-full of tested strategies that improve student learning."

—Michele Vaughn, Whitehouse High School, Texas

"Spreading the content delivery out over six weeks was perfect. I will definitely recommend the courses to other instructors in my district."

—Diane Stonebrink, Estrella Mountain Community, Arizona

New vocabulary teaching strategies from Dr. Robert Marzano! **NEW!**

TEACHING BASIC AND ADVANCED VOCABULARY
A Framework for Direct Instruction

Dr. Robert J. Marzano

Authored by field expert and vocabulary specialist Dr. Robert J. Marzano, *Teaching Basic and Advanced Vocabulary* provides strategies to help build general background knowledge of instrumental vocabulary by introducing terms in semantic clusters. This innovative approach is designed to maximize students' understanding of new words by creating a framework of meaning through context.

Support strategies for basic and advanced terms!

Features:

- More than **8,000 basic and advanced vocabulary terms**
- **Semantic clusters** that group related words together
- Comparison, classification, analogy and metaphor **activities to strengthen comprehension skills**
- **Snapshot assessment** for comprehension evaluation

COMPONENTS

Text

See p. 142 for Teaching Basic and Advanced Vocabulary *ISBN/Price listings*

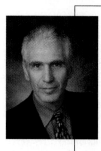

"... Teaching Basic and Advanced Vocabulary *is focused on providing a framework for direct instruction in basic terms—those words that are critical to understanding and using the English language. To this end, 2,845 basic terms have been identified and listed in the book.*

Teaching Basic and Advanced Vocabulary *also explains how a district, school, or individual teacher might use semantic clusters in a whole-class approach to direct instruction that focuses on advanced vocabulary."*

—Dr. Robert J. Marzano

1. Modals—related clusters: 3, 4, 342, 411

Word	Importance	Part of Speech	Word	Importance	Part of Speech
can	1	v	shall	1	v
cannot	1	v	should	1	v
could	1	v	will	1	v
may	1	v	would	1	v
might	1	v	ought	4	v
must	1	v	used to	4	v

Example of semantic clusters from *Teaching Basic and Advanced Vocabulary*

For secondary basal materials using Dr. Marzano's strategies, see *Milestones* on page 8.

For customer support, call **(877) NEED-ESL** or visit **elt.heinle.com** For pricing, ISBNs, and ordering information see pp. 122 – 144

The perfect companion piece to Teaching Basic and Advanced Vocabulary!

NEW!

SNAPSHOT ONLINE ASSESSMENT OF BASIC VOCABULARY

Dr. Robert J. Marzano

Dr. Robert Marzano's unique new online assessment system quickly determines a student's level of understanding vocabulary terms that are essential to their comprehension of English. Using the semantic cluster system introduced in Dr. Marzano's *Teaching Basic and Advanced Vocabulary* book, this tool quickly identifies knowledge of basic terms so that instruction will be focused and efficient.

- **Twenty-minute testing time** quickly identifies a student's vocabulary knowledge.
- **Adaptive test** places students at the appropriate starting point in Dr. Marzano's vocabulary learning curriculum.
- Range of vocabulary terms comes directly from **Dr. Marzano's research on the essential vocabulary** that is foundational to English and to general literacy.

COMPONENTS
Online Assessment

See p. 140 for Snapshot Online Assessment of Basic Vocabulary *ISBN/Price listings*

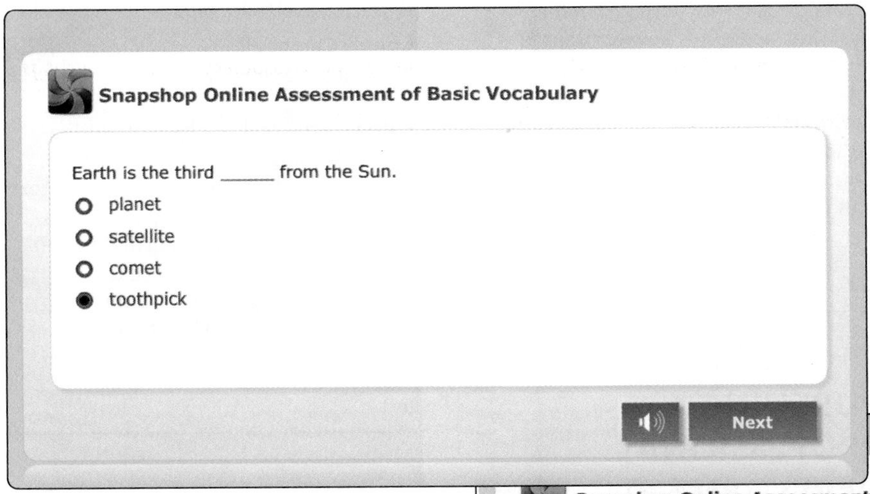

Snapshop Online Assessment of Basic Vocabulary

Earth is the third _____ from the Sun.
- ○ planet
- ○ satellite
- ○ comet
- ● toothpick

Next

◀ Tests can be administered to a whole class, or to an individual student. ▼

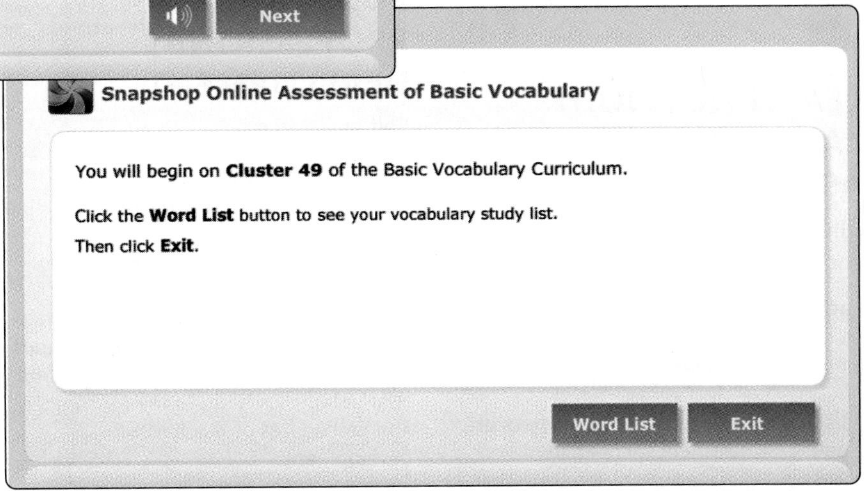

Bundle a *Snapshot Online Assessment* site license with *Teaching Basic and Advanced Vocabulary*. Ask your Heinle representative for details.

Snapshop Online Assessment of Basic Vocabulary

You will begin on **Cluster 49** of the Basic Vocabulary Curriculum.

Click the **Word List** button to see your vocabulary study list.
Then click **Exit**.

Word List   Exit

TeacherSource

Donald Freeman, *Series Editor*

"The TeacherSource series offers you a point of view on second/foreign language teaching.

As a reader, you will find that each book has its own personality; it is not anonymous. It comes as a story, not as a directive, and is meant to create a relationship with you rather than assume your attention."

Donald Freeman

EXPLORING SECOND LANGUAGE READING
Issues and Strategies

Neil J. Anderson,
Brigham Young University

Exploring Second Language Reading: Issues and Strategies is a comprehensive exploration of ESL reading. This text provides an overview of the key issues and practical strategies for teaching reading effectively.

Text
_____

Also see Neil Anderson's series *ACTIVE Skills for Reading* on p. 64.

LEARNING ABOUT LANGUAGE ASSESSMENT
Dilemmas, Decisions, and Directions

Kathleen M. Bailey,
Monterey Institute of International Studies

This text provides a practical analysis of language assessment theory and accessible explanations of the statistics involved.

Text
_____

TEACHING ESL K – 12
Views from the Classroom

Helene Becker, Else Hamayan

Teaching ESL K – 12: Views from the Classroom addresses how to prepare English language learners to successfully enter the demands of mainstream classrooms, curricula, and schools. The authors artfully blend insightful classroom and school-based experience with frameworks of research and policy.

Text
_____

PURSUING PROFESSIONAL DEVELOPMENT
Self as Source

Kathleen M. Bailey,
Monterey Institute of International Studies
Andy Curtis
David Nunan, *University of Hong Kong*

Intended for individual study or teacher-preparation programs, this text provides an up-to-date overview of key ideas and a comprehensive guide to the techniques and procedures of teacher self-development.

Text
_____

TEACHING SECOND-LANGUAGE WRITING
Interacting with Text

Cherry Campbell,
Sonoma State University

Based on the philosophy that writing should be taught in conjunction with social and cultural expectations, this text teaches a variety of writing strategies, such as self-editing and portfolio writing, and provides practical advice on assessing writing and providing constructive feedback to students.

Text
_____

DOING TEACHER RESEARCH
From Inquiry to Understanding

Donald Freeman,
School for International Training

This text focuses on the intersection of teaching and research. By examining how research can fit within and transform the work of teaching, it offers a different perspective to teachers doing research.

Text
_____

For customer support, call **(877) NEED-ESL** or visit **elt.heinle.com** ■ For pricing, ISBNs, and ordering information see pp. 122 – 144

DESIGNING LANGUAGE COURSES

A Guide for Teachers

Kathleen Graves,
School for International Training

This clear and comprehensive text provides a practical guide to designing language courses by encouraging teachers to explore ways of evaluating materials and planning and organizing content.

Text

TEACHING BILINGUAL CHILDREN

Beliefs and Behaviors

Suzanne Irujo,
Boston University, Emeritus

Based on a vivid account of Matilde's classroom, this text is a comprehensive exploration of bilingual education theory and practice.

Text

UNDERSTANDING LANGUAGE TEACHING

Reasoning in Action

Karen E. Johnson,
Pennsylvania State University

Teachers are encouraged to reflect on their classroom practice by thinking critically about their own teaching, their colleagues' teaching, and the environments in which they work.

Text

TEACHING LANGUAGE

From Grammar to Grammaring

Diane Larsen-Freeman,
University of Michigan

A must-read for every language teaching professional, *Teaching Language: From Grammar to Grammaring* explores the regular, predictable elements of language as well as the potential creativity of its underlying system. By combining a wide range of viewpoints with her own personal experiences and studies, Diane Larsen-Freeman challenges the static descriptive ideas of grammar, based on rules, and promotes the more fluid and dynamic notions of reason-driven grammaring, which she defines as "the ability to use grammar structures accurately, meaningfully, and appropriately."

Text

Also see Diane Larsen-Freeman and Marianne Celce-Murcia's updated edition of *The Grammar Book* on p. 117.

TEACHING CULTURE

Perspectives in Practice

Patrick Moran

Teaching Culture: Perspectives in Practice offers multiple viewpoints on the interrelationship between language and culture and how they serve to teach meaning, offer a lens of identity, and provide a mechanism for social participation. Authentic classroom experiences engage the reader and offer teachers invaluable support as they expand their ideas about how language and culture work together.

Text

LEARNING NEW LANGUAGES

A Guide to Second Language Acquisition

Tom Scovel,
San Francisco State University

This text explores a wide range of issues that influence how a person learns a second language. By using P.L.A.C.E. as an acronym, standing for People, Language, Attention, Cognition, and Emotion, the text offers an accessible way to examine both the practical and theoretical sides of each issue.

Text

WORKING WITH TEACHING METHODS

What's at Stake?

Earl W. Stevick

By examining different methods of language teaching, this text models a way for teachers to analyze their own teaching by thinking critically about approaches, techniques, and materials.

Text

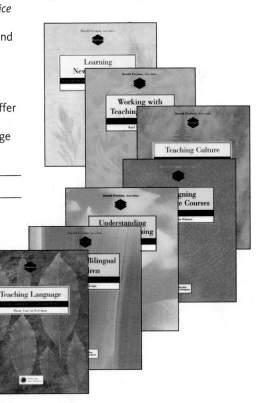

Special Offer!

TeacherSource—*The Ultimate Collection*

Includes all TeacherSource books! 978-0-8384-4370-5 $302.75

THE LEXICAL APPROACH

The State of ELT and a Way Forward

Michael Lewis

The Lexical Approach develops current thinking, synthesizing the best insights of previous theory, corpus linguistics, discourse analysis, and modern approaches to grammar. Principles of *The Lexical Approach* include:

- The grammar/vocabulary dichotomy is invalid; collocation is used as an organizing principle; the Observe-Hypothesize-Experiment cycle replaces the Present-Practice-Produce paradigm; and, most importantly, language consists of grammaticalized lexis—not lexicalized grammar.

Text

IMPLEMENTING THE LEXICAL APPROACH

Putting Theory into Practice

Michael Lewis

Implementing the Lexical Approach develops the theoretical position set out in Michael Lewis' highly acclaimed *The Lexical Approach*.

- It provides teachers with comprehensive, step-by-step classroom changes to ensure more effective teaching and more efficient learning.

Text

TEACHING COLLOCATION

Further Developments in the Lexical Approach

Michael Lewis, *Editor*

Teaching Collocation provides further follow-up to *The Lexical Approach*.

- Contains papers by Jane Conzett, Peter Hargreaves, Jimmie Hill, Michael Hoey, Michael Lewis, Morgan Lewis, and George Woolard about collocation in everyday classroom teaching.

- Readers will learn the importance of collocation and idioms, practical ways of introducing the idea to students, examples of good classroom practices, and teachers' experiences.

Text

PRACTICAL TECHNIQUES

For Language Teaching

Michael Lewis, Jimmie Hill

Practical Techniques is a highly practical, jargon-free basic teacher training handbook for new teachers of ESL/EFL.

- This text includes basic principles, discussion on classroom management, notes on preparation, and a thorough overview of basic techniques.

Text

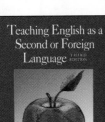

Professional Development & Resources

EXPLORING SECOND LANGUAGE CLASSROOM RESEARCH

A Comprehensive Guide

David Nunan, Kathleen M. Bailey

Exploring Second Language Classroom Research is a comprehensive introductory manual for beginning and advanced researchers. The text is illustrated with a variety of qualitative and quantitative data and includes tasks for reflection and application.

Text

TEACHING ENGLISH AS A SECOND OR FOREIGN LANGUAGE

Third Edition

Marianne Celce-Murcia, *Editor*

This best-selling methodology resource gives experienced and prospective teachers the theoretical background and practical applications they need to succeed. New contributions from more than 40 acknowledged specialists in the field cover methodology, language skills, integrated approaches, learner variables, and teacher skills. Discussion questions and activities, methods, materials, and other resources make this ideal for classroom and/or personal use.

Text

THE GRAMMAR BOOK

An ESL/EFL Teacher's Course, Second Edition

Marianne Celce-Murcia, Diane Larsen-Freeman

In this highly acclaimed revision, grammatical descriptions and teaching suggestions are organized into sections dealing with form, meaning, and use. *The Grammar Book* helps teachers and future teachers grasp the linguistic system and details of English grammar, providing more information on how structures are used at the discourse level.

Text

THE POWER OF CONTEXT

in Language Teaching and Learning

Jan Frodesen, Christine A. Holten, *Editors*

The Power of Context in Language Teaching and Learning provides a highly accessible, in-depth study of the relationship between discourse and the context of language teaching and learning. This text contains a strong combination of theory and practice that will benefit any language teacher or student. Contributions from 30 renowned specialists provide a variety of insights and perspectives, with an emphasis on practical applications.

Text

ESSENTIALS OF TEACHING ACADEMIC ENGLISH SERIES

Oral Communication: **John Murphy**
Reading: **Sharon Seymour, Laura Walsh**
Writing: **Joy M. Reid**
Vocabulary: **Averil Coxhead**

The four books in the *Essentials* series, one for each skill area, provide helpful information for instructors who wish to teach academic English. These short, easy-to-read volumes are suitable for instructors for professional development or program administrators for pre-service or in-service training. They are ideal as the basis for workshops or brown bag discussions.

Texts

LANGUAGE: THE SOCIAL MIRROR

Fourth Edition

Elaine Chaika

Language: The Social Mirror focuses on the ways language is used and how this use affects society and the individual. Thoroughly revised, the fourth edition presents a modern study of sociolinguistics through updated case studies and current research findings.

Topics include:

Bilingualism

Business

Global Dialects

Gender and Language

Text

LANGUAGE LEARNING STRATEGIES

What Every Teacher Should Know

Rebecca L. Oxford

This text provides ESL/EFL teachers with practical recommendations for developing their students' second language strategies.

- Detailed suggestions for strategy use in the four language skills
- Case studies and models for setting up programs
- A practical approach that translates research into suitable information
- A strong research base from a wide range of sources

Text

SECOND LANGUAGE TEACHING & LEARNING

David Nunan

Second Language Teaching & Learning is the first professional title to offer a practical introduction to the theoretical foundations of task-based language teaching.

- Provides comprehensive coverage of the topics typically addressed in methodology courses: language, the learner, the learning process, and classroom teaching
- Includes illustrative scenarios and topics for discussion and writing
- Provides the pedagogical overview that ESL/EFL teachers need to teach successfully with *Go for it!*, *Expressions,* and *Listen In*

Text

ASSESSING LANGUAGE ABILITY IN THE CLASSROOM

Second Edition

Andrew D. Cohen

This second edition presents various principles for guiding teachers through the assessment process (dictation, cloze summary, oral interview, role-plays and portfolio assessment techniques).

Text

DUAL LANGUAGE INSTRUCTION

A Handbook for Enriched Education

Nancy Cloud, Fred Genesee, Else Hamayan

This popular volume provides a comprehensive, theoretical framework and practical guide to implementing, evaluating, administering, and maintaining successful two-way immersion, developmental bilingual, and foreign language immersion programs.

Text

THE ELEMENTS OF LANGUAGE CURRICULUM

A Systematic Approach to Program Development

James Dean Brown

The Elements of Language Curriculum provides a practical, comprehensive overview of the different phases and activities involved in developing and implementing a sound, rational, and effective language program.

Text

THE TAPESTRY OF LANGUAGE LEARNING

The Individual in the Communicative Classroom

Rebecca L. Oxford, Robin C. Scarcella

This teacher resource book weaves together language learning strategies, learning styles, theme- and task-based instruction, and the relatedness of skills. Teachers will also find practical ideas and strategies to implement in class.

Text

Also see *Tapestry Reading*, **p. 68;** *Tapestry Writing*, **p. 80; and** *Tapestry Listening & Speaking*, **p. 90**

MEMORY, MEANING & METHOD

A View of Language Teaching, Second Edition

Earl W. Stevick

This thoroughly revised edition updates and restates Earl Stevick's classic account of what occurs in the learning and teaching of languages.

Text

RAISING SILENT VOICES

Educating Linguistic Minorities for the 21st Century

Henry T. Trueba

Raising Silent Voices examines the ways teachers can identify minority students' capabilities and work with them towards more effective classroom communication.

Text

TEACHING AND LEARNING VOCABULARY

I.S.P. Nation

Teaching and Learning Vocabulary examines the principles of vocabulary acquisition and presents a unified approach to vocabulary teaching and learning.

Text

TEACHING VOCABULARY:

Strategies and Techniques

I.S.P. Nation

Written especially for teachers, *Teaching Vocabulary: Strategies and Techniques* thoroughly examines over 60 teaching techniques and suggests clear, research-based principles for vocabulary learning. This unified approach presents vocabulary instruction through listening, speaking, reading and writing development.

Text

METHODOLOGY IN TESOL

A Book of Readings

Michael H. Long, Jack C. Richards, *Editors*

This comprehensive anthology contains articles which present the rationale behind current methodology and identify specific applications suitable for many teaching situations.

Text

Academic Spelling Power — p. 100

Text (160 pp.) ....978-0-618-48121-7 — $17.25

Academic Word Power — p. 99

Book 1 (144 pp.)	978-0-618-39768-6	$17.25
Book 2 (144 pp.)	978-0-618-39769-3	$17.25
Book 3 (144 pp.)	978-0-618-39770-9	$17.25
Book 4 (144 pp.)	978-0-618-39774-7	$17.25

Access Reading — p. 48

Book 1
Text (128 pp.)	978-1-4130-0772-5	$21.25
Text/Audio CD Pkg.	978-1-4130-9462-6	$27.50
Audio CD	978-1-4130-0773-2	$24.50
Instructor's Manual	978-1-4130-0774-9	$11.75

Book 2
Text (128 pp.)	978-1-4130-0680-3	$21.25
Text/Audio CD Pkg.	978-1-4130-9464-0	$27.50
Audio CD	978-1-4130-0776-3	$24.50
Instructor's Manual	978-1-4130-0775-6	$11.75

Book 3
Text (144 pp.)	978-1-4130-0778-7	$21.25
Text/Audio CDs Pkg.	978-1-4130-9466-4	$27.50
Audio CDs (2)	978-1-4130-0780-0	$43.00
Instructor's Manual	978-1-4130-0779-4	$11.75

Book 4
Text (144 pp.)	978-1-4130-0782-4	$21.25
Text/Audio CDs Pkg.	978-1-4130-9468-8	$27.50
Audio CDs (2)	978-1-4130-0783-1	$43.00
Instructor's Manual	978-1-4130-0701-5	$11.75

Across the Board* — p. 70

Text (288 pp.) ....978-0-0303-2482-6 — $29.75

*Across the Board is Book 3 of the Steps to Academic Reading series.

ACTIVE Skills for Communication — p. 84

Intro
Student Text	978-1-4130-2034-2	$27.25
Student Text with Student Audio CD Pkg.	978-1-4240-0905-3	$39.75
Workbook	978-1-4240-0110-1	$11.00
Classroom Audio CD	978-1-4240-0121-7	$39.75
Student Audio CD	978-1-4240-0125-5	$20.00
Teacher's Edition	978-1-4240-0102-6	$29.75

Level 1
Student Text	978-1-4130-2031-1	$27.25
Student Text with Student Audio CD Pkg.	978-1-4240-0908-4	$39.75
Workbook	978-1-4240-0107-1	$11.00
Classroom Audio CD	978-1-4240-0118-7	$39.75
Student Audio CD	978-1-4240-0122-4	$20.00
Teacher's Edition	978-1-4240-0089-0	$29.75

Level 2
Student Text	978-1-4130-2032-8	$27.25
Student Text with Student Audio CD Pkg.	978-1-4240-0909-1	$39.75
Workbook	978-1-4240-0108-8	$11.00
Classroom Audio CD	978-1-4240-0119-4	$39.75
Student Audio CD	978-1-4240-0123-1	$20.00
Teacher's Edition	978-1-4240-0090-6	$29.75

ACTIVE Skills for Reading, 2/e — p. 64

Intro
Text (176 pp.)	978-1-4240-0231-3	$29.50
Text/Audio CD Pkg.	978-1-4240-9423-3	$35.50
Audio CD	978-1-4240-0233-7	$23.00
Teacher's Guide	978-1-4240-0232-0	$32.25

Book 1
Text (176 pp.)	978-1-4240-0186-6	$29.50
Text/Audio CDs Pkg.	978-1-4240-9419-6	$35.50
Audio CDs (2)	978-1-4240-0187-3	$43.00
Teacher's Guide	978-1-4240-0188-0	$32.25

Book 2
Text (176 pp.)	978-1-4240-0208-5	$29.50
Text/Audio CDs Pkg.	978-1-4240-9420-2	$35.50
Audio CDs (2)	978-1-4240-0210-8	$43.00
Teacher's Guide	978-1-4240-0209-2	$32.25

Book 3
Text (216 pp.)	978-1-4240-0211-5	$29.50
Text/Audio CD Pkg.	978-1-4240-9347-2	$35.50
Audio CD	978-1-4240-0213-9	$23.00
Teacher's Guide	978-1-4240-0212-2	$32.25

Book 4
Text (240 pp.)	978-1-4240-0236-8	$29.50
Text/Audio CD Pkg.	978-1-4240-9422-6	$35.50
Audio CD	978-1-4240-0238-2	$23.00
Teacher's Guide	978-1-4240-0237-5	$32.25

Assessment CD-ROM with ExamView® (Intro – 2)	978-1-4240-0235-1	$119.00
Assessment CD-ROM with ExamView® (Books 3 & 4)	978-1-4240-0794-3	$119.00

Advanced Grammar Book, The, 2/e — p. 60

Text (448 pp.)	978-0-8384-4715-4	$41.75
Workbook	978-0-8384-4717-8	$22.50
Text/Workbook Pkg.	978-0-8384-8683-2	$57.75
Instructor's Manual	978-0-8384-8099-1	$15.25

Advanced Listening Comprehension, 3/e* — p. 91

Text (224 pp.)	978-1-4130-0396-3	$33.25
Text/Audio CDs Pkg.	978-1-4130-7529-8	$44.75
Audio CDs (5)	978-1-4130-0603-2	$119.00
DVD	978-1-4130-0605-6	$121.75
Video (VHS)	978-1-4130-0604-9	$121.75

*Advanced Listening Comprehension is Book 3 of the Listening and Notetaking series.

Against All Odds — p. 100

Text (228 pp.)	978-0-8384-2855-9	$33.50
Audio Tapes (2)	978-0-8384-2856-6	$40.75

A Good Read — p. 65

Level 1
Student Book	978-1-4240-0422-5	$25.25
Audio CD	978-1-4240-0423-2	$22.00
Teacher's Guide	978-1-4240-0424-9	$22.00

Level 2
Student Book	978-1-4240-0425-6	$25.25
Audio CD	978-1-4240-0426-3	$22.00
Teacher's Guide	978-1-4240-0427-0	$22.00

Level 3
Student Book	978-1-4240-0428-7	$25.25
Audio CD	978-1-4240-0429-4	$22.00
Teacher's Guide	978-1-4240-0430-0	$22.00

All Clear: Listening and Speaking — p. 90

Level 1, 2/e
Text (240 pp.)	978-1-4130-1703-8	$30.75
Text/Audio CDs Pkg.	978-1-4240-9921-4	$36.25
Audio CDs (2)	978-1-4130-2117-2	$42.00

Level 2, 3/e
Text (240 pp.)	978-1-4130-1704-5	$30.75
Text/Audio CDs Pkg.	978-1-4240-9925-2	$36.25
Audio CDs (2)	978-1-4130-2118-9	$42.00

Level 3, 2/e
Text (240 pp.)	978-1-4130-1705-2	$30.75
Text/Audio CDs Pkg.	978-1-4240-9435-6	$36.25
Audio CDs (3)	978-1-4130-2119-6	$62.50

Assessment CD-ROM with ExamView® (Levels 1 – 3) ..978-1-4240-0626-7 — $113.25

Amazing Stories to Tell and Retell — p. 70

Book 1 (160 pp.)	978-0-3958-8440-9	$25.25
Book 2 (188 pp.)	978-0-3958-8441-6	$25.25
Book 3 (208 pp.)	978-0-3959-4913-9	$25.25

American Business Vocabulary — p. 108

Text (96 pp.) ....978-0-9067-1769-1 — $19.50

American Short Stories, 2/e — p. 70

Text (240 pp.) ....978-0-0302-1334-2 — $32.25

American Vocabulary Program — p. 99

Text 1 (96 pp.)	978-0-9067-1767-7	$19.50
Text 2 (96 pp.)	978-0-9067-1770-7	$19.50
Text 3 (96 pp.)	978-0-9067-1771-4	$19.50

Applied English Grammar — p. 60

Text (466 pp.) ....978-0-0303-3528-0 — $40.25

Assessing Language Ability in the Classroom, 2/e — p. 118

Text (400 pp.) ....978-0-8384-4262-3 — $42.00

At Home in Two Lands, 2/e — p. 68

Text (240 pp.)	978-1-4130-2730-3	$28.25
Audio CD	978-1-4240-0442-3	$21.50
Assessment CD-ROM with ExamView®*	978-1-4240-0843-8	$119.00

*For At Home in Two Lands, 2/e and Far From Home, 3/e

For customer support, call **(877) NEED-ESL** or visit **elt.heinle.com** ■ For pricing, ISBNs, and ordering information see pp. 122 – 144

B

Basic Composition for ESL, 3/e — p. 82
Text (272 pp.) 978-0-8384-3004-0 $32.50

Best Practice — p. 108

Elementary
Text (160 pp.) 978-1-4130-0902-6 $25.75
Workbook....................................978-1-4130-0903-3 $13.50
Audio CDs (2) 978-1-4130-0906-4 $43.00
Teacher's Resource Book 978-1-4130-0904-0 $17.00
Assessment CD-ROM with ExamView® 978-1-4130-0907-1 $69.25

Pre-Intermediate
Text (160 pp.) 978-1-4130-0908-8 $25.75
Workbook....................................978-1-4130-0913-2 $13.50
Audio CDs (2) 978-1-4130-0910-1 $43.00
Teacher's Resource Book 978-1-4130-0912-5 $17.00
Assessment CD-ROM with ExamView® 978-1-4130-1469-3 $69.25

Intermediate
Text (176 pp.) 978-1-4130-2185-1 $25.75
Workbook....................................978-1-4130-2859-1 $13.50
Audio CDs (2) 978-1-4130-2856-0 $43.00
Teacher's Resource Book 978-1-4130-2858-4 $17.00
Assessment CD-ROM with ExamView® 978-1-4240-0886-5 $69.25

Upper-Intermediate
Text (176 pp.) 978-1-4240-0065-4 $25.75
Workbook....................................978-1-4240-0066-1 $13.50
Audio CDs (2) 978-1-4240-0069-2 $43.00
Teacher's Resource Book 978-1-4240-0068-5 $17.00
Assessment CD-ROM with ExamView® 978-1-4240-1617-4 $69.25

Better English Every Day — p. 48
Book 1 (257 pp.)........................978-0-0306-9601-5 $21.50
Book 2 (243 pp.) 978-0-0306-9603-9 $21.50
Book 3 (282 pp.) 978-0-0306-9604-6 $21.50
Instructor's Manual (164 pp.) ...978-0-0306-9602-2 $15.25

Between the Lines, 3/e* — p. 70
Text (352 pp.) 978-0-0303-3994-3 $29.75

*Between the Lines is Book 5 of the Steps to Academic Reading series.

Big Picture, The — p. 100
Text (208 pp.) 978-0-395-91712-1 $29.50

Blueprints — p. 80
Book 1 (224 pp.) 978-0-618-14409-9 $33.75
Book 2 (272 pp.) 978-0-618-14410-5 $33.75

Bridge to College Success — p. 104
Text (272 pp.) 978-0-8384-2907-5 $38.00
Audio Tapes (2)..........................978-0-8384-3007-1 $56.00
Videos (VHS) (2) 978-0-8384-3009-5 $110.00

Building Bridges — p. 22

Level 1
Text (108 pp.) 978-0-8384-1844-4 $31.25
Audio Tape.................................978-0-8384-2230-4 $35.50
Teacher's Manual 978-0-8384-2227-4 $37.25
Activity Masters 978-0-8384-2224-3 $33.50

Level 2
Text (138 pp.) 978-0-8384-1845-1 $31.25
Audio Tape.................................978-0-8384-2231-1 $35.50
Teacher's Manual 978-0-8384-2228-1 $37.25
Activity Masters 978-0-8384-2225-0 $33.50

Level 3
Text (122 pp.) 978-0-8384-1846-8 $31.25
Audio Tape.................................978-0-8384-2232-8 $35.50
Teacher's Manual 978-0-8384-2229-8 $37.25
Activity Masters 978-0-8384-2226-7 $33.50

Business Concepts for English Practice, 2/e — p. 108
Text (202 pp.) 978-0-8384-4077-3 $36.25
Instructor's Manual 978-0-8384-4210-4 $13.25

Business Language Practice — p. 108
Text (160 pp.) 978-0-9067-1754-7 $19.50

C

Can't Stop Talking, 2/e — p. 96
Text (177 pp.) 978-0-8384-2914-3 $27.75

Catalyst: Writing From Reading — p. 77

Book 1
Text (168 pp.) 978-0-618-47478-3 $31.00
Audio CDs (2) 978-1-4240-1749-2 $38.00

Book 2
Text (240 pp.) 978-0-618-54974-0 $31.00
Audio CDs (2) 978-1-4240-1750-8 $38.00

Cause & Effect, 4/e* — p. 65
Text (304 pp.) 978-1-4130-0416-8 $28.50
Text/Audio CD Pkg. 978-1-4130-6240-3 $34.50
Audio CD 978-1-4130-1330-6 $25.75
Answer Key and Video Transcripts (Books 3 & 4)* 978-1-4130-0612-4 $6.75
Assessment CD-ROM with ExamView® (Books 3 & 4)* ...978-1-4130-1327-6 $119.00
CNN® DVD (Books 3 & 4)* 978-1-4130-1588-1 $53.75
CNN® Video (Books 3 & 4)* 978-1-4130-0611-7 $53.75

*Cause & Effect, 4/e is Book 3 of the Reading & Vocabulary Development series.

Classic Graphic Novel Collection, The — p. 20

Frankenstein
5-Pack 978-1-4240-3658-5 $81.00
25-Pack 978-1-4240-4676-8 $405.00
Audio CD 978-1-4240-4574-7 $20.50
Workbook...................................978-1-111-00571-9 $8.00
Teacher's Manual 978-1-4240-4631-7 $22.00

Great Expectations
5-Pack 978-1-4240-3659-2 $81.00
25-Pack 978-1-4240-4882-3 $405.00
Audio CD 978-1-4240-4572-3 $20.50
Workbook...................................978-1-111-00568-9 $8.00
Teacher's Manual 978-1-4240-4629-4 $22.00

Henry V
5-Pack 978-1-4240-3660-8 $81.00
25-Pack 978-1-4240-4674-4 $405.00
Audio CD 978-1-4240-4571-6 $20.50
Workbook...................................978-1-4240-5342-1 $8.00
Teacher's Manual 978-1-4240-4628-7 $22.00

Jane Eyre
5-Pack 978-1-111-02404-8 $81.00
25-Pack 978-1-111-03130-5 $405.00
Audio CD 978-1-4240-4573-0 $20.50
Workbook...................................978-1-111-00569-6 $8.00
Teacher's Manual 978-1-4240-4630-0 $22.00

Macbeth
5-Pack 978-1-4240-3661-5 $81.00
25-Pack 978-1-4240-4675-1 $405.00
Audio CD 978-1-4240-4578-5 $20.50
Workbook...................................978-1-111-00573-3 $8.00
Teacher's Manual 978-1-4240-4565-5 $22.00

College Oral Communication — p. 85

Book 1
Text (288 pp.) 978-0-618-23016-7 $31.25
Text/Audio CD Pkg. 978-1-4282-0302-0 $36.75
Text/Audio CD/College Vocabulary 1 Pkg. ...978-1-4282-0308-2 $45.00
Audio CD 978-0-618-23037-2 $20.50

Book 2
Text (270 pp.) 978-0-618-23017-4 $31.25
Text/Audio CD Pkg. 978-1-4282-0301-3 $36.75
Text/Audio CD/College Vocabulary 2 Pkg. ...978-1-4282-0309-9 $45.00
Audio CD 978-0-618-23038-9 $20.50

Book 3
Text (238 pp.) 978-0-618-23018-1 $31.25
Text/Audio CD Pkg. 978-1-4282-0299-3 $36.75
Text/Audio CD/College Vocabulary 3 Pkg. ...978-1-4282-0310-5 $45.00
Audio CD 978-0-618-23039-6 $20.50

Book 4
Text (206 pp.) 978-0-618-23019-8 $31.25
Text/Audio CD Pkg. 978-1-4282-0300-6 $36.75
Text/Audio CD/College Vocabulary 4 Pkg. ...978-1-4282-0311-2 $45.00
Audio CD 978-0-618-23040-2 $20.50

College Reading — p. 67

Book 1
Text (256 pp.) 978-0-618-23020-4 $31.25
Text/College Vocabulary 1 Pkg. ...978-1-4282-0298-6 $42.50

Book 2
Text (274 pp.) 978-0-618-23021-1 $31.25
Text/College Vocabulary 2 Pkg. ...978-1-4130-5110-0 $42.50

College Reading (continued)

Book 3
Text (318 pp.)	978-0-618-23022-8	$31.25
Text/College Vocabulary 3 Pkg.	978-1-4282-0322-8	$42.50

Book 4
Text (288 pp.)	978-0-618-23023-5	$31.25
Text/College Vocabulary 4 Pkg.	978-1-4282-0297-9	$42.50

College Vocabulary p. 98
Book 1 (96 pp.)	978-0-618-23024-2	$12.50
Book 2 (96 pp.)	978-0-618-23025-9	$12.50
Book 3 (112 pp.)	978-0-618-23026-6	$12.50
Book 4 (130 pp.)	978-0-618-23027-3	$12.50

College Writing p. 79

Book 1
Text (274 pp.)	978-0-618-23028-0	$31.25
Text/College Vocabulary 1 Pkg.	978-1-4282-0296-2	$42.50

Book 2
Text (238 pp.)	978-0-618-23029-7	$31.25
Text/College Vocabulary 2 Pkg.	978-1-4282-0295-5	$42.50

Book 3
Text (290 pp.)	978-0-618-23030-3	$31.25
Text/College Vocabulary 3 Pkg.	978-1-4282-0312-9	$42.50

Book 4
Text (288 pp.)	978-0-618-2-3031-0	$31.25
Text/College Vocabulary 4 Pkg.	978-1-4282-0313-6	$42.50

Collins COBUILD Advanced Dictionary of American English p. 29
Softcover (1680 pp.) with CD-ROM	978-1-4240-0363-1	$34.50
CD-ROM Site License*	978-1-4240-0810-0	*

*For pricing or to purchase, call Technology Services at 800-423-0563 or contact your Heinle representative.

Collins COBUILD Advanced Dictionary of American English, English/Japanese p. 30
Softcover (1712 pp.) with CD-ROM	978-1-4240-0079-1	$34.50

Collins COBUILD Advanced Dictionary of American English, English/Korean p. 30
Softcover (1704 pp.) with CD-ROM	978-1-4240-1673-0	$32.00

Collins COBUILD Basic Dictionary of American English p. 25
Softcover (632 pp.) with CD-ROM	978-1-4240-0081-4	$17.75

Collins COBUILD English/Español Glossary p. 30
Softcover (400 pp.)	978-1-4240-1964-9	$9.00

Collins COBUILD English/Spanish Student's Dictionary of American English p. 30
Softcover (1008 pp.) with CD-ROM	978-1-4240-1962-5	$29.25

Collins COBUILD Intermediate Dictionary of American English p. 28
Softcover (1232 pp.) with CD-ROM	978-1-4240-0776-9	$29.25
CD-ROM Site License*	978-1-111-05415-1	*

*For pricing or to purchase, call Technology Services at 800-423-0563 or contact your Heinle representative.

Collins COBUILD School Dictionary of American English p. 27
Softcover (1232 pp.) with CD-ROM	978-1-4240-0787-5	$29.25
Hardcover with CD-ROM	978-1-4240-1895-6	$39.75
CD-ROM SIte License*	978-1-111-05416-8	*

*For pricing or to purchase, call Technology Services at 800-423-0563 or contact your Heinle representative.

Collins Escolar Plus Dictionary (English/Portuguese/Português/Inglês) p. 30
Softcover (1056 pp.)	978-1-4240-7588-1	$29.25

Communicating Effectively in English, 2/e p. 93
Text (252 pp.)	978-0-5341-7268-8	$43.00
Instructor's Manual	978-0-5341-7269-5	$15.75

Communication Strategies, 2/e p. 92

Level 1
Text (120 pp.)	978-9-8142-3259-3	$30.50
Teacher's Guide	978-9-8142-3260-9	$33.50
Audio CD	978-9-8142-3261-6	$22.50

Level 2
Text (120 pp.)	978-9-8142-3262-3	$30.50
Teacher's Guide	978-9-8142-3263-0	$33.50
Audio CD	978-9-8142-3264-7	$22.50

Level 3
Text (120 pp.)	978-9-8126-5914-9	$30.50
Teacher's Guide	978-9-8142-3265-4	$33.50
Audio CD	978-9-8142-3266-1	$22.50

Level 4
Text (120 pp.)	978-9-8142-3267-8	$30.50
Teacher's Guide	978-9-8142-3268-5	$33.50
Audio CD	978-9-8142-3269-2	$22.50

Communicative Ideas, 2/e p. 116
Text (128 pp.)	978-0-9067-1738-7	$32.75

Complete Guide to the TOEFL® Test iBT Edition., The p. 102
Text (856 pp.)/CD-ROM Pkg.	978-1-4130-2303-9	$46.50
Interactive CD-ROM	978-1-4130-2328-2	$47.25
Text/CD-ROM/Audio CDs Pkg.	978-1-4130-2305-3	$62.50
Text/CD-ROM/Audio CDs/ Answer Key Pkg.	978-1-4240-9939-9	$63.50
Audio CDs (13)	978-1-4130-2308-4	$265.50
Audio Script and Answer Key	978-1-4130-2311-4	$45.25

Complete Guide to the TOEIC® Test, 3/e p. 104
Text (348 pp.)	978-1-4240-0296-2	$38.50
Text/Audio CDs/Answer Key Pkg.	978-1-4240-9945-0	$65.75
Audio CDs (5)	978-1-4240-0377-8	$107.00
Audio Script and Answer Key	978-1-4240-0309-9	$10.50

Composition Practice, 3/e p. 80
Book 1 (112 pp.)	978-0-8384-1993-9	$31.00
Book 2 (160 pp.)	978-0-8384-1998-4	$31.00
Book 3 (176 pp.)	978-0-8384-1999-1	$31.00
Book 4 (208 pp.)	978-0-8384-2000-3	$31.00

Concepts & Comments, 3/e* p. 65
Text (264 pp.)	978-1-4130-0417-5	$28.50
Text/Audio CD Pkg.	978-1-4130-6245-8	$34.50
Audio CD	978-1-4130-1328-3	$25.75
Answer Key and Video Transcripts (Books 3 & 4)*	978-1-4130-0612-4	$6.75
Assessment CD-ROM with ExamView® (Books 3 & 4)*	978-1-4130-1327-6	$119.00
CNN® Video (Books 3 & 4)*	978-1-4130-0611-7	$53.75
CNN® DVD (Books 3 & 4)*	978-1-4130-1588-1	$53.75

*Concepts & Comments, 3/e is Book 4 of the Reading & Vocabulary Development series.

Concepts for Today, 2/e* p. 66
Text (288 pp.)	978-1-4130-0812-8	$28.50
Text/Audio CD Pkg.	978-1-4130-8249-4	$34.50
Audio CD	978-0-7593-9817-7	$25.75
Instructor's Manual with Answer Key (Books 3 – 5)*	978-0-7593-9816-0	$17.00
CNN® Video (Books 3 – 5)*	978-0-7593-9815-3	$71.75
Assessment CD-ROM with ExamView® (Books 1 – 5)*	978-1-4130-0132-7	$134.75

*Concepts for Today, 2/e is Book 4 of the Reading for Today series.

Correction p. 116
Text (128 pp.)	978-0-9067-1791-2	$33.75

Crossroads Café p. 48
Photo Stories A: Episodes 1 – 13 (232 pp.)	978-0-8384-6608-7	$24.50
Photo Stories B: Episodes 14 – 26 (238 pp.)	978-0-8384-6607-0	$24.50
Worktext A: Episodes 1 – 13 (222 pp.)	978-0-8384-6612-4	$24.50
Worktext B: Episodes 14 – 26 (222 pp.)	978-0-8384-6606-3	$24.50
Partner Guide	978-0-8384-6614-8	$9.00
Teacher's Resource Book A: Episodes 1 – 13	978-0-8384-6436-6	$64.25
Teacher's Resource Book B: Episodes 14 – 26	978-0-8384-6434-2	$64.25
Reproducible Handouts: Episodes 1 – 26	978-0-8384-6615-5	$75.00
Assessment Pkg. A: Episodes 1 – 13	978-0-8384-8061-8	$150.00
Assessment Pkg. B: Episodes 14 – 26	978-0-8384-8062-5	$150.00
DVD Pack (4) (includes Episodes A&B) with Single Site License	978-1-58370-042-6	$1,653.75
Each additional Set*		$250.00 Pack
DVD Set A (2) with Single Site License	978-1-58370-040-2	$876.50
Each additional Set*		$250.00 Pack
DVD Set B (2) with Single Site License	978-1-5837-0041-9	$876.50
Each additional Set*		$250.00 Pack

*Available to license holders only

DVDs can now be purchased directly from Heinle. Some restrictions apply.

Crossroads Café can also be ordered directly from INTELECOM, 150 E. Colorado Boulevard, Suite 300, Pasadena, CA 91105-1937 Tel: 800-576-2988 or 626-796-7300 Fax: 626-577-4282

Culturally Speaking, 3/e p. 93
Text (192 pp.)	978-1-4240-0404-1	$34.25
Audio CD	978-1-4240-5119-9	$26.75

D

Designing Language Courses p. 115
Text (240 pp.)	978-0-8384-7909-4	$30.00

Destinations		p. 77

Book 1

Text (300 pp.)	978-1-4130-1935-3	$31.00
Grammar Workbook	978-1-4130-2244-5	$16.50
Text/Grammar Workbook Pkg.	978-1-4240-9346-5	$43.00
Instructor's Manual: Writing and Grammar	978-1-4130-2247-6	$19.50
Assessment CD-ROM with ExamView®	978-1-4130-2241-4	$119.00

Book 2

Text (264 pp.)	978-1-4130-1936-0	$31.00
Grammar Workbook	978-1-4130-2245-2	$16.50
Text/Grammar Workbook Pkg.	978-1-4130-6057-7	$43.00
Instructor's Manual: Writing and Grammar	978-1-4130-2248-3	$19.50
Assessment CD-ROM with ExamView®	978-1-4130-2242-1	$119.00

Developing Composition Skills, 2/e		p. 81
Text (304 pp.)	978-0-8384-2655-5	$35.25
Instructor's Manual	978-0-8384-2658-6	$14.00
CNN® Video	978-0-8384-2659-3	$77.25

Developing Reading Skills		p. 70

Beginning, 2/e

Text (193 pp.)	978-0-8384-4987-5	$31.75

Intermediate 1, 2/e

Text (224 pp.)	978-0-8384-5774-0	$31.75
Answer Key	978-0-8384-5775-7	$15.75

Advanced, 3/e

Text (280 pp.)	978-0-8384-5276-9	$31.75

Developing Vocabulary Skills, 2/e		p. 100
Text (272 pp.)	978-0-8384-4672-0	$38.50
Answer Key/Instructor's Manual	978-0-8384-4673-7	$15.75

Discoveries in Academic Writing		p. 82
Text (352 pp.)	978-0-1550-7255-8	$38.75
Instructor's Manual	978-0-1550-7256-5	$39.50

Doing Teacher Research		p. 114
Text (272 pp.)	978-0-8384-7900-1	$30.00

Downtown		p. 40

Basic

Text (240 pp.)	978-1-4240-1656-3	$18.50
Workbook	978-1-4240-1670-9	$11.00
Text/Workbook Pkg.	978-1-4240-9095-2	$26.00
Text/Audio CDs Pkg.	978-1-4240-4164-0	$23.00
Text/Workbook/Audio CDs Pkg.	978-1-4240-9844-6	$31.75
Audio CDs (2)	978-1-4240-1739-3	$44.00
Transparencies	978-1-4240-6018-4	$30.50
Teacher's Edition	978-1-4266-3410-9	$24.50
Assessment CD-ROM with ExamView®	978-1-4240-1671-6	$57.00

Level 1

Text (224 pp.)	978-0-8384-4374-3	$18.50
Workbook	978-0-8384-5046-8	$11.00
Text/Workbook Pkg.	978-1-4240-9840-8	$26.00
Text/Audio CDs Pkg.	978-1-4240-9913-9	$23.00
Text/Workbook/Audio CDs Pkg.	978-1-4240-9844-6	$31.75
Text/Grammar Café Pkg.	978-1-4240-2071-3	$24.75
Audio CDs (2)	978-0-8384-5049-9	$44.00
Teacher's Edition with Art Bank CD-ROM	978-0-8384-5047-5	$24.50

Level 2

Text (240 pp.)	978-0-8384-4379-8	$18.50
Workbook	978-0-8384-5163-2	$11.00
Text/Workbook Pkg.	978-1-4240-9851-4	$26.00
Text/Audio CDs Pkg.	978-1-4240-8812-6	$23.00
Text/Workbook/Audio CDs Pkg.	978-1-4240-9841-5	$31.75
Text/Grammar Café Pkg.	978-1-4240-2072-0	$24.75
Audio CDs (2)	978-0-8384-5171-7	$44.00
Teacher's Edition with Art Bank CD-ROM	978-0-8384-5165-6	$24.50

Level 3

Text (224 pp.)	978-0-8384-4380-4	$18.50
Workbook	978-0-8384-5327-8	$11.00
Text/Workbook Pkg.	978-1-4240-9849-1	$26.00
Text/Audio CDs Pkg.	978-1-4240-8814-0	$23.00
Text/Workbook/Audio CDs Pkg.	978-1-4240-9842-2	$31.75
Text/Grammar Café Pkg.	978-1-4240-2073-7	$24.75
Audio CDs (2)	978-0-8384-5330-8	$44.00
Teacher's Edition with Art Bank CD-ROM	978-0-8384-5328-5	$24.50

Level 4

Text (243 pp.)	978-0-8384-4381-1	$18.50
Workbook	978-0-8384-5582-1	$11.00
Text/Workbook Pkg.	978-1-4240-9850-7	$26.00
Text/Audio CDs Pkg.	978-1-4240-8813-3	$23.00
Text/Workbook/Audio CDs Pkg.	978-1-4240-9847-7	$31.75
Text/Grammar Café Pkg.	978-1-4240-2070-6	$24.75
Audio CDs (2)	978-0-8384-5671-2	$44.00
Teacher's Edition with Art Bank CD-ROM	978-0-8384-5620-0	$24.50

Picture Cards (Levels Basic, 1, & 2)	978-1-111-00674-7	$50.00
Transparencies (Levels 1 & 2)	978-0-8384-5105-2	$61.25
Assessment CD-ROM with ExamView® (Levels 1 & 2)	978-0-8384-5700-9	$113.25
Assessment CD-ROM with ExamView® (Levels 3 & 4)	978-1-4240-2266-7	$113.25

Dual Language Instruction		p. 118
Text (240 pp.)	978-0-8384-8801-0	$47.50

E

Elements of Language Curriculum, The		p. 118
Text (272 pp.)	978-0-8384-5810-5	$42.00

ELT Advantage		p. 110
Assessing Language Ability in Young Adults and Adults, Andrew Cohen	978-1-4240-0864-3	*
Communicative Teaching for the ESL/EFL Classroom, Kevin Keating	978-1-4240-1729-4	*
Content-Based Instruction for Language Learners, Kathleen M. Bailey	978-1-4240-0866-7	*
Developing ESL/EFL Listening Comprehension, Patricia Dunkel	978-1-4240-1727-0	*
An Introduction to Corpora in English Language Teaching, Michael McCarthy, Anne O'Keeffe, Steve Walsh	978-1-4240-1723-2	*
An Introduction to Language Assessment in the K-12 Classroom, Natalie Kuhlman	978-1-4240-0412-6	*
An Introduction to Task-Based Teaching, David Nunan	978-1-4130-2878-2	*
An Introduction to Teaching English to Young Learners, Annie Hughes	978-1-4240-1731-7	*
An Introduction to Teaching ESL/EFL, Tom Scovel	978-1-4240-0143-9	*
Language Learning Technologies for K-12 Teachers, Joyce Nutta	978-1-4240-1725-6	*
Making the Most of Learner's Dictionaries (American Edition), Michela Clari	978-1-4240-1615-0	*
Practical Ideas for the Adult ESL/EFL Classroom, Rob Jenkins	978-1-4240-0144-6	*
Pursuing Professional Development, Andy Curtis	978-1-4130-2880-5	*
Teaching ESL/EFL Reading, Neil J. Anderson	978-1-4240-0142-2	*
Teaching Grammar for ESL/EFL, Diane Larsen-Freeman	978-1-4240-2814-6	*
Teaching Lexically, Hugh Dellar and Andrew Walkley	978-1-4130-2879-9	*
Teaching ESL/EFL Vocabulary, I.S.P. Nation	978-1-4240-2816-0	*

*Pricing for ELT Advantage		
Total # of courses	**Discount**	**$ per course**
1 course	No discount	$99.00
25-49 courses	10% discount	$89.00
50-74 courses	15% discount	$84.25
75-99 courses	20% discount	$79.25
100 or more courses	25% discount	$74.25
Passcodes expire one year from date of issue. Prices subject to change without notice.		

For bulk or purchase orders, go to: elt.heinle.com/eltorderingworksheet
Single copy purchases can be made online at: eltadvantage.heinle.com

English for Academic Success series

See individual titles: *College Oral Communication, College Reading, College Vocabulary,* and *College Writing*

English for Business		p. 107
Text with Audio CD	978-1-4130-2088-5	$24.50
Teacher's Resource Book	978-1-4240-0011-1	$23.75

English for Health Sciences		p. 107
Text with Audio CD	978-1-4130-2089-2	$24.50
Teacher's Resource Book	978-1-4240-0012-8	$23.75

English for Professional Success		p. 107
Text with Audio CD	978-1-4130-2087-8	$24.50
Teacher's Resource Book	978-1-4240-0007-4	$23.75

English for Science and Engineering		p. 107
Text with Audio CD	978-1-4130-2091-5	$24.50
Teacher's Resource Book	978-1-4240-0013-5	$23.75

English for the Humanities — p. 107
Text with Audio CD	978-1-4130-2090-8	$24.50
Teacher's Resource Book	978-1-4240-0014-2	$23.75

English in Action — p. 44
Level 1
Text (256 pp.)	978-0-8384-2811-5	$19.00
Workbook with Audio CD	978-0-8384-5185-4	$12.00
Text/Workbook Pkg.	978-0-8384-7050-3	$28.00
Text/Audio CDs Pkg.	978-0-8384-0722-6	$24.75
Text/Audio CDs/Workbook Pkg.	978-1-4130-9015-4	$32.75
Text/Grammar Café Pkg.	978-1-4240-2078-2	$24.25
Audio CDs (2)	978-0-8384-0534-5	$44.00
Teacher's Guide	978-0-8384-5184-7	$29.75

Level 2
Text (246 pp.)	978-0-8384-2828-3	$19.00
Workbook with Audio CD	978-0-8384-5194-6	$12.00
Text/Workbook Pkg.	978-0-8384-7051-0	$28.00
Text/Audio CDs Pkg.	978-0-8384-0723-3	$24.75
Text/Audio CDs/Workbook Pkg.	978-1-4130-9016-1	$32.75
Text/Grammar Café Pkg.	978-1-4240-2080-5	$24.25
Audio CDs (2)	978-0-8384-0536-9	$44.00
Teacher's Guide	978-0-8384-5193-9	$29.75

Level 3
Text (272 pp.)	978-0-8384-2829-0	$19.00
Workbook with Audio CD	978-0-8384-5199-1	$12.00
Text/Workbook Pkg.	978-0-8384-7052-7	$28.00
Text/Audio CDs Pkg.	978-0-8384-0724-0	$24.75
Text/Audio CDs/Workbook Pkg.	978-1-4130-9017-8	$32.75
Text/Grammar Café Pkg.	978-1-4240-2081-2	$24.25
Audio CDs (2)	978-0-8384-0538-3	$44.00
Teacher's Guide	978-0-8384-5196-0	$29.75

Level 4
Text (288 pp.)	978-0-8384-2830-6	$19.00
Workbook with Audio CD	978-0-8384-5202-8	$12.00
Text/Workbook Pkg.	978-0-8384-7053-4	$28.00
Text/Audio CDs Pkg.	978-0-8384-0725-7	$24.75
Text/Audio CDs/Workbook Pkg.	978-1-4130-9018-5	$32.75
Text/Grammar Café Pkg.	978-1-4240-2079-9	$24.25
Audio CDs (3)	978-0-8384-0539-0	$44.00
Teacher's Guide	978-0-8384-5201-1	$29.75

Assessment CD-ROM with ExamView® (Levels 1 – 4)	978-1-4130-1499-0	$131.00

English Observed — p. 116
Text (104 pp.)	978-0-9067-1792-9	$24.75

English Verb, The — p. 116
Text (180 pp.)	978-0-9067-1740-0	$38.00

Essential Academic Vocabulary — p. 100
Text (254 pp.)	978-0-618-44542-4	$28.00

Essentials of Teaching Academic English series — p. 117
See individual titles: *Essentials of Teaching Academic Oral Communication, Essentials of Teaching Academic Reading, Essentials of Teaching Academic Vocabulary,* and *Essentials of Teaching Academic Writing*

Essentials of Teaching Academic Oral Communication — p. 117
Text (160 pp.)	978-0-618-22492-0	$11.25

Essentials of Teaching Academic Reading — p. 117
Text (160 pp.)	978-0-618-23012-9	$11.25

Essentials of Teaching Academic Vocabulary — p. 117
Text (176 pp.)	978-0-618-23014-3	$11.25

Essentials of Teaching Academic Writing — p. 117
Text (176 pp.)	978-0-618-23013-6	$11.25

Expanding Reading Skills — p. 70
Intermediate, 2/e
Text (222 pp.)	978-0-8384-2644-9	$32.75
Answer Key	978-0-8384-4208-1	$15.75

Advanced, 2/e
Text (222 pp.)	978-0-8384-3098-9	$32.75

Exploring Second Language Classroom Research — p. 117
Text (432 pp.)	978-1-4240-2705-7	$29.25

Exploring Second Language Reading — p. 114
Text (144 pp.)	978-0-8384-6685-8	$30.00

Expressions — p. 96
Intro
Text (112 pp.)	978-0-8384-2596-1	$22.50
Text (112 pp.)/Audio CDs Pkg.	978-0-8384-2842-9	$23.75
Workbook	978-0-8384-2601-2	$14.50
Teacher's Annotated Edition	978-0-8384-2600-5	$29.50
Audio CDs (2)	978-0-8384-2598-5	$56.25

Book 1
Text (144 pp.)	978-0-8384-2240-3	$22.50
Workbook	978-0-8384-2241-0	$14.50
Teacher's Annotated Edition	978-0-8384-2242-7	$29.50
Audio CDs (2)	978-0-8384-2390-5	$56.25

Book 2
Text (144 pp.)	978-0-8384-2245-8	$22.50
Workbook	978-0-8384-2246-5	$14.50
Teacher's Annotated Edition	978-0-8384-2249-6	$29.50
Audio CDs (2)	978-0-8384-2389-9	$56.25

Book 3
Text (144 pp.)	978-0-8384-2278-6	$22.50
Workbook	978-0-8384-2279-3	$14.50
Teacher's Annotated Edition	978-0-8384-2286-1	$29.50
Audio CDs (2)	978-0-8384-2388-2	$56.25

Teacher Resource CD Pkg. with ExamView® (Intro – 3)	978-0-8384-4471-9	$78.50

F

Facts & Figures, 4/e* — p. 65
Text (262 pp.)	978-1-4130-0418-2	$28.50
Text/Audio CD Pkg.	978-1-4130-6290-8	$34.50
Audio CD	978-1-4130-1332-0	$25.75
Answer Key and Video Transcripts (Books 1 & 2)*	978-1-4130-0609-4	$6.75
Assessment CD-ROM with ExamView® (Books 1 & 2)*	978-1-4130-0613-1	$122.00
CNN® DVD (Books 1 & 2)*	978-1-4130-1587-4	$53.75
CNN® Video (Books 1 & 2)*	978-1-4130-0610-0	$53.75

*Facts & Figures, 4/e is Book 1 of the *Reading & Vocabulary Development* series.

Far From Home, 3/e — p. 68
Text (240 pp.)	978-1-4130-1721-2	$28.25
Audio CD	978-1-4240-0445-4	$21.50
Assessment CD-ROM with ExamView®*	978-1-4240-0843-8	$119.00

*For *At Home in Two Lands, 2/e* and *Far From Home, 3/e*

Financial English — p. 108
Text (160 pp.)	978-1-8993-9600-9	$28.25

Footprint Reading Library — p. 18
Level 1
Incredible Animals

Arctic Whale Danger!
5-Pack	978-1-4240-3744-5	$42.50
25-Pack	978-1-4240-3676-9	$175.00

Happy Elephants
5-Pack	978-1-4240-3784-1	$42.50
25-Pack	978-1-4240-3951-7	$175.00

Monkey Party
5-Pack	978-1-4240-3791-9	$42.50
25-Pack	978-1-4240-3953-1	$175.00

Fascinating Places

The Future of a Village
5-Pack	978-1-4240-4694-2	$42.50
25-Pack	978-1-4240-3699-8	$175.00

Life on the Orinoco
5-Pack	978-1-4240-3787-2	$42.50
25-Pack	978-1-4240-3954-8	$175.00

The Lost City of Machu Picchu
5-Pack	978-1-4240-4700-0	$42.50
25-Pack	978-1-4240-3705-6	$175.00

Remarkable People

Columbus and the New World
5-Pack	978-1-4240-3762-9	$42.50
25-Pack	978-1-4240-3635-6	$175.00

Dreamtime Painters
5-Pack	978-1-4240-3774-2	$42.50
25-Pack	978-1-4240-3647-9	$175.00

The Young Riders of Mongolia
5-Pack	978-1-4240-4702-4	$42.50
25-Pack	978-1-4240-3712-4	$175.00

Exciting Activities

Alaskan Ice Climbing
5-Pack 978-1-4240-3742-1 $42.50
25-Pack 978-1-4240-3674-5 $175.00

Don't Believe Your Eyes!
5-Pack 978-1-4240-3773-5 $42.50
25-Pack 978-1-4240-3646-2 $175.00

The Story of the Hula
5-Pack 978-1-4240-4705-5 $42.50
25-Pack 978-1-4240-3710-0 $175.00

Amazing Science

The Giant's Causeway
5-Pack 978-1-4240-4696-6 $42.50
25-Pack 978-1-4240-3701-8 $175.00

Snow Magic!
5-Pack 978-1-4240-4688-1 $42.50
25-Pack 978-1-4240-3688-2 $175.00

Volcano Trek
5-Pack 978-1-4240-4709-3 $42.50
25-Pack 978-1-4240-3713-1 $175.00

Level 1 Collection (Bound Anthology) 978-1-4240-4513-6 $42.00
Teacher's Manual 978-1-4240-4383-5 $21.00
DVD 978-1-4240-1253-4 $104.75
Audio CD 978-1-4240-4449-8 $31.50
Assessment CD-ROM with ExamView® 978-1-4240-4394-1 $105.00
Footprint Reading Library
  Online E-Book Collection – Level 1 ....978-1-4240-7309-2 $20.00

Level 2

Incredible Animals

Farley the Red Panda
5-Pack 978-1-4240-3779-7 $42.50
25-Pack 978-1-4240-3946-3 $175.00

Gorilla Watching Tours
5-Pack 978-1-4240-3783-4 $42.50
25-Pack 978-1-4240-3950-0 $175.00

Puffin Rescue!
5-Pack 978-1-4240-4685-0 $42.50
25-Pack 978-1-4240-3690-5 $175.00

Fascinating Places

A Disappearing World
5-Pack 978-1-4240-3739-1 $42.50
25-Pack 978-1-4240-3671-4 $175.00

The Knife Markets of Sanaa
5-Pack 978-1-4240-4692-8 $42.50
25-Pack 978-1-4240-3702-5 $175.00

A Special Kind of Neighborhood
5-Pack 978-1-4240-3736-0 $42.50
25-Pack 978-1-4240-3668-4 $175.00

Remarkable People

The Last of the Cheju Divers
5-Pack 978-1-4240-4698-0 $42.50
25-Pack 978-1-4240-3698-1 $175.00

Peruvian Weavers
5-Pack 978-1-4240-4684-3 $42.50
25-Pack 978-1-4240-3689-9 $175.00

Taiko Master
5-Pack 978-1-4240-4690-4 $42.50
25-Pack 978-1-4240-3695-0 $175.00

Exciting Activities

Cheese-Rolling Races
5-Pack 978-1-4240-3760-5 $42.50
25-Pack 978-1-4240-3633-2 $175.00

Making a Thai Boxing Champion
5-Pack 978-1-4240-3785-8 $42.50
25-Pack 978-1-4240-3957-9 $175.00

Water Sports Adventure
5-Pack 978-1-4240-4710-9 $42.50
25-Pack 978-1-4240-3714-8 $175.00

Amazing Science

Dinosaur Search
5-Pack 978-1-4240-3772-8 $42.50
25-Pack 978-1-4240-3645-5 $175.00

The Memory Man
5-Pack 978-1-4240-4697-3 $42.50
25-Pack 978-1-4240-3707-0 $175.00

Wild Animal Trackers
5-Pack 978-1-4240-4712-3 $42.50
25-Pack 978-1-4240-3716-2 $175.00

Level 2 Collection (Bound Anthology) 978-1-4240-4514-3 $42.00
Teacher's Manual 978-1-4240-4384-2 $21.00
DVD 978-1-4240-1254-1 $104.75
Audio CD 978-1-4240-4450-4 $31.50
Assessment CD-ROM with ExamView® 978-1-4240-4396-5 $105.00
Footprint Reading Library
  Online E-Book Collection – Level 2 ....978-1-4240-7311-5 $20.00

Level 3

Incredible Animals

Birds in Paradise
5-Pack 978-1-4240-3752-0 $42.50
25-Pack 978-1-4240-3624-0 $175.00

Cambodia Animal Rescue
5-Pack 978-1-4240-3758-2 $42.50
25-Pack 978-1-4240-3631-8 $175.00

Night Hunt
5-Pack 978-1-4240-3790-2 $42.50
25-Pack 978-1-4240-3682-0 $175.00

Fascinating Places

The Adventure Capital of the World
5-Pack 978-1-4240-4691-1 $42.50
25-Pack 978-1-4240-3696-7 $175.00

Butler School
5-Pack 978-1-4240-3754-4 $42.50
25-Pack 978-1-4240-3626-4 $175.00

One Village Makes a Difference
5-Pack 978-1-4240-4679-9 $42.50
25-Pack 978-1-4240-3684-4 $175.00

Remarkable People

A Real Winner
5-Pack 978-1-4240-3740-7 $42.50
25-Pack 978-1-4240-3672-1 $175.00

One Boy's Journey
5-Pack 978-1-4240-4678-2 $42.50
25-Pack 978-1-4240-3678-3 $175.00

Living With a Volcano
5-Pack 978-1-4240-3788-9 $42.50
25-Pack 978-1-4240-3955-5 $175.00

Exciting Activities

Making a Deal
5-Pack 978-1-4240-3789-6 $42.50
25-Pack 978-1-4240-3956-2 $175.00

Dangerous Dining
5-Pack 978-1-4240-3766-7 $42.50
25-Pack 978-1-4240-3639-4 $175.00

Flying Pumpkins!
5-Pack 978-1-4240-3780-3 $42.50
25-Pack 978-1-4240-3947-0 $175.00

Amazing Science

Killer Bees!
5-Pack 978-1-4240-3786-5 $42.50
25-Pack 978-1-4240-3948-7 $175.00

Wind Power
5-Pack 978-1-4240-4713-0 $42.50
25-Pack 978-1-4240-3717-9 $175.00

The Missing Snows of Kilimanjaro
5-Pack 978-1-4240-4703-1 $42.50
25-Pack 978-1-4240-3703-2 $175.00

Level 3 Collection (Bound Anthology) 978-1-4240-4538-9 $42.00
Teacher's Manual 978-1-4240-4385-9 $21.00
DVD 978-1-4240-1255-8 $104.75
Audio CD 978-1-4240-4451-1 $31.50
Assessment CD-ROM with ExamView® 978-1-4240-4398-9 $105.00
Footprint Reading Library
  Online E-Book Collection – Level 3 ....978-1-4240-7314-6 $20.00

Level 4

Incredible Animals

Blue Cows?
5-Pack 978-1-4240-3753-7 $42.50
25-Pack 978-1-4240-3625-7 $175.00

Footprint Reading Library (continued)

Level 4 (continued)

Cupid the Dolphin
5-Pack .... 978-1-4240-3764-3 — $42.50
25-Pack .... 978-1-4240-3637-0 — $175.00

Wild Animal Town
5-Pack .... 978-1-4240-4711-6 — $42.50
25-Pack .... 978-1-4240-3715-5 — $175.00

Fascinating Places

The Lost Temples of the Maya
5-Pack .... 978-1-4240-4701-7 — $42.50
25-Pack .... 978-1-4240-3706-3 — $175.00

Mount Fuji
5-Pack .... 978-1-4240-3792-6 — $42.50
25-Pack .... 978-1-4240-3679-0 — $175.00

The Three Rivers of Zambia
5-Pack .... 978-1-4240-4706-2 — $42.50
25-Pack .... 978-1-4240-3711-7 — $175.00

Remarkable People

One Woman's Choice
5-Pack .... 978-1-4240-4680-5 — $42.50
25-Pack .... 978-1-4240-3685-1 — $175.00

The Olympians
5-Pack .... 978-1-4240-4704-8 — $42.50
25-Pack .... 978-1-4240-3709-4 — $175.00

Zoo Dentists
5-Pack .... 978-1-4240-4707-9 — $42.50
25-Pack .... 978-1-4240-3718-6 — $175.00

Exciting Activities

The Art of Making Silk
5-Pack .... 978-1-4240-4687-4 — $42.50
25-Pack .... 978-1-4240-3697-4 — $175.00

Capoeira: The Fighting Dance
5-Pack .... 978-1-4240-3759-9 — $42.50
25-Pack .... 978-1-4240-3632-5 — $175.00

Gliding Across the Gobi
5-Pack .... 978-1-4240-3782-7 — $42.50
25-Pack .... 978-1-4240-3949-4 — $175.00

Amazing Science

Orangutan Language
5-Pack .... 978-1-4240-4677-5 — $42.50
25-Pack .... 978-1-4240-3687-5 — $175.00

Saving the Pandas
5-Pack .... 978-1-4240-4686-7 — $42.50
25-Pack .... 978-1-4240-3691-2 — $175.00

Solar Cooking
5-Pack .... 978-1-4240-4689-8 — $42.50
25-Pack .... 978-1-4240-3694-3 — $175.00

Level 4 Collection (Bound Anthology) .... 978-1-4240-4515-0 — $42.00
Teacher's Manual .... 978-1-4240-4386-6 — $21.00
DVD .... 978-1-4240-1256-5 — $104.75
Audio CD .... 978-1-4240-4452-8 — $31.50
Assessment CD-ROM with ExamView® ... 978-1-4240-4399-6 — $105.00
Footprint Reading Library
   Online E-Book Collection – Level 4 ... 978-1-4240-7317-7 — $20.00

Level 5

Incredible Animals

Beagle Patrol
5-Pack .... 978-1-4240-3750-6 — $42.50
25-Pack .... 978-1-4240-3621-9 — $175.00

Giant Cave Crocs!
5-Pack .... 978-1-4240-3776-6 — $42.50
25-Pack .... 978-1-4240-3943-2 — $175.00

Fascinating Places

Opal Town
5-Pack .... 978-1-4240-4681-2 — $42.50
25-Pack .... 978-1-4240-3686-8 — $175.00

Confucianism in China
5-Pack .... 978-1-4240-3763-6 — $42.50
25-Pack .... 978-1-4240-3636-3 — $175.00

Remarkable People

Bird Girl
5-Pack .... 978-1-4240-3746-9 — $42.50
25-Pack .... 978-1-4240-3617-2 — $175.00

The Life of a Geisha
5-Pack .... 978-1-4240-4699-7 — $42.50
25-Pack .... 978-1-4240-3704-9 — $175.00

Exciting Activities

Chuckwagon Racing
5-Pack .... 978-1-4240-3756-8 — $42.50
25-Pack .... 978-1-4240-3628-8 — $175.00

Para-Life Rescue
5-Pack .... 978-1-4240-4683-6 — $42.50
25-Pack .... 978-1-4240-3683-7 — $175.00

Amazing Science

Mysterious Crop Circles
5-Pack .... 978-1-4240-3793-3 — $42.50
25-Pack .... 978-1-4240-3680-6 — $175.00

Tornado Chase
5-Pack .... 978-1-4240-4708-6 — $42.50
25-Pack .... 978-1-4240-3708-7 — $175.00

Level 5 Collection (Bound Anthology) .... 978-1-4240-4516-7 — $42.00
Teacher's Manual .... 978-1-4240-4387-3 — $21.00
DVD .... 978-1-4240-1257-2 — $104.75
Audio CD .... 978-1-4240-4453-5 — $31.50
Assessment CD-ROM with ExamView® ... 978-1-4240-4420-7 — $105.00
Footprint Reading Library
   Online E-Book Collection – Level 5 ... 978-1-4240-7320-7 — $20.00

Level 6

Incredible Animals

Polar Bear Trouble
5-Pack .... 978-1-4240-3732-2 — $42.50
25-Pack .... 978-1-4240-3664-6 — $175.00

Cheetahs in Focus
5-Pack .... 978-1-4240-3735-3 — $42.50
25-Pack .... 978-1-4240-3667-7 — $175.00

Fascinating Places

The Black Diamonds of Provence
5-Pack .... 978-1-4240-4693-5 — $42.50
25-Pack .... 978-1-4240-3693-6 — $175.00

Shark Alley
5-Pack .... 978-1-4240-3747-6 — $42.50
25-Pack .... 978-1-4240-3618-9 — $175.00

Remarkable People

A Chinese Artist in Harlem
5-Pack .... 978-1-4240-3738-4 — $42.50
25-Pack .... 978-1-4240-3670-7 — $175.00

The Gauchos of Argentina
5-Pack .... 978-1-4240-4695-9 — $42.50
25-Pack .... 978-1-4240-3700-1 — $175.00

Exciting Activities

The Great Kite Fight
5-Pack .... 978-1-4240-3765-0 — $42.50
25-Pack .... 978-1-4240-3638-7 — $175.00

Extreme Sky Diving
5-Pack .... 978-1-4240-3768-1 — $42.50
25-Pack .... 978-1-4240-3641-7 — $175.00

Amazing Science

Aquarium on Wheels
5-Pack .... 978-1-4240-3743-8 — $42.50
25-Pack .... 978-1-4240-3675-2 — $175.00

How's the Weather?
5-Pack .... 978-1-4240-3781-0 — $42.50
25-Pack .... 978-1-4240-3952-4 — $175.00

Level 6 Collection (Bound Anthology) .... 978-1-4240-4517-4 — $42.00
Teacher's Manual .... 978-1-4240-4389-7 — $21.00
DVD .... 978-1-4240-1258-9 — $104.75
Audio CD .... 978-1-4240-4520-4 — $31.50
Assessment CD-ROM with ExamView® ... 978-1-4240-4421-4 — $105.00
Footprint Reading Library
   Online E-Book Collection – Level 6 ... 978-1-4240-7323-8 — $20.00

Level 7

Incredible Animals

Save the Koalas
5-Pack 978-1-4240-3733-9 $42.50
25-Pack 978-1-4240-3665-3 $175.00

The King of the Spiders
5-Pack 978-1-4240-3731-5 $42.50
25-Pack 978-1-4240-3663-9 $175.00

Fascinating Places

The Hidden Treasures of Egypt
5-Pack 978-1-4240-3745-2 $42.50
25-Pack 978-1-4240-3677-6 $175.00

The Barcelona Street Life
5-Pack 978-1-4240-3748-3 $42.50
25-Pack 978-1-4240-3619-6 $175.00

Remarkable People

Dinosaur Builder
5-Pack 978-1-4240-3755-1 $42.50
25-Pack 978-1-4240-3627-1 $175.00

Snake Detective
5-Pack 978-1-4240-3751-3 $42.50
25-Pack 978-1-4240-3623-3 $175.00

Exciting Activities

Canyaking Adventure
5-Pack 978-1-4240-3761-2 $42.50
25-Pack 978-1-4240-3634-9 $175.00

Spacewalk
5-Pack 978-1-4240-3769-8 $42.50
25-Pack 978-1-4240-3642-4 $175.00

Amazing Science

The Amazing Human Body
5-Pack 978-1-4240-3775-9 $42.50
25-Pack 978-1-4240-3942-5 $175.00

Saving the Amazon
5-Pack 978-1-4240-3777-3 $42.50
25-Pack 978-1-4240-3944-9 $175.00

Level 7 Collection (Bound Anthology) 978-1-4240-4518-1 $42.00
Teacher's Manual 978-1-4240-4391-0 $21.00
DVD 978-1-4240-1259-6 $104.75
Audio CD 978-1-4240-4455-9 $31.50
Assessment CD-ROM with Exam*View*® 978-1-4240-4422-1 $105.00
Footprint Reading Library
 Online E-Book Collection – Level 7 ....978-1-4240-7326-9 $20.00

Level 8

Incredible Animals

The Perfect Swarm
5-Pack 978-1-4240-3734-6 $42.50
25-Pack 978-1-4240-3666-0 $175.00

Red Devils
5-Pack 978-1-4240-3737-7 $42.50
25-Pack 978-1-4240-3669-1 $175.00

Fascinating Places

Forgotten China
5-Pack 978-1-4240-3741-4 $42.50
25-Pack 978-1-4240-3673-8 $175.00

The Orient Express
5-Pack 978-1-4240-3749-0 $42.50
25-Pack 978-1-4240-3620-2 $175.00

Remarkable People

Natacha's Animal Rescue
5-Pack 978-1-4240-3794-0 $42.50
25-Pack 978-1-4240-3681-3 $175.00

Afganistan's Heroic Artists
5-Pack 978-1-4240-3757-5 $42.50
25-Pack 978-1-4240-3629-5 $175.00

Exciting Activities

Living in the Slow Lane
5-Pack 978-1-4240-3767-4 $42.50
25-Pack 978-1-4240-3640-0 $175.00

Firewalking
5-Pack 978-1-4240-3770-4 $42.50
25-Pack 978-1-4240-3643-1 $175.00

Amazing Science

Mars on Earth
5-Pack 978-1-4240-3771-1 $42.50
25-Pack 978-1-4240-3644-8 $175.00

Alternative Future
5-Pack 978-1-4240-3778-0 $42.50
25-Pack 978-1-4240-3945-6 $175.00

Level 8 Collection (Bound Anthology) 978-1-4240-4519-8 $42.00
Teacher's Manual 978-1-4240-4393-4 $21.00
DVD 978-1-4240-1260-2 $104.75
Audio CD 978-1-4240-4456-6 $31.50
Assessment CD-ROM with Exam*View*® 978-1-4240-4423-8 $105.00
Footprint Reading Library
 Online E-Book Collection – Level 8 ....978-1-4240-7329-0 $20.00

Footprint Reading Library: The Complete
 Online E-Book Collection (all 8 levels)* 978-1-111-03406-1 $35.00

*For 1 year access

Foundations Reading Library*   p. 20

Level 1

Sarah's Surprise
5-pack 978-1-4240-9659-6 $38.25
25-Pack 978-1-4240-0725-7 $183.75

Goodbye, Hello
5-pack 978-1-4240-9754-8 $38.25
25-Pack 978-1-4240-0759-2 $183.75

Rain! Rain! Rain!
5-pack 978-1-4240-9662-6 $38.25
25-Pack 978-1-4240-0724-0 $183.75

Bad Dog? Good Dog!
5-pack 978-1-4240-9761-6 $38.25
25-Pack 978-1-4240-0751-6 $183.75

Get the Ball!
5-pack 978-1-4240-9756-2 $38.25
25-Pack 978-1-4240-0760-8 $183.75

The Tickets
5-pack 978-1-4240-9643-5 $38.25
25-Pack 978-1-4240-0721-9 $183.75

Level 1 Collection 978-1-4240-0689-2 $42.00
Activity Book 978-1-4240-0051-7 $11.50
Audio CD 978-1-4240-0058-6 $21.50
Lesson Planner 978-1-4240-0094-4 $22.00

Level 2

Sk8 for Jake
5-pack 978-1-4240-9694-7 $38.25
25-Pack 978-1-4240-0728-8 $183.75

The New Guitar
5-pack 978-1-4240-9666-4 $38.25
25-Pack 978-1-4240-0744-8 $183.75

Trouble at the Zoo
5-pack 978-1-4240-9646-6 $38.25
25-Pack 978-1-4240-0717-2 $183.75

Singer Wanted!
5-pack 978-1-4240-9657-2 $38.25
25-Pack 978-1-4240-0727-1 $183.75

Old Boat, New Boat
5-pack 978-1-4240-9667-1 $38.25
25-Pack 978-1-4240-0742-4 $183.75

The Cave
5-pack 978-1-4240-9652-7 $38.25
25-Pack 978-1-4240-0733-2 $183.75

Level 2 Collection 978-1-4240-0690-8 $42.00
Activity Book 978-1-4240-0052-4 $11.50
Audio CDs (2) 978-1-4240-0059-3 $44.00
Lesson Planner 978-1-4240-0095-1 $22.00

Level 3

Slam Dunk for Mark
5-pack 978-1-4240-9655-8 $38.25
25-Pack 978-1-4240-0729-5 $183.75

Kung Fu Kid
5-pack 978-1-4240-9672-5 $38.25
25-Pack 978-1-4240-0737-0 $183.75

Foundations Reading Library* (continued)

Level 3 (continued)

A Good Friend
5-pack	978-1-4240-9764-7	$38.25
25-Pack	978-1-4240-0749-3	$183.75

Quick Thinking
5-pack	978-1-4240-9664-0	$38.25
25-Pack	978-1-4240-0746-2	$183.75

I Always Win!
5-pack	978-1-4240-9765-4	$38.25
25-Pack	978-1-4240-0755-4	$183.75

Quiz Night
5-pack	978-1-4240-9663-3	$38.25
25-Pack	978-1-4240-0747-9	$183.75

Level 3 Collection	978-1-4240-0566-6	$42.00
Activity Book	978-1-4240-0053-1	$11.50
Audio CDs (2)	978-1-4240-0060-9	$44.00
Lesson Planner	978-1-4240-0096-8	$22.00

Level 4

I Spy
5-pack	978-1-4240-9766-1	$38.25
25-Pack	978-1-4240-0736-3	$183.75

Go Jimmy Go!
5-pack	978-1-4240-9755-5	$38.25
25-Pack	978-1-4240-0761-5	$183.75

Do I Tell?
5-pack	978-1-4240-9759-3	$38.25
25-Pack	978-1-4240-0754-7	$183.75

Lost at Sea
5-pack	978-1-4240-9670-1	$38.25
25-Pack	978-1-4240-0739-4	$183.75

The Shipwreck
5-pack	978-1-4240-9648-0	$38.25
25-Pack	978-1-4240-0715-8	$183.75

Mystery on the Island
5-pack	978-1-4240-9642-8	$38.25
25-Pack	978-1-4240-0722-6	$183.75

Level 4 Collection	978-1-4240-0572-7	$42.00
Activity Book	978-1-4240-0054-8	$11.50
Audio CDs (2)	978-1-4240-0061-6	$44.00
Lesson Planner	978-1-4240-0097-5	$22.00

Level 5

Who's Best?
5-pack	978-1-4240-9644-2	$38.25
25-Pack	978-1-4240-0719-6	$183.75

The Big Test
5-pack	978-1-4240-9653-4	$38.25
25-Pack	978-1-4240-0731-8	$183.75

Where's Lorena?
5-pack	978-1-4240-9645-9	$38.25
25-Pack	978-1-4240-0718-9	$183.75

Boys vs. Girls
5-pack	978-1-4240-9760-9	$38.25
25-Pack	978-1-4240-0752-3	$183.75

Think Daniela!
5-pack	978-1-4240-9763-0	$38.25
25-Pack	978-1-4240-0713-4	$183.75

The Bear's Mouth
5-pack	978-1-4240-9654-1	$38.25
25-Pack	978-1-4240-0730-1	$183.75

Level 5 Collection	978-1-4240-0691-5	$42.00
Activity Book	978-1-4240-0055-5	$11.50
Audio CDs (2)	978-1-4240-0062-3	$44.00
Lesson Planner	978-1-4240-0098-2	$22.00

Level 6

The Lost Wallet
5-pack	978-1-4240-9650-3	$38.25
25-Pack	978-1-4240-0735-6	$183.75

No, You Can't!
5-pack	978-1-4240-9665-7	$38.25
25-Pack	978-1-4240-0745-5	$183.75

Does He Love Me?
5-pack	978-1-4240-9757-9	$38.25
25-Pack	978-1-4240-0757-8	$183.75

A Helping Hand
5-pack	978-1-4240-9762-3	$38.25
25-Pack	978-1-4240-0750-9	$183.75

Trouble at Sea
5-pack	978-1-4240-9647-3	$38.25
25-Pack	978-1-4240-0716-5	$183.75

The Old Promise
5-pack	978-1-4240-9649-7	$38.25
25-Pack	978-1-4240-0714-1	$183.75

Level 6 Collection	978-1-4240-0692-2	$42.00
Activity Book	978-1-4240-0056-2	$11.50
Audio CDs (2)	978-1-4240-0063-0	$44.00
Lesson Planner	978-1-4240-0099-9	$22.00

Level 7

Let's Party!
5-pack	978-1-4240-9671-8	$38.25
25-Pack	978-1-4240-0738-7	$183.75

Do It!
5-pack	978-1-4240-9758-6	$38.25
25-Pack	978-1-4240-0748-6	$183.75

My Mom, the Movie Star
5-pack	978-1-4240-9668-8	$38.25
25-Pack	978-1-4240-0741-7	$183.75

The Secret Tunnel
5-pack	978-1-4240-9658-9	$38.25
25-Pack	978-1-4240-0726-4	$183.75

Love Online
5-pack	978-1-4240-9669-5	$38.25
25-Pack	978-1-4240-0740-0	$183.75

The Golden Monkey
5-pack	978-1-4240-9651-0	$38.25
25-Pack	978-1-4240-0734-9	$183.75

Level 7 Collection	978-1-4240-0693-9	$42.00
Activity Book	978-1-4240-0057-9	$11.50
Audio CDs (2)	978-1-4240-0064-7	$44.00
Lesson Planner	978-1-4240-0100-2	$22.00

*Multiple packaging options available for this series. Please ask your Heinle representative for more information.

From College to Careers — p. 92
Text (206 pp.)	978-0-618-38213-2	$29.50
Text/Audio CD Pkg.	978-0-618-60725-9	$35.50
Audio CD	978-0-618-38215-6	$21.50

From Great Paragraphs to Great Essays, 2/e — P. 72
See *Great Writing* series.

G

Gateway to Science — p. 34
Softcover (304 pp.)	978-1-4240-1621-1	$31.75
Hardcover (304 pp.)	978-1-4240-0331-0	$43.50
Workbook with Labs	978-1-4240-0332-7	$17.00
Audio CDs (4)	978-1-4240-0334-1	$81.75
Teacher's Edition	978-1-4240-0333-4	$89.50
Assessment Book	978-1-4240-0894-0	$113.50
Teacher Resources CD-ROM with ExamView® and Classroom Presentation Tool	978-1-4240-0335-8	$117.75

Getting Together — p. 96
Text (178 pp.)	978-0-1552-9598-8	$33.75

Go for it!, 2/e — p. 22

Book 1
Text (144 pp.)	978-0-8384-0494-2	$21.50
Workbook	978-1-4130-0016-0	$13.50
Teacher's Edition	978-1-4130-0015-3	$32.25
Classroom Audio CDs (2)	978-1-4240-0103-3	$48.50

Book 2
Text (144 pp.)	978-1-4130-0019-1	$21.50
Workbook	978-1-4130-0021-4	$13.50
Teacher's Edition	978-1-4130-0020-7	$32.25
Classroom Audio CDs (2)	978-1-4240-0105-7	$48.50

Book 3
Text (144 pp.)	978-1-4130-0024-5	$21.50
Workbook	978-1-4130-0026-9	$13.50
Teacher's Edition	978-1-4130-0025-2	$32.25
Classroom Audio CDs (2)	978-1-4130-0023-8	$48.50

Book 4

Text (144 pp.)	978-1-4130-0029-0	$21.50
Workbook	978-1-4130-0031-3	$13.50
Teacher's Edition	978-1-4130-0030-6	$32.25
Classroom Audio CDs (2)	978-1-4130-0028-3	$48.50
Assessment CD-ROM with ExamView® (Books 1 & 2)	978-1-4130-0085-6	$140.75
Assessment CD-ROM with ExamView® (Books 3 & 4)	978-1-4130-1775-5	$140.75

Grammar Book, The, 2/e — p. 117

Text (800 pp.)	978-0-8384-4725-3	$69.25

Grammar Café — p. 58

Level 1	978-1-4240-0644-1	$28.25
Level 2	978-1-4240-1690-7	$28.25
Level 3	978-1-4240-1691-4	$28.25
Level 4	978-1-4240-1692-1	$28.25
Level 5	978-1-4240-1694-5	$28.25
Level 6	978-1-4240-1693-8	$28.25

See individual grammar programs for additional *Grammar Café* packages.

Grammar Challenge — p. 38

See the *Stand Out* series.

Grammar Clips — p. 58

DVD	978-1-4240-0449-2	$27.25
Workbook	978-1-4240-0448-5	$17.75

Grammar Connection — p. 54

Book 1

Text (262 pp.)	978-1-4130-0830-2	$37.25
Workbook	978-1-4130-0834-0	$20.75
Text/Audio CD Pkg.	978-1-4240-9635-0	$38.25
Text/Workbook Pkg.	978-1-4240-9675-6	$48.25
Text/Grammar Café Pkg.	978-1-4240-9036-5	$43.00
Audio CD (2)	978-1-4130-0831-9	$43.00
Teacher's Annotated Edition (with Activity Bank and Classroom Presentation Tool CD-ROM)	978-1-4240-0214-6	$41.75
Assessment CD-ROM with ExamView®	978-1-4130-0850-0	$119.00

Book 2

Text (304 pp.)	978-1-4130-0835-7	$37.25
Workbook	978-1-4130-0839-5	$20.75
Text/Audio CDs Pkg.	978-1-4240-9602-2	$38.25
Text/Workbook Pkg.	978-1-4240-9600-8	$48.25
Text/Grammar Café Pkg.	978-1-4240-9043-3	$43.00
Audio CDs (2)	978-1-4130-0836-4	$43.00
Teacher's Annotated Edition (with Activity Bank and Classroom Presentation Tool CD-ROM)	978-1-4240-0216-0	$41.75
Assessment CD-ROM with ExamView®	978-1-4240-0408-9	$119.00

Book 3

Text (304 pp.)	978-1-4130-0840-1	$37.25
Workbook	978-1-4130-0844-9	$20.75
Text/Audio CDs Pkg.	978-1-4240-9604-6	$38.25
Text/Workbook Pkg.	978-1-4240-9613-8	$48.25
Text/Grammar Café Pkg.	978-1-4240-9038-9	$43.00
Audio CDs (2)	978-1-4130-0841-8	$43.00
Teacher's Annotated Edition (with Activity Bank and Classroom Presentation Tool CD-ROM)	978-1-4240-0219-1	$41.75
Assessment CD-ROM with ExamView®	978-1-4240-0409-6	$119.00

Book 4

Text (304pp.)	978-1-4130-0845-6	$37.25
Workbook	978-1-4130-0849-4	$20.75
Text/Audio CDs Pkg.	978-1-4240-9619-0	$38.25
Text/Workbook Pkg.	978-1-4240-9676-3	$48.25
Text/Grammar Café Pkg.	978-1-4240-9041-9	$43.00
Audio CDs (2)	978-1-4130-0846-3	$43.00
Teacher's Annotated Edition (with Activity Bank and Classroom Presentation Tool CD-ROM)	978-1-4240-0221-4	$41.75
Assessment CD-ROM with ExamView®	978-1-4240-0410-2	$119.00

Book 5

Text (305 pp.)	978-1-4240-0034-0	$37.25
Workbook	978-1-4240-0041-8	$20.75
Text/Audio CDs Pkg.	978-1-4240-9628-2	$38.25
Text/Workbook Pkg.	978-1-4240-9632-9	$48.25
Text/Grammar Café Pkg.	978-1-4240-9044-0	$43.00
Audio CDs (2)	978-1-4240-0038-8	$43.00
Teacher's Annotated Edition (with Activity Bank and Classroom Presentation Tool CD-ROM)	978-1-4240-0222-1	$41.75
Assessment CD-ROM with ExamView®	978-1-4240-0411-9	$119.00

Grammar Dimensions, 4/e — p. 50

Book 1

School Edition (496 pp.)	978-1-4130-2740-2	$37.50
Enhanced College Edition (496 pp.)	978-1-4240-9039-6	$37.50
Split Text 1A	978-1-4240-0336-5	$20.50
Split Text 1B	978-1-4240-0337-2	$20.50
Text/Audio CD Pkg.	978-1-4240-9425-7	$38.50
Workbook	978-1-4240-0352-5	$22.00
Audio CD	978-1-4240-0356-3	$40.50
Lesson Planner	978-1-4240-0360-0	$113.25
Assessment CD-ROM with ExamView®		

Book 2

School Edition (432 pp.)	978-1-4130-2741-9	$37.50
Enhanced College Edition (432 pp.)	978-1-4240-9042-6	$37.50
Split Text 2A	978-1-4240-0338-9	$20.50
Split Text 2B	978-1-4240-0339-6	$20.50
Text/Audio CD Pkg.	978-1-4240-9427-1	$38.50
Workbook	978-1-4240-0353-2	$22.00
Audio CD	978-1-4240-0349-5	$20.50
Lesson Planner	978-1-4240-0357-0	$40.50
Assessment CD-ROM with ExamView®	978-1-4240-0831-5	$113.25

Book 3

School Edition (480 pp.)	978-1-4130-2742-6	$37.50
Enhanced College Edition (480 pp.)	978-1-4240-9037-2	$37.50
Split Text 3A	978-1-4240-0340-2	$20.50
Split Text 3B	978-1-4240-0341-9	$20.50
Text/Audio CD Pkg.	978-1-4240-9429-5	$38.50
Workbook	978-1-4240-0354-9	$22.00
Audio CD	978-1-4240-0350-1	$20.50
Lesson Planner	978-1-4240-0358-7	$40.50
Assessment CD-ROM with ExamView®	978-1-4240-0832-2	$113.25

Book 4

School Edition (512 pp.)	978-1-4130-2752-5	$37.50
Enhanced College Edition (512 pp.)	978-1-4240-9040-2	$37.50
Split Text 4A	978-1-4240-0342-6	$20.50
Split Text 4B	978-1-4240-0343-3	$20.50
Text/Audio CDs Pkg.	978-1-4240-9431-8	$38.50
Workbook	978-1-4240-0355-6	$22.00
Audio CDs (2)	978-1-4240-0351-8	$41.00
Lesson Planner	978-1-4240-0359-4	$40.50
Assessment CD-ROM with ExamView®	978-1-4240-0833-9	$113.25

Grammar Expert — p. 59

Basic (112 pp.)	978-9-6040-3288-4	$19.50
Book 1 (144 pp.)	978-9-6040-3286-0	$19.50
Book 2 (160 pp.)	978-9-6040-3284-6	$19.50
Book 3 (176 pp.)	978-9-6040-3290-7	$19.50
Assessment CD-ROM with ExamView® (Basic – 3)	978-9-6040-3289-1	$59.50

Grammar in Context, 4/e — p. 52

Basic

School Edition (320 pp.)	978-1-4130-0638-4	$35.25
Enhanced College Edition (320 pp.)	978-1-4240-2554-1	$35.25
Text/Audio CDs Pkg.	978-1-4130-6691-3	$36.25
Text/Interactive CD-ROM Pkg.	978-1-4240-9724-1	$40.50
Audio CDs (2)	978-1-4130-0825-8	$42.75
Teacher's Annotated Edition	978-1-4130-0827-2	$42.00
Assessment CD-ROM with ExamView®	978-1-4130-1952-0	$113.25

Book 1

School Edition (464 pp.)	978-1-4130-0736-7	$35.25
Enhanced College Edition (464 pp.)	978-1-4240-9033-4	$35.25
Split Text 1A (Lessons 1 – 7)	978-1-4130-0737-4	$21.00
Split Text 1B (Lessons 8 – 14)	978-1-4130-0738-1	$21.00
Text/Audio CDs Pkg.	978-1-4130-7377-5	$36.25
Text/Interactive CD-ROM Pkg.	978-1-4240-9725-8	$40.50
Audio CDs (2)	978-1-4130-0739-8	$42.75
Teacher's Annotated Edition	978-1-4130-0741-1	$42.00
Assessment CD-ROM with ExamView®	978-1-4130-0829-6	$113.25

Book 2

School Edition (528 pp.)	978-1-4130-0742-8	$35.25
Enhanced College Edition (528 pp.)	978-1-4240-2556-5	$35.25
Split Text 2A (Lessons 1 – 7)	978-1-4130-0743-5	$21.00
Split Text 2B (Lessons 8 – 14)	978-1-4130-0744-2	$21.00
Text/Audio CDs Pkg.	978-1-4130-7379-9	$36.25
Text/Interactive CD-ROM Pkg.	978-1-4240-9723-4	$40.50
Audio CDs (3)	978-1-4130-0745-9	$64.25
Teacher's Annotated Edition	978-1-4130-0747-3	$42.00
Assessment CD-ROM with ExamView®	978-1-4130-1950-6	$113.25

Book 3

School Edition (544 pp.)	978-1-4130-0748-0	$35.25
Enhanced College Edition (544 pp.)	978-1-4240-9027-3	$35.25
Split Text 3A (Lessons 1 – 5)	978-1-4130-0822-7	$21.00
Split Text 3B (Lessons 6 – 10)	978-1-4130-0823-4	$21.00
Text/Audio CDs Pkg.	978-1-4130-7381-2	$36.25

Grammar in Context, 4/e (continued)

Book 3 (continued)

Text/Interactive CD-ROM Pkg.	978-1-4240-9726-5	$40.50
Audio CDs (4)	978-1-4130-0749-7	$81.75
Teacher's Annotated Edition	978-1-4130-0821-0	$42.00
Assessment CD-ROM with ExamView®	978-1-4130-1951-3	$113.25

Basic – 3

Interactive CD-ROM	978-1-4130-1452-5	$31.75
Instructional Video	978-1-4130-1451-8	$70.25
Instructional DVD	978-1-4130-2219-3	$70.25

Grammar Links
p. 56

Basic

Text (304 pp.)	978-0-618-15026-7	$36.00
Text/Audio CD Pkg.	978-1-4282-0286-3	$37.00
Text/Grammar Café Pkg.	978-1-4240-9031-0	$41.25
Audio CD	978-0-618-15030-4	$21.50

Book 1, 2/e

Text (478 pp.)	978-0-618-27412-3	$36.00
Workbook	978-0-618-27421-5	$19.75
Split Text 1A	978-0-618-27415-4	$21.25
Split Workbook 1A	978-0-618-27424-6	$10.75
Split Text 1B	978-0-618-27416-1	$21.25
Split Workbook 1B	978-0-618-27425-3	$10.75
Text/Workbook Pkg.	978-1-4282-0314-3	$46.50
Text/Audio CD Pkg.	978-1-4282-0287-0	$37.00
Text/Audio CD/Workbook Pkg.	978-1-4282-0285-6	$48.00
Text/Grammar Café Pkg.	978-1-4240-9030-3	$41.25
Audio CD	978-0-618-35300-2	$21.50

Book 2, 2/e

Text (432 pp.)	978-0-618-27413-0	$36.00
Workbook	978-0-618-27422-2	$19.75
Split Text 2A	978-0-618-27417-8	$21.25
Split Workbook 2A	978-0-618-27426-0	$10.75
Split Text 2B	978-0-618-27418-5	$21.25
Split Workbook 2B	978-0-618-27427-7	$10.75
Text/Workbook Pkg.	978-1-4282-0315-0	$46.50
Text/Audio CD Pkg.	978-1-4282-0289-4	$37.00
Text/Audio CD/Workbook Pkg.	978-1-4282-0288-7	$48.00
Text/Grammar Café Pkg.	978-1-4240-9029-7	$41.25
Audio CD	978-0-618-35301-9	$21.50

Book 3, 2/e

Text (512 pp.)	978-0-618-27414-7	$36.00
Workbook	978-0-618-27423-9	$19.75
Split Text 3A	978-0-618-27419-2	$21.25
Split Workbook 3A	978-0-618-27428-4	$10.75
Split Text 3B	978-0-618-27420-8	$21.25
Split Workbook 3B	978-0-618-27429-1	$10.75
Text/Workbook Pkg.	978-1-4282-0316-7	$46.50
Text/Audio CD Pkg.	978-1-4282-0290-0	$37.00
Text/Audio CD/Workbook Pkg.	978-1-4282-0294-8	$48.00
Text/Grammar Café Pkg.	978-1-4240-9028-0	$41.25
Audio CD	978-0-618-35302-6	$21.50

Great Writing series, The
p. 72

Great Writing 1: Great Sentences for Great Paragraphs, 3/e

Text	978-1-4240-4989-9	$32.25
Assessment CD-ROM with ExamView®	978-1-4240-6371-0	$107.75
Classroom Presentation Tool CD-ROM	978-1-4240-6515-8	$108.00

Great Writing 2: Great Paragraphs, 3/e

Text	978-1-4240-5100-7	$32.25
Assessment CD-ROM with ExamView®	978-1-4240-6212-6	$107.75
Classroom Presentation Tool CD-ROM	978-1-4240-6516-5	$108.00

Great Writing 3: From Great Paragraphs to Great Essays, 2/e

Text	978-1-4240-6210-2	$32.25
Assessment CD-ROM with ExamView®	978-1-4240-6213-3	$107.75
Classroom Presentation Tool CD-ROM	978-1-4240-6513-4	$108.00

Great Writing 4: Great Essays, 3/e

Text	978-1-4240-5101-4	$32.25
Assessment CD-ROM with ExamView®	978-1-4240-6214-0	$107.75
Classroom Presentation Tool CD-ROM	978-1-4240-6514-1	$108.00

Great Writing 5: Greater Essays, 2/e

Text	978-1-4240-6211-9	$32.25
Assessment CD-ROM with ExamView®	978-1-4240-6215-7	$107.75
Classroom Presentation Tool CD-ROM	978-1-4240-6512-7	$108.00

H

Heart of the Matter, The
p. 96

Text (184 pp.)	978-0-8384-7857-8	$31.50
Text/Audio Tapes Pkg.	978-0-8384-6087-0	$37.50
Audio Tapes (2)	978-0-8384-7866-0	$60.50
Video (VHS)	978-0-8384-6088-7	$182.00

Heinle Phonics & Intervention Kit, The
p. 13

Phonics/Intervention Kit	978-1-4240-3219-8	$236.25

Heinle Picture Dictionary, The
p. 32

Text (272 pp.)	978-0-8384-4400-9	$19.00
Text/Beginning Workbook Pkg.	978-1-4240-9826-2	$27.75
Text/Intermediate Workbook Pkg.	978-1-4240-9827-9	$27.75
Text/Audio CDs Pkg.	978-1-4130-7481-9	$30.50
Text/Interactive CD-ROM Pkg.	978-1-4240-9703-6	$20.00
Text/Beginning Workbook /Interactive CD-ROM Pkg.	978-1-4240-9045-7	$28.75
Text/Intermediate Workbook/ Interactive CD-ROM Pkg.	978-1-4240-9047-1	$28.75
Text/Audio CDs/Interactive CD-ROM Pkg.	978-1-4240-4170-1	$31.50
Beginning Workbook with Audio CD	978-0-8384-4401-6	$12.25
Intermediate Workbook with Audio CD	978-1-4130-1467-9	$12.25
Audio CDs (6)	978-0-8384-4405-4	$126.00
Lesson Planner with Activity Bank and Classroom Presentation Tool CD-ROM	978-0-8384-4413-9	$34.25
Transparencies	978-1-4130-1708-3	$263.25
Interactive CD-ROM	978-0-8384-4410-8	$43.00
Heinle Picture Dictionary Online Site License*	978-1-4240-0049-4	*

*For pricing or to purchase, call Technology Services at 800-423-0563 or contact your Heinle representative.

Bilingual Editions

Brazilian Portuguese	978-1-4130-0550-9	$19.00
Chinese, Simplified	978-1-4240-0112-5	$19.00
Chinese, Traditional	978-1-4130-0553-0	$19.00
Haitian Creole	978-1-4130-1819-6	$19.00
Japanese	978-1-4130-0551-6	$19.00
Korean	978-1-4130-0552-3	$19.00
Spanish	978-1-4130-0549-3	$19.00

Heinle Picture Dictionary for Children, The
p. 31

Softcover (160 pp.)	978-1-4130-2256-8	$18.00
Hardcover (160 pp.)	978-1-4240-0711-0	$26.00
Workbook	978-1-4240-0421-8	$12.75
Audio CDs (3)	978-1-4240-0416-4	$61.25
Sing-Along Audio CD	978-1-4240-0942-8	$45.00
Interactive CD-ROM	978-1-4240-0418-8	$39.75
Lesson Planner (contains Audio CDs and Activity Bank CD-ROM)	978-1-4240-0419-5	$47.50
Transparencies	978-1-4240-0712-7	$113.50
Classroom Presentation Tool CD-ROM	978-1-4240-0870-4	$113.50

Bilingual Editions

Spanish	978-1-4240-0876-6	$18.00
British English (softcover)	978-1-4240-0849-0	$17.00

Heinle Reading Library: Academic Content Collection, The
p. 16

Level A (Beginning/Early Intermediate)

The Pilgrims

5-pack	978-1-4130-6443-8	$51.00
25-Pack	978-1-4130-2104-2	$229.75

Rain Forests

5-pack	978-1-4130-6441-4	$51.00
25-Pack	978-1-4130-2105-9	$229.75

The Hopi

5-pack	978-1-4240-9712-8	$51.00
25-Pack	978-1-4240-9721-0	$229.75

How Do I Become a Firefighter?

5-pack	978-1-4240-9710-4	$51.00
25-Pack	978-1-4240-9719-7	$229.75

The Solar System

5-pack	978-1-4130-6437-7	$51.00
25-Pack	978-1-4130-2106-6	$229.75

Frida Kahlo

5-pack	978-1-4240-9711-1	$51.00
25-Pack	978-1-4240-9720-3	$229.75

Audio CD (Level A)	978-1-4130-2862-1	$57.75
Workbook (Level A)	978-1-4240-0325-9	$14.25

Level B (Intermediate)

Arctic
5-pack	978-1-4130-6438-4	$51.00
25-Pack	978-1-4130-2108-0	$229.75

Photosynthesis
5-pack	978-1-4240-9713-5	$51.00
25-Pack	978-1-4240-9722-7	$229.75

Anne Frank
5-pack	978-1-4240-9707-4	$51.00
25-Pack	978-1-4240-9716-6	$229.75

Space Travel
5-pack	978-1-4130-6444-5	$51.00
25-Pack	978-1-4130-2109-7	$229.75

Alexander Graham Bell
5-pack	978-1-4240-9706-7	$51.00
25-Pack	978-1-4240-9715-9	$229.75

The Oregon Trail
5-pack	978-1-4130-6442-1	$51.00
25-Pack	978-1-4130-2107-3	$229.75

Audio CD (Level B)	978-1-4240-0439-3	$57.75
Workbook (Level B)	978-1-4240-0326-6	$14.25

Level C (Early Advanced/Advanced)

The Navajo
5-pack	978-1-4130-6440-7	$51.00
25-Pack	978-1-4130-2111-0	$229.75

Dolphins
5-pack	978-1-4130-6439-1	$51.00
25-Pack	978-1-4130-2110-3	$229.75

Tony Hawk
5-pack	978-1-4240-9714-2	$51.00
25-Pack	978-1-4240-9705-0	$229.75

Life in a Cave
5-pack	978-1-4240-9708-1	$51.00
25-Pack	978-1-4240-9717-3	$229.75

The Statue of Liberty
5-pack	978-1-4130-6445-2	$51.00
25-Pack	978-1-4130-2112-7	$229.75

Energy
5-pack	978-1-4240-9709-8	$51.00
25-Pack	978-1-4240-9718-0	$229.75

Audio CD (Level C)	978-1-4240-0440-9	$57.75
Workbook (Level C)	978-1-4240-0327-3	$14.25

Levels A – C

Teacher Guide with Reproducible Masters
(for all 18 readers)	978-1-4240-0328-0	$29.50

Heinle Reading Library: Biography Collection, The   p. 16

Level A (Beginning/Early Intermediate)

Benjamin Franklin
5-Pack	978-1-4240-9792-0	$51.00
25-Pack	978-1-4240-0648-9	$229.75
Audio CD	978-1-4240-0577-2	$31.00

Clara Barton
5-Pack	978-1-4240-9793-7	$51.00
25-Pack	978-1-4240-0649-6	$229.75
Audio CD	978-1-4240-0578-9	$31.00

Level B (Intermediate)

Eleanor Roosevelt
5-Pack	978-1-4240-9794-4	$51.00
25-Pack	978-1-4240-0650-2	$229.75
Audio CD	978-1-4240-0580-2	$31.00

Jackie Robinson
5-Pack	978-1-4240-9796-8	$51.00
25-Pack	978-1-4240-0652-6	$229.75
Audio CD	978-1-4240-0588-8	$31.00

Level C (Early Advanced)

Martin Luther King, Jr.
5-Pack	978-1-4240-9790-6	$51.00
25-Pack	978-1-4240-0653-3	$229.75
Audio CD	978-1-4240-0592-5	$31.00

Babe Ruth
5-Pack	978-1-4240-9791-3	$51.00
25-Pack	978-1-4240-0647-2	$229.75
Audio CD	978-1-4240-0574-1	$31.00

George Washington
5-Pack	978-1-4240-9795-1	$51.00
25-Pack	978-1-4240-0651-9	$229.75
Audio CD	978-1-4240-0582-6	$31.00

Heinle Reading Library: Illustrated Classics Collection, The*   p. 16

Level A (Beginning/Early Intermediate)

The Legend of Sleepy Hollow
5-pack	978-1-4130-9102-1	$51.00
25-Pack	978-1-4130-2122-6	$229.75
Workbook 5-pack	978-1-4130-1238-5	$25.50
Workbook 25-Pack	978-1-4130-2140-0	$114.75
Audio CD	978-1-4130-1108-1	$31.00

Aesop's Fables
5-pack	978-1-4130-9091-8	$51.00
25-Pack	978-1-4130-2123-3	$229.75
Workbook 5-pack	978-1-4130-1220-0	$25.50
Workbook 25-Pack	978-1-4130-2141-7	$114.75
Audio CD	978-1-4130-1094-7	$31.00

The Strange Case of Dr. Jekyll and Mr. Hyde
5-pack	978-1-4130-9093-2	$51.00
25-Pack	978-1-4130-2124-0	$229.75
Workbook 5-pack	978-1-4130-1230-9	$25.50
Workbook 25-Pack	978-1-4130-2142-4	$114.75
Audio CD	978-1-4130-1101-2	$31.00

The Red Badge of Courage
5-pack	978-1-4130-9103-8	$51.00
25-Pack	978-1-4130-2125-7	$229.75
Workbook 5-pack	978-1-4130-1246-0	$25.50
Workbook 25-Pack	978-1-4130-2143-1	$114.75
Audio CD	978-1-4130-1106-7	$31.00

The Invisible Man
5-pack	978-1-4130-9094-9	$51.00
25-Pack	978-1-4130-2126-4	$229.75
Workbook 5-pack	978-1-4130-1232-3	$25.50
Workbook 25-Pack	978-1-4130-2144-8	$114.75
Audio CD	978-1-4130-1099-2	$31.00

Moby Dick
5-pack	978-1-4130-9098-7	$51.00
25-Pack	978-1-4130-2127-1	$229.75
Workbook 5-pack	978-1-4130-1242-2	$25.50
Workbook 25-Pack	978-1-4130-2145-5	$114.75
Audio CD	978-1-4130-1104-3	$31.00

Dracula**
5-pack	978-1-4240-9852-1	$51.00
25-Pack	978-1-4240-0659-5	$229.75
Audio CD	978-1-4240-0579-6	$31.00

The Phantom of the Opera**
5-pack	978-1-4240-9772-2	$51.00
25-Pack	978-1-4240-0674-8	$229.75
Audio CD	978-1-4240-0595-6	$31.00

Tales of Mystery and Terror**
5-pack	978-1-4240-9769-2	$51.00
25-Pack	978-1-4240-0682-3	$229.75
Audio CD	978-1-4240-0601-4	$31.00

Three Musketeers**
5-pack	978-1-4240-9733-3	$51.00
25-Pack	978-1-4240-0683-0	$229.75
Audio CD	978-1-4240-0605-2	$31.00

The Time Machine**
5-pack	978-1-4240-9806-4	$51.00
25-Pack	978-1-4240-0684-7	$229.75
Audio CD	978-1-4240-0606-9	$31.00

The Adventures of Tom Sawyer**
5-pack	978-1-4240-9404-2	$51.00
25-Pack	978-1-4240-0685-4	$229.75
Audio CD	978-1-4240-0607-6	$31.00

The Adventures of Huckleberry Finn**
5-pack	978-1-4240-9934-4	$51.00
25-Pack	978-1-4240-0656-4	$229.75
Audio CD	978-1-4240-0587-1	$31.00

Sherlock Holmes and the Case of the Hound of the Baskervilles**
5-pack	978-1-4240-9799-9	$51.00
25-Pack	978-1-4240-0680-9	$229.75
Audio CD	978-1-4240-0600-7	$31.00

Heinle Reading Library: Illustrated Classics Collection, The* (continued)

Level A (continued)

Pollyanna**
5-pack	978-1-4240-9674-9	$51.00
25-Pack	978-1-4240-0675-5	$229.75
Audio CD	978-1-4240-0596-3	$31.00

Jane Eyre**
5-pack	978-1-4240-9822-4	$51.00
25-Pack	978-1-4240-0667-0	$229.75
Audio CD	978-1-4240-0589-5	$31.00

Level B (Intermediate)

Treasure Island
5-pack	978-1-4130-9104-5	$51.00
25-Pack	978-1-4130-2128-8	$229.75
Workbook 5-pack	978-1-4130-1250-7	$25.50
Workbook 25-Pack	978-1-4130-2146-2	$114.75
Audio CD	978-1-4130-1110-4	$31.00

David Copperfield
5-pack	978-1-4130-9092-5	$51.00
25-Pack	978-1-4130-2129-5	$229.75
Workbook 5-pack	978-1-4130-1228-6	$25.50
Workbook 25-Pack	978-1-4130-2147-9	$114.75
Audio CD	978-1-4130-1098-5	$31.00

Ivanhoe
5-pack	978-1-4130-9095-6	$51.00
25-Pack	978-1-4130-2130-1	$229.75
Workbook 5-pack	978-1-4130-1234-7	$25.50
Workbook 25-Pack	978-1-4130-2148-6	$114.75
Audio CD	978-1-4130-1100-5	$31.00

Journey to the Center of the Earth
5-pack	978-1-4130-9096-3	$51.00
25-Pack	978-1-4130-2131-8	$229.75
Workbook 5-pack	978-1-4130-1236-1	$25.50
Workbook 25-Pack	978-1-4130-2149-3	$114.75
Audio CD	978-1-4130-1102-9	$31.00

Pride and Prejudice
5-pack	978-1-4130-9099-4	$51.00
25-Pack	978-1-4130-2132-5	$229.75
Workbook 5-pack	978-1-4130-1244-6	$25.50
Workbook 25-Pack	978-1-4130-2150-9	$114.75
Audio CD	978-1-4130-1105-0	$31.00

The Call of the Wild
5-pack	978-1-4130-9101-4	$51.00
25-Pack	978-1-4130-2133-2	$229.75
Workbook 5-pack	978-1-4130-1224-8	$25.50
Workbook 25-Pack	978-1-4130-2151-6	$114.75
Audio CD	978-1-4130-1096-1	$31.00

The House of the Seven Gables**
5-pack	978-1-4240-9907-8	$51.00
25-Pack	978-1-4240-0664-9	$229.75
Audio CD	978-1-4240-0586-4	$31.00

Oliver Twist**
5-pack	978-1-4240-9770-8	$51.00
25-Pack	978-1-4240-0665-6	$229.75
Audio CD	978-1-4240-0594-9	$31.00

Anne of Green Gables**
5-pack	978-1-4240-9837-8	$51.00
25-Pack	978-1-4240-0658-8	$229.75
Audio CD	978-1-4240-0576-5	$31.00

The Man in the Iron Mask**
5-pack	978-1-4240-9731-9	$51.00
25-Pack	978-1-4240-0670-0	$229.75
Audio CD	978-1-4240-0591-8	$31.00

Heidi**
5-pack	978-1-4240-9906-1	$51.00
25-Pack	978-1-4240-0663-2	$229.75
Audio CD	978-1-4240-0585-7	$31.00

The Secret Garden**
5-pack	978-1-4240-9789-0	$51.00
25-Pack	978-1-4240-0679-3	$229.75
Audio CD	978-1-4240-0599-4	$31.00

The Mutiny on the HMS Bounty**
5-pack	978-1-4240-9740-1	$51.00
25-Pack	978-1-4240-0672-4	$229.75
Audio CD	978-1-4240-0593-2	$31.00

King Arthur and the Knights of the Round Table**
5-pack	978-1-4240-9656-5	$51.00

25-Pack	978-1-4240-0668-7	$229.75
Audio CD	978-1-4240-0590-1	$31.00

The Prince and the Pauper**
5-pack	978-1-4240-9775-3	$51.00
25-Pack	978-1-4240-0676-2	$229.75
Audio CD	978-1-4240-0604-5	$31.00

The Merry Adventures of Robin Hood**
5-pack	978-1-4240-9786-9	$51.00
25-Pack	978-1-4240-0678-6	$229.75
Audio CD	978-1-4240-0598-7	$31.00

Level C (Early Advanced)

The Adventures of Sherlock Holmes
5-pack	978-1-4130-9089-5	$51.00
25-Pack	978-1-4130-2134-9	$229.75
Workbook 5-pack	978-1-4130-1218-7	$25.50
Workbook 25-Pack	978-1-4130-2152-3	$114.75
Audio CD	978-1-4130-1107-4	$31.00

The Swiss Family Robinson
5-pack	978-1-4130-9100-7	$51.00
25-Pack	978-1-4130-2135-6	$229.75
Workbook 5-pack	978-1-4130-1248-4	$25.50
Workbook 25-Pack	978-1-4130-2153-0	$114.75
Audio CD	978-1-4130-1109-8	$31.00

20,000 Leagues Under the Sea
5-pack	978-1-4130-9087-1	$51.00
25-Pack	978-1-4130-2136-3	$229.75
Workbook 5-pack	978-1-4130-1216-3	$25.50
Workbook 25-Pack	978-1-4130-2154-7	$114.75
Audio CD	978-1-4130-1093-0	$31.00

Black Beauty
5-pack	978-1-4130-9090-1	$51.00
25-Pack	978-1-4130-2137-0	$229.75
Workbook 5-pack	978-1-4130-1222-4	$25.50
Workbook 25-Pack	978-1-4130-2155-4	$114.75
Audio CD	978-1-4130-1095-4	$31.00

Little Women
5-pack	978-1-4130-9097-0	$51.00
25-Pack	978-1-4130-2138-7	$229.75
Workbook 5-pack	978-1-4130-1240-8	$25.50
Workbook 25-Pack	978-1-4130-2156-1	$114.75
Audio CD	978-1-4130-1103-6	$31.00

A Christmas Carol
5-pack	978-1-4130-9088-8	$51.00
25-Pack	978-1-4130-2139-4	$229.75
Workbook 5-pack	978-1-4130-1225-5	$25.50
Workbook 25-Pack	978-1-4130-2157-8	$114.75
Audio CD	978-1-4130-1097-8	$31.00

The Count of Monte Cristo**
5-pack	978-1-4240-9704-3	$51.00
25-Pack	978-1-4240-0671-7	$229.75
Audio CD	978-1-4240-0602-1	$31.00

The Wind in the Willows**
5-pack	978-1-4240-9773-9	$51.00
25-Pack	978-1-4240-0688-5	$229.75
Audio CD	978-1-4240-0610-6	$31.00

Great Expectations**
5-pack	978-1-4240-9876-7	$51.00
25-Pack	978-1-4240-0661-8	$229.75
Audio CD	978-1-4240-0583-3	$31.00

White Fang**
5-pack	978-1-4240-9406-6	$51.00
25-Pack	978-1-4240-0687-8	$229.75
Audio CD	978-1-4240-0609-0	$31.00

Rebecca of Sunnybrook Farm**
5-pack	978-1-4240-9776-0	$51.00
25-Pack	978-1-4240-0677-9	$229.75
Audio CD	978-1-4240-0597-0	$31.00

The War of the Worlds**
5-pack	978-1-4240-4134-3	$51.00
25-Pack	978-1-4240-0686-1	$229.75
Audio CD	978-1-4240-0608-3	$31.00

A Little Princess**
5-pack	978-1-4240-9698-5	$51.00
25-Pack	978-1-4240-0669-4	$229.75
Audio CD	978-1-4240-0575-8	$31.00

Gulliver's Travels**
5-pack	978-1-4240-9878-1	$51.00

25-Pack	978-1-4240-0662-5	$229.75
Audio CD	978-1-4240-0584-0	$31.00

The Hunchback of Notre Dame**

	978-1-4240-9947-4	$51.00
5-pack	978-1-4240-0666-3	$229.75
25-Pack	978-1-4240-0603-8	$31.00
Audio CD		

A Tale of Two Cities**

	978-1-4240-9753-1	$51.00
5-pack	978-1-4240-0673-1	$229.75
25-Pack	978-1-4240-0611-3	$31.00
Audio CD		

Frankenstein**

	978-1-4240-9864-4	$51.00
5-pack	978-1-4240-0660-1	$229.75
25-Pack	978-1-4240-0581-9	$31.00
Audio CD		

Levels A – C

Teacher Guide	978-1-4130-0634-6	$24.50

*Multiple packaging options available. Please ask your Heinle representative for more information.

**Workbooks not available at this time.

Heinle Reading Library: Milestones Introductory Reading Library   p. 16

The Cave

5-pack	978-1-4240-2514-5	$36.75
25-pack	978-1-4240-2533-6	$183.75

Goodbye, Hello!

5-pack	978-1-4240-2504-6	$36.75
25-pack	978-1-4240-2542-8	$183.75

Where's Lorena?

5-pack	978-1-4240-2520-6	$36.75
25-pack	978-1-4240-2525-1	$183.75

Think Daniela!

5-pack	978-1-4240-2519-0	$36.75
25-pack	978-1-4240-2526-8	$183.75

The Tickets

5-pack	978-1-4240-2518-3	$36.75
25-pack	978-1-4240-2527-5	$183.75

Sk8 for Jake

5-pack	978-1-4240-2511-4	$36.75
25-pack	978-1-4240-2543-5	$183.75

Bad Dog? Good Dog

5-pack	978-1-4240-2502-2	$36.75
25-pack	978-1-4240-2539-8	$183.75

The Bear's Mouth

5-pack	978-1-4240-2513-8	$36.75
25-pack	978-1-4240-2531-2	$183.75

No, You Can't

5-pack	978-1-4240-2507-7	$36.75
25-pack	978-1-4240-2537-4	$183.75

Old Boat, New Boat

5-pack	978-1-4240-2508-4	$36.75
25-pack	978-1-4240-2536-7	$183.75

Who's Best

5-pack	978-1-4240-2521-3	$36.75
25-pack	978-1-4240-2524-4	$183.75

The Shipwreck

5-pack	978-1-4240-2517-6	$36.75
25-pack	978-1-4240-2528-2	$183.75

I Always Win!

5-pack	978-1-4240-2505-3	$36.75
25-pack	978-1-4240-2541-1	$183.75

Trouble at the Zoo

5-pack	978-1-4240-2522-0	$36.75
25-pack	978-1-4240-2523-7	$183.75

Quiz Night

5-pack	978-1-4240-2509-1	$36.75
25-pack	978-1-4240-2535-0	$183.75

Slam Dunk for Mark

5-pack	978-1-4240-2512-1	$36.75
25-pack	978-1-4240-2532-9	$183.75

Go Jimmy Go!

5-pack	978-1-4240-2503-9	$36.75
25-pack	978-1-4240-2540-4	$183.75

Singer Wanted

5-pack	978-1-4240-2510-7	$36.75
25-pack	978-1-4240-2534-3	$183.75

The Golden Monkey

5-pack	978-1-4240-2515-2	$36.75
25-pack	978-1-4240-2530-5	$183.75

The New Guitar

5-pack	978-1-4240-2516-9	$36.75
25-pack	978-1-4240-2529-9	$183.75

My Mom, the Movie Star

5-pack	978-1-4240-2506-0	$36.75
25-pack	978-1-4240-2538-1	$183.75

Teacher's Set (1 of each title)	978-1-4240-2500-8	$108.00

Heinle Reading Library: Mini-Reader Collection, The   p. 16

First Day of School

5-Pack	978-1-4130-6449-0	$15.50
25-Pack	978-1-4130-2158-5	$82.75

Here is My Family

5-Pack	978-1-4130-6451-3	$15.50
25-Pack	978-1-4130-2159-2	$82.75

After School Work

5-Pack	978-1-4130-6447-6	$15.50
25-Pack	978-1-4130-2160-8	$82.75

Teenagers in the Morning

5-Pack	978-1-4130-6455-1	$15.50
25-Pack	978-1-4130-2161-5	$82.75

Saturday Afternoon

5-Pack	978-1-4130-6454-4	$15.50
25-Pack	978-1-4130-2162-2	$82.75

Friends at Lunch

5-Pack	978-1-4130-6450-6	$15.50
25-Pack	978-1-4130-2163-9	$82.75

Working at the Supermarket

5-Pack	978-1-4130-6456-8	$15.50
25-Pack	978-1-4130-2164-6	$82.75

Career Day at School

5-Pack	978-1-4130-6448-3	$15.50
25-Pack	978-1-4130-2165-3	$82.75

Holiday Scrapbook

5-Pack	978-1-4130-6452-0	$15.50
25-Pack	978-1-4130-2166-0	$82.75

Joel's Senior Yearbook

5-Pack	978-1-4130-6453-7	$15.50
25-Pack	978-1-4130-2167-7	$82.75

Classroom Library (5 of each title)	978-1-4130-2168-4	$147.50
Audio CD	978-1-4240-0774-5	$31.00

Heinle TOEFL® Test Assistant series, The   p. 104

Grammar Text (178 pp.)	978-0-8384-4252-4	$36.00
Listening Text/Tapes Pkg.	978-0-8384-4699-7	$50.00
Listening Text (182 pp.)	978-0-8384-4697-3	$36.00
Listening Tapes (3)	978-0-8384-4698-0	$110.50
Reading Text (144 pp.)	978-0-8384-4276-0	$36.00
Vocabulary Text (182 pp.)	978-0-8384-4280-7	$36.00
Test of Written English Text	978-0-8384-4281-4	$36.00

Heinle's BASIC Newbury House Dictionary of American English, 2/e   p. 36

Softcover (632 pp.)	978-0-8384-2656-2	$26.25
Hardcover (632 pp.)	978-0-7593-9808-5	$34.25
Softcover with CD-ROM	978-1-4130-7297-6	$28.25
Hardcover with CD-ROM	978-1-4130-7060-6	$36.25
Heinle Newbury House Dictionary CD-ROM	978-0-8384-2661-6	$15.00

Heinle's Newbury House Dictionary with Integrated Thesaurus, 4/e   p. 36

Softcover (1232 pp.) with CD-ROM	978-0-8384-2657-9	$29.75
Hardcover (1232 pp.)	978-0-8837-7017-7	$34.25
Hardcover with CD-ROM	978-1-4130-9227-1	$44.00
CD-ROM (dual platform)	978-0-8384-2661-6	$15.00
CD-ROM Site License *	978-1-4130-0215-7	*

*For pricing or to purchase, call Technology Services at 800-423-0563 or contact your Heinle representative.

Hot Topics   p. 69

Book 1

Text (192 pp.)	978-1-4130-0702-2	$28.00
Text/Audio CDs Pkg.	978-1-4130-6305-9	$33.75
Audio CDs (2)	978-1-4130-0703-9	$48.50
CNN® DVD	978-1-4130-1568-3	$51.50
CNN® Video	978-1-4130-1569-0	$51.50

Hot Topics (continued)

Book 2
Text (192 pp.)	978-1-4130-0706-0	$28.00
Text/Audio CDs Pkg.	978-1-4130-6310-3	$33.75
Audio CDs (2)	978-1-4130-0707-7	$48.50
CNN® DVD	978-1-4130-1570-6	$51.50
CNN® Video	978-1-4130-0705-3	$51.50

Book 3
Text (216 pp.)	978-1-4130-0710-7	$28.00
Text/Audio CDs Pkg.	978-1-4130-6338-7	$33.75
Audio CDs (3)	978-1-4130-0711-4	$64.25
CNN® DVD	978-1-4130-1571-3	$51.50
CNN® Video	978-1-4130-1572-0	$51.50

Books 1 – 3
Instructor's Manual	978-1-4130-0714-5	$20.25
Assessment CD-ROM with ExamView®	978-1-4130-0713-8	$128.00

I

Idea Exchange — p. 82
Book 1 (208 pp.)	978-0-0303-4481-7	$32.00
Book 2 (208 pp.)	978-0-0303-4488-6	$32.00

IELTS express — p. 104

Intermediate
Coursebook (128 pp)	978-1-4130-0955-2	$21.50
Workbook (96 pp)	978-1-4130-0959-0	$13.50
Audio CDs (2)	978-1-4130-0956-9	$48.50
Workbook Audio CD	978-1-4130-0974-3	$24.50
Workbook with Audio CDs	978-1-4130-0960-6	$15.00
Teacher's Book	978-1-4130-0958-3	$24.50
DVD	978-1-4130-0970-5	$33.50
Video (VHS)	978-1-4130-2869-0	$33.50

Upper-Intermediate
Coursebook (128 pp)	978-1-4130-0963-7	$21.50
Workbook (96 pp)	978-1-4130-0967-5	$13.50
Audio CDs (2)	978-1-4130-0964-4	$48.50
Workbook Audio CD	978-1-4130-0968-2	$24.50
Workbook with Audio CDs	978-1-4130-0971-2	$15.00
Teacher's Book	978-1-4130-0966-8	$24.50
DVD	978-1-4130-1397-9	$33.50
Video (VHS)	978-1-4130-2868-3	$33.50

IELTS Practice Tests — p. 104
Text with Answer Key (256 pp.)	978-1-4130-0975-0	$19.75
Text without Answer Key (208 pp.)	978-1-4130-0976-7	$18.50
Audio CDs (3)	978-1-4130-0977-4	$48.50
Assessment CD-ROM with ExamView®	978-1-4130-0979-8	$128.00

Implementing the Lexical Approach — p. 116
Text (224 pp.)	978-1-8993-9660-3	$37.25

Impressions — p. 68
Book 1 (176 pp.)	978-0-618-41026-2	$27.50
Book 2 (160 pp.)	978-0-618-41027-9	$27.50

In Context, 3/e* — p. 70
Text (320 pp.)	978-0-0303-4002-4	$29.75

In Context is Book 4 of the Steps to Academic Reading series.

In Detail — p. 48

Book 1
Text (160 pp.)	978-0-8384-4530-3	$21.50
Workbook	978-0-8384-4531-0	$15.00
Text/Workbook Pkg.	978-1-4130-9599-9	$32.75
Text/Workbook/Audio CDs Pkg.	978-1-4130-8415-3	$38.50
Audio CDs (2)	978-0-8384-4559-4	$53.50
Teacher's Edition	978-0-8384-4533-4	$27.00

Book 2
Text (160 pp.)	978-0-8384-4557-0	$21.50
Workbook	978-0-8384-4558-7	$15.00
Text/Workbook Pkg.	978-1-4130-8800-7	$32.75
Text/Workbook/Audio CDs Pkg.	978-1-4240-9809-5	$38.50
Audio CDs (2)	978-0-8384-4606-5	$53.50
Teacher's Edition	978-0-8384-4604-1	$27.00

Books 1 & 2
Assessment CD-ROM with ExamView®	978-0-8384-4612-6	$59.50
CNN® Video	978-0-8384-5172-4	$51.00

Independent Writing, 2/e — p. 82
Text (216 pp.)	978-0-8384-4206-7	$36.50

Inside Out/Outside In — p. 70
Text (360 pp.)	978-0-3959-8605-9	$29.00

Inside the News — p. 70
Text (109 pp.)	978-0-1550-6435-5	$31.25

Insights for Today, 3/e* — p. 66
Text (312 pp.)	978-1-4130-0809-8	$28.50
Text/Audio CD Pkg.	978-1-4130-8730-7	$34.50
Audio CD	978-0-7593-9819-1	$25.75
Instructor's Manual with Answer Key (Books 1 & 2)*	978-0-7593-9826-9	$17.00
CNN® Video (Books 1 & 2)*	978-0-7593-9825-2	$71.75
Assessment CD-ROM with ExamView® (Books 1 – 5)*	978-1-4130-0132-7	$134.75

Insights for Today, 3/e is Book 2 of the Reading for Today series.

Intercom 2000, 3/e — p. 48

Level 1
Text (186 pp.)	978-0-8384-1800-0	$22.25
Workbook	978-0-8384-1801-7	$15.50
Instructor's Edition	978-0-8384-1802-4	$40.75
Lab Audio Tapes (5)	978-0-8384-1803-1	$162.25

Level 2
Text (186 pp.)	978-0-8384-1807-9	$22.25
Workbook	978-0-8384-1808-6	$15.50
Instructor's Edition	978-0-8384-1809-3	$40.75
Lab Audio Tapes (4)	978-0-8384-1810-9	$130.25

Level 3
Text (186 pp.)	978-0-8384-1813-0	$22.25
Workbook	978-0-8384-1814-7	$15.50
Instructor's Edition	978-0-8384-1815-4	$40.75
Lab Audio Tapes (4)	978-0-8384-1816-1	$130.25

Level 4
Text (186 pp.)	978-0-8384-1819-2	$22.25
Workbook	978-0-8384-1820-8	$15.50
Instructor's Edition	978-0-8384-1821-5	$40.75
Lab Audio Tapes (5)	978-0-8384-1822-2	$162.25

Tests (Levels 1 & 2)	978-0-8384-2164-2	$73.00
Tests (Levels 3 & 4)	978-0-8384-2165-9	$73.00

Intermediate Listening Comprehension, 3/e* — p. 91
Text (208 pp.)	978-1-4130-0397-0	$33.25
Text/Audio CDs Pkg.	978-1-4130-6911-2	$44.75
Audio CDs (8)	978-1-4130-0596-7	$171.50
DVD	978-1-4130-0598-1	$121.75
Video (VHS)	978-1-4130-0597-4	$121.75

Intermediate Listening Comprehension is Book 1 of the Listening and Notetaking series.

Introductory Guide to the TOEIC® Test — p. 104
Text (208 pp.)	978-1-4130-0891-3	$28.50
Audio CDs (4)	978-1-4130-1058-9	$85.75
Answer Key	978-1-4130-1318-4	$12.25
Text/Answer Key/Audio CDs Pkg.	978-1-4130-1392-4	$42.00

Issues for Today, 3/e* — p. 66
Text (256 pp.)	978-1-4130-0815-9	$28.50
Text/Audio CD Pkg.	978-1-4130-8252-4	$34.50
Audio CD	978-0-7593-9821-4	$25.75
Instructor's Manual with Answer Key (Books 3 – 5)*	978-0-7593-9816-0	$17.00
CNN® Video (Books 3 – 5)*	978-0-7593-9815-3	$71.75
Assessment CD-ROM with ExamView® (Books 1 – 5)*	978-1-4130-0132-7	$134.75

Issues for Today, 3/e is Book 3 of the Reading for Today series.

K

Key Concepts: Listening, Note Taking, and Speaking Across the Disciplines — p. 88

Book 1
Text (143 pp.)	978-0-618-38240-8	$30.00
Text/Audio CD Pkg.	978-1-4282-0307-5	$36.25
Audio CD	978-0-618-38243-9	$21.50

Book 2
Text (160 pp.)	978-0-618-38241-5	$30.00
Text/Audio CD Pkg.	978-1-4282-0306-8	$36.25
Audio CD	978-0-618-38245-3	$21.50

Key Concepts: Reading and Writing Across the Disciplines — p. 76
Book 1 (256 pp.)	978-0-618-47461-5	$27.25
Book 2 (256 pp.)	978-0-618-47462-2	$27.25

Milestones (continued)

Intro (continued)
E-Book (Online)	978-1-4240-3187-0	$60.00
Workbook with Test Preparation	978-1-4240-3204-4	$15.00
Teacher's Edition	978-1-4240-0893-3	$120.00
Teacher's Resource CD-ROM with ExamView®	978-1-4240-3215-0	$180.00
MilestonesTracker Online Assessment and Remediation System	978-1-4240-2811-5	$200.00
Assessment Book	978-1-4240-3432-1	$120.00
Audio Program	978-1-4240-3353-9	$120.00
Independent Practice CD-ROM	978-1-4240-3229-7	$60.00

Level A
Student Edition	978-1-4240-0887-2	$60.00
E-Book (CD-ROM)	978-1-4240-4320-0	$60.00
E-Book (Online)	978-1-4240-3188-7	$60.00
Workbook with Test Preparation	978-1-4240-2744-6	$15.00
Teacher's Edition	978-1-4240-0890-2	$120.00
Teacher's Resource CD-ROM with ExamView®	978-1-4240-3220-4	$180.00
Assessment Book	978-1-4240-3433-8	$120.00
MilestonesTracker Online Assessment and Remediation System	978-1-4240-4984-4	$200.00
Graphic Reader Blackline Master Companion	978-1-4240-3426-0	$60.00
Audio Program	978-1-4240-3357-7	$120.00
Independent Practice CD-ROM	978-1-4240-3331-7	$60.00

Level B
Student Edition	978-1-4240-0888-9	$60.00
E-Book (CD-ROM)	978-1-4240-4348-4	$60.00
E-Book (Online)	978-1-4240-3189-4	$60.00
Workbook with Test Preparation	978-1-4240-3209-9	$15.00
Teacher's Edition	978-1-4240-0891-9	$120.00
Teacher's Resource CD-ROM with ExamView®	978-1-4240-3222-8	$180.00
Assessment Book	978-1-4240-3434-5	$120.00
MilestonesTracker Online Assessment and Remediation System	978-1-4240-4982-0	$200.00
Graphic Reader Blackline Master Companion	978-1-4240-3427-7	$60.00
Audio Program	978-1-4240-3358-4	$120.00
Independent Practice CD-ROM	978-1-4240-3336-2	$60.00

Level C
Student Edition	978-1-4240-0889-6	$60.00
E-Book (CD-ROM)	978-1-4240-4321-7	$60.00
E-Book (Online)	978-1-4240-3190-0	$60.00
Workbook with Test Preparation	978-1-4240-3212-9	$15.00
Teacher's Edition	978-1-4240-0892-6	$120.00
Teacher's Resource CD-ROM with ExamView®	978-1-4240-3224-2	$180.00
Assessment Book	978-1-4240-3435-2	$120.00
MilestonesTracker Online Assessment and Remediation System	978-1-4240-4983-7	$200.00
Graphic Reader Blackline Master Companion	978-1-4240-3428-4	$60.00
Audio Program	978-1-4240-3359-1	$120.00
Independent Practice CD-ROM	978-1-4240-3341-6	$60.00

Levels Intro – C
Online Professional Development Program	978-1-4240-2916-7	$500.00
The Heinle Phonics & Intervention Kit	978-1-4240-3219-8	$225.00
(66 Decodable Readers; Audio CD; Transparencies; Teacher Guide)		

Milestones Reading Library | p. 16

See *Heinle Reading Library, The*

MilestonesTracker Online Assessment and Remediation System | p. 12

See the *Milestones* series.

More Grammar Practice | p. 59
Workbook 1 (144 pp.)	978-0-8384-1893-2	$18.75
Workbook 2 (144 pp.)	978-0-8384-1902-1	$18.75
Workbook 3 (144 pp.)	978-0-8384-1947-2	$18.75
Answer Key (Books 1 – 3)	978-0-8384-1948-9	$12.50

Multicultural Workshop, The | p. 70
Book 1 (192 pp.)	978-0-8384-4834-2	$31.00
Book 2 (192 pp.)	978-0-8384-4835-9	$31.00
Book 3 (294 pp.)	978-0-8384-5020-8	$31.00
The Multicultural Workshop Box	978-0-8384-5021-5	$515.75

N

New Arrival English | p. 22
Text (128 pp.)	978-0-8384-2253-3	$31.25
Teacher's Manual	978-0-8384-2254-0	$48.25
Audio Tapes (2)	978-0-8384-2255-7	$62.50
Activity Masters	978-0-8384-2256-4	$55.75

New Business Matters, 2/e | p. 108
Coursebook (176 pp.)	978-0-7593-9856-6	$29.00
Workbook	978-0-7593-9859-7	$17.00
Teacher's Book	978-0-7593-9857-3	$34.75
Audio CDs (2)	978-0-7593-9853-5	$53.50
Assessment CD-ROM with ExamView®	978-0-7593-9852-8	$71.25
CNN® Video	978-0-7593-9855-9	$71.00

New Grammar in Action, The | p. 59

Basic
Text (256 pp.)	978-0-8384-1119-3	$19.75
Text/Audio CD Pkg.	978-1-4240-4727-7	$27.25
Audio CD	978-1-4240-4521-1	$29.25

Book 1
Text (208 pp.)	978-0-8384-6719-0	$19.75
Text/Audio CD Pkg.	978-1-4240-4724-6	$27.25
Audio CD	978-1-4240-4522-8	$29.25

Book 2
Text (197 pp.)	978-0-8384-6723-7	$19.75
Text/Audio CD Pkg.	978-1-4240-4725-3	$27.25
Audio CD	978-1-4240-4523-5	$29.25

Book 3
Text (203 pp.)	978-0-8384-6728-2	$19.75
Text/Audio CD Pkg.	978-1-4240-4769-7	$27.25
Audio CD	978-1-4240-4524-2	$29.25
Answer Key (Basic – 3)	978-0-8384-1736-2	$8.00
Assessment Booklet (Basic – 3)	978-0-8384-1123-0	$67.00
Correlation Guide (1 – 3)	978-0-8384-9931-3	$10.50

Non-Stop Discussion Workbook, The, 2/e | p. 96
Workbook (162 pp.)	978-0-8384-2938-9	$27.75

Noteworthy, 3/e* | p. 91
Text (288 pp.)	978-1-4130-0398-7	$33.25
Text/Audio CDs Pkg.	978-1-4130-7502-1	$44.75
Audio CDs (5)	978-1-4130-0593-6	$119.00
DVD	978-1-4130-0600-1	$121.75
Video (VHS)	978-1-4130-0599-8	$121.75

*Noteworthy is Book 2 of the *Listening and Notetaking* series.

Now Hear This!, 3/e | p. 86
Text (176 pp.)	978-1-4240-0379-2	$28.25
Text/Audio CDs Pkg.	978-1-4240-4715-4	$42.00
Audio CDs	978-1-4240-1614-3	$102.00

O

On Speaking Terms | p. 87

Book 1
Text	978-0-618-39600-9	$28.00
Text/Audio CD Pkg.	978-1-4240-4188-6	$33.00

Book 2
Text	978-0-618-39602-3	$28.00
Text/Audio CD Pkg.	978-1-4240-4193-0	$33.00

One Step at a Time | p. 82
Book 1 (200 pp.)	978-0-8384-5030-7	$39.00
Book 2 (200 pp.)	978-0-8384-5031-4	$39.00

One to One | p. 116
Text (160 pp.)	978-0-9067-1761-5	$35.50

Online Tutorial for the TOEFL® iBT | p. 103
Complete Edition (includes Listening, Speaking, Reading, Writing, and Practice Tests)	978-1-4240-6860-9	$36.75
Listening/Speaking with Practice Tests	978-1-4240-6862-3	$21.00
Reading/Writing with Practice Tests	978-1-4240-6861-6	$21.00
Complete Edition: Online Tutorial/Complete Guide to the TOEFL iBT Text/CD-ROM Pkg.	978-1-111-02477-2	$54.00
Complete Edition: Online Tutorial/Complete Guide to the TOEFL iBT Text/CD-ROM/Audio Pkg.	978-1-111-02476-5	$75.00

Out of the Ordinary* | p. 70
Text (238 pp.)	978-0-1550-6033-3	$29.75

*Out of the Ordinary is Book 2 of the *Steps to Academic Reading* series.

P

Past, Present & Future, 4/e | p. 82
Text (375 pp.)	978-0-8384-5282-0	$38.00

For customer support, call **(877) NEED-ESL** or visit **elt.heinle.com** ■ For pricing, ISBNs, and ordering information see pp. 122 – 144

Power of Context, The — p. 117
Text (288 pp.) ....978-1-4130-0131-0 — $43.00

Practical English, 2/e — p. 48
Level 1
Text (260 pp.) ....978-0-1557-0912-6 — $21.50
Audio Tape ....978-0-1557-0919-5 — $25.75
Level 2
Text (260 pp.) ....978-0-1557-0920-1 — $21.50
Audio Tape ....978-0-1557-0927-0 — $25.75
Level 3
Text (260 pp.) ....978-0-1557-0928-7 — $21.50
Audio Tape ....978-0-1557-0935-5 — $25.75

Practical Techniques — p. 116
Text (138 pp.) ....978-0-9067-1755-4 — $38.00

Practice: Grammar — p. 60
Text (176 pp.) ....978-0-8384-2192-5 — $18.50
Practice: Grammar and Vocabulary Answer Key ....978-0-8384-2572-5 — $3.00

Practice: Vocabulary — p. 100
Text (176 pp.) ....978-0-8384-2206-9 — $18.50
Practice: Grammar and Vocabulary Answer Key ....978-0-8384-2572-5 — $3.00

Presenting in English — p. 108
Text (128 pp.) ....978-1-8993-9630-6 — $27.50
Audio Tape (American English version) ....978-1-8993-9675-7 — $31.25

Problem/Solution — p. 60
Text (240 pp.) ....978-0-8384-4125-1 — $42.00

Professional English series — p. 106
See individual titles: *English for Business, English for Health Sciences, English for Humanities, English for Professional Success,* and *English for Science and Engineering*

Pronouncing American English, 2/e — p. 96
Text (338 pp.) ....978-0-8384-6332-1 — $40.75
Text/Audio CDs Pkg. ....978-1-4240-9055-6 — $59.25
Audio CDs (10) ....978-1-4240-1822-2 — $193.00
Answer Key/Instructor's Manual ....978-0-8384-6334-5 — $13.50

Pursuing Professional Development — p. 114
Text (278 pp.) ....978-0-8384-1130-8 — $30.00

R

Raising Silent Voices — p. 119
Text (224 pp.) ....978-0-8384-2709-5 — $42.00

Read to Succeed — p. 70
Book 1
Text (240 pp.) ....978-0-618-32470-5 — $29.25
Text/Audio CD Pkg. ....978-1-4282-0291-7 — $35.00
Audio CD ....978-0-618-35295-1 — $21.50
Book 2
Text (256 pp.) ....978-0-618-32471-2 — $29.25
Text/Audio CD Pkg. ....978-1-4240-9019-8 — $35.00
Audio CD ....978-0-618-35296-8 — $21.50

Read, Write, Edit — p. 78
Text (208 pp.) ....978-0-618-14495-2 — $35.50

Reading Advantage, 2/e — p. 70
Level 1
Text (96 pp.) ....978-1-4130-0114-3 — $22.25
Text/Audio CD Pkg. ....978-1-4130-8257-9 — $28.25
Audio CD ....978-1-4130-0126-6 — $27.00
Teacher's Guide ....978-1-4130-0118-1 — $13.50
Level 2
Text (96 pp.) ....978-1-4130-0115-0 — $22.25
Text/Audio CD Pkg. ....978-1-4130-8259-3 — $28.25
Audio CD ....978-1-4130-0127-3 — $27.00
Teacher's Guide ....978-1-4130-0119-8 — $13.50
Level 3
Text (96 pp.) ....978-1-4130-0116-7 — $22.25
Text/Audio CD Pkg. ....978-1-4130-8261-6 — $28.25
Audio CD ....978-1-4130-0128-0 — $27.00
Teacher's Guide ....978-1-4130-0120-4 — $13.50
Level 4
Text (96 pp.) ....978-1-4130-0117-4 — $22.25
Text/Audio CDs Pkg. ....978-1-4240-8809-6 — $28.25
Audio CDs (2) ....978-1-4130-0129-7 — $27.00
Teacher's Guide ....978-1-4130-0121-1 — $13.50

Reading & Vocabulary Development series — p. 65
See individual titles: *Facts & Figures, Thoughts & Notions, Cause & Effect,* and *Concepts & Comments*

Reading & Writing Challenge — p. 38
See the *Stand Out* series.

Reading Explorer — p. 62
Level 1
Student Book ....978-1-4240-4362-0 — $28.25
Student Book/Student CD-ROM pkg. ....978-1-4240-4761-1 — $32.00
Teacher's Guide ....978-1-4240-4551-8 — $23.00
DVD ....978-1-4240-5125-0 — $23.75
Audio CD ....978-1-4240-4554-9 — $39.75
Student CD-ROM ....978-1-4240-5006-2 — $22.00
CD-ROM Site License* ....978-1-4240-6863-0 — *
Assessment CD-ROM with Exam*View*® ....978-1-4240-4569-3 — $119.00
Level 2
Student Book ....978-1-4240-4364-4 — $28.25
Student Book/Student CD-ROM pkg. ....978-1-4240-4762-8 — $32.00
Teacher's Guide ....978-1-4240-4550-1 — $23.00
DVD ....978-1-4240-5126-7 — $23.75
Audio CD ....978-1-4240-4553-2 — $39.75
Student CD-ROM ....978-1-4240-5007-9 — $22.00
CD-ROM Site License* ....978-1-4240-6864-7 — *
Assessment CD-ROM with Exam*View*® ....978-1-4240-4568-6 — $119.00
Level 3
Student Book ....978-1-4240-4370-5 — $28.25
Student Book/Student CD-ROM pkg. ....978-1-4240-4764-2 — $32.00
Teacher's Guide ....978-1-4240-4549-5 — $23.00
DVD ....978-1-4240-5127-4 — $23.75
Audio CD ....978-1-4240-4556-3 — $39.75
Student CD-ROM ....978-1-4240-5008-6 — $22.00
CD-ROM Site License* ....978-1-4240-6865-4 — *
Assessment CD-ROM with Exam*View*® ....978-1-4240-4567-9 — $119.00
Level 4
Student Book ....978-1-4240-4373-6 — $28.25
Student Book/Student CD-ROM pkg. ....978-1-4240-4763-5 — $32.00
Teacher's Guide ....978-1-4240-4555-6 — $23.00
DVD ....978-1-4240-5128-1 — $23.75
Audio CD ....978-1-4240-4552-5 — $39.75
Student CD-ROM ....978-1-4240-5009-3 — $22.00
CD-ROM Site License* ....978-1-4240-6866-1 — *
Assessment CD-ROM with Exam*View*® ....978-1-4240-4566-2 — $119.00

*For pricing or to purchase, call Technology Services at 800-423-0563 or contact your Heinle representative.

Reading for Today series — p. 66
See individual titles: *Themes for Today, Insights for Today, Issues for Today, Concepts for Today,* and *Topics for Today*

Reading Matters, 2/e — p. 69
Book 1 (272 pp.) ....978-0-618-47512-4 — $26.50
Book 2 (274 pp.) ....978-0-618-47513-1 — $26.50
Book 3 (304 pp.) ....978-0-618-47514-8 — $26.50
Book 4 (304 pp.) ....978-0-618-47515-5 — $26.50

Reading the News — p. 69
Text (112 pp.) ....978-1-4240-0381-5 — $27.00
Text/Audio CDs Pkg. ....978-1-4240-9432-5 — $33.00
Audio CDs (2) ....978-1-4240-0380-8 — $46.25
Instructor's Manual ....978-1-4240-0382-2 — $25.75

Refining Composition Skills, 5/e — p. 81
Text (448 pp.) ....978-0-8384-0223-8 — $38.75
Instructor's Manual ....978-0-8384-0224-5 — $15.75
CNN® Video ....978-0-8384-0225-2 — $62.00

Reflections, 2/e — p. 70
Text (224 pp.) ....978-0-8384-4846-5 — $29.25

Rethinking America — p. 68
Level 1
Text (240 pp.) ....978-0-8384-4750-5 — $27.75
CNN® Video ....978-0-8384-0811-7 — $62.00
Level 2
Text (254 pp.) ....978-0-8384-4741-3 — $27.75
CNN® Video ....978-0-8384-0820-9 — $62.00
Level 3
Text (256 pp.) ....978-0-8384-4732-1 — $27.75
CNN® Video ....978-0-8384-0829-2 — $62.00

Instructor's Manual (Books 1 – 3) ....978-0-8384-0031-9 — $21.00

Sam and Pat
p. 48

Book 1

Text (128 pp.)	978-1-4130-1964-3	$17.25
Audio CD	978-1-4130-1966-7	$24.50

Book 2

Text (160 pp.)	978-1-4130-1965-0	$17.25
Audio CD	978-1-4130-1967-4	$24.50

Say It Naturally, 2/e
p. 96

Text/Audio Tape Pkg. 1	978-0-0302-2197-2	$36.75
Text/Audio Tape Pkg. 2	978-0-0302-2198-9	$36.75

Second Language Teaching & Learning
p. 118

Text (336 pp.)	978-0-8384-0838-4	$35.00

Shooting Stars
p. 22

Level 1

Student Book (128 pp.)	978-1-4240-1826-0	$28.25
Teacher's Book (128 pp.)	978-1-4240-1883-3	$22.50
Classroom Audio CDs (2)	978-1-4240-1885-7	$41.00
Student Audio CDs (2)	978-1-4240-1972-4	$41.00

Level 2

Student Book (128 pp.)	978-1-4240-1827-7	$28.25
Teacher's Book (128 pp.)	978-1-4240-1896-3	$22.50
Classroom Audio CDs (2)	978-1-4240-1886-4	$41.00
Student Audio CDs (2)	978-1-4240-1980-9	$41.00

Level 3

Student Book (128 pp.)	978-1-4240-1828-4	$28.25
Teacher's Book (128 pp.)	978-1-4240-1897-0	$22.50
Classroom Audio CDs (2)	978-1-4240-1887-1	$41.00
Student Audio CDs (2)	978-1-4240-1981-6	$41.00

Level 4

Student Book (128 pp.)	978-1-4240-1829-1	$28.25
Teacher's Book (128 pp.)	978-1-4240-1898-7	$22.50
Classroom Audio CDs (2)	978-1-4240-1888-8	$41.00
Student Audio CDs (2)	978-1-4240-1982-3	$41.00

Level 5

Student Book (128 pp.)	978-1-4240-1830-7	$28.25
Teacher's Book (128 pp.)	978-1-4240-1899-4	$22.50
Classroom Audio CDs (2)	978-1-4240-1889-5	$41.00
Student Audio CDs (2)	978-1-4240-1983-0	$41.00

Level 6

Student Book (128 pp.)	978-1-4240-1831-4	$28.25
Teacher's Book (128 pp.)	978-1-4240-1900-7	$22.50
Classroom Audio CDs (2)	978-1-4240-1890-1	$41.00
Student Audio CDs (2)	978-1-4240-1984-7	$41.00

Assessment CD-ROM with Exam*View*®	978-1-4240-4564-8	$120.00

Skillbuilder
p. 22

See *Voices in Literature*.

Snapshot Online Assessment of Basic Vocabulary*
p. 113

Online Assessment - 1 year access	978-1-111-00004-2	$45.00

*Related product: See *Teaching Basic and Advanced Vocabulary*.

So to Speak
p. 94

Book 1

Text (144 pp.)	978-0-3958-7383-0	$27.00
Text/Audio CD Pkg.	978-1-4282-0292-4	$33.75
Audio CD	978-0-618-20885-2	$21.50

Book 2

Text (146 pp.)	978-0-3958-7406-6	$27.00
Text/Audio CD Pkg.	978-1-4282-0293-1	$33.75
Audio CD	978-0-618-20887-6	$21.50

Sound Bites
p. 96

Text (256 pp.)	978-0-618-25972-4	$28.50
Text/Audio CD Pkg.	978-1-4282-0284-9	$34.50
Audio CD	978-0-618-25994-6	$21.50

Sounds Great
p. 96

Book 1

Text (203 pp.)	978-0-8384-3964-7	$30.75
Text/Audio Tapes Pkg.	978-0-8384-0544-4	$42.25
Audio Tapes (5)	978-0-8384-4211-1	$187.50
Instructor's Manual	978-0-8384-4272-2	$15.75

Book 2

Text (192 pp.)	978-0-8384-4273-9	$30.75
Text/Audio Tapes Pkg.	978-0-8384-7458-7	$42.25
Audio Tapes (5)	978-0-8384-4274-6	$187.50

Instructor's Manual	978-0-8384-4275-3	$15.75

Sourcework
p. 82

Text (240 pp.)	978-0-618-41287-7	$33.75

Speak Up, 2/e
p. 96

Book 1

Text (112 pp.)	978-0-8384-4996-7	$34.50
Text/Audio Tapes Pkg.	978-0-8384-9682-4	$40.50
Audio Tapes (2)	978-0-8384-4997-4	$66.50

Book 2

Text (124 pp.)	978-0-8384-4998-1	$34.50
Text/Audio Tapes Pkg.	978-0-8384-9683-1	$40.50
Audio Tapes (2)	978-0-8384-4999-8	$66.50

Tapescript/Answer Key (Books 1 & 2)	978-0-8384-5018-5	$16.25

Stand Out, 2/e
p. 38

Basic

Text (208 pp.)*	978-1-4240-0254-2	$18.50
Grammar Challenge	978-1-4240-1600-6	$12.50
Reading & Writing Challenge	978-1-4130-0720-6	$12.50
Text/Audio CDs Pkg.	978-1-4240-9310-6	$23.50
Text/DVD Pkg.	978-1-4354-3473-8	$19.50
Text/Grammar Café Pkg.	978-1-4240-2051-5	$23.50
Audio CDs (2)	978-1-4240-0964-0	$41.00
Lifeskills Video on DVD	978-1-4240-9569-8	$39.75
Lesson Planner (contains Activity Bank CD-ROM & Audio CD)	978-1-4240-1927-4	$32.75
Online Lesson Planner	978-1-111-03314-9	$40.00
Assessment CD-ROM with Exam*View*®	978-1-4240-0999-2	$113.25
Classroom Presentation Tool	978-1-4240-1853-6	$113.50
Technology Tool Kit	978-1-4240-6558-5	$150.00

Level 1

Text (208 pp.)*	978-1-4240-0256-6	$18.50
Grammar Challenge	978-1-4240-0987-9	$12.50
Reading & Writing Challenge	978-1-4130-0721-3	$12.50
Text/Audio CD Pkg.	978-1-4240-9313-7	$23.50
Text/DVD Pkg.	978-1-4354-3474-5	$19.50
Text/Grammar Café Pkg.	978-1-4240-2052-2	$23.50
Audio CDs (2)	978-1-4240-0966-4	$41.00
Lifeskills Video on DVD	978-1-4240-9567-4	$39.75
Lesson Planner (contains Activity Bank CD-ROM & Audio CD)	978-1-4240-1929-8	$32.75
Online Lesson Planner	978-1-111-03313-2	$40.00
Assessment CD-ROM with Exam*View*®	978-1-4240-0974-9	$113.25
Classroom Presentation Tool	978-1-4240-1854-3	$113.50
Technology Tool Kit	978-1-4240-6559-2	$150.00

Level 2

Text (208 pp.)*	978-1-4240-0258-0	$18.50
Grammar Challenge	978-1-4240-0991-6	$12.50
Reading & Writing Challenge	978-1-4130-0722-0	$12.50
Text/Audio CD Pkg.	978-1-4240-9302-1	$23.50
Text/DVD Pkg.	978-1-4354-3475-2	$19.50
Text/Grammar Café Pkg.	978-1-4240-2053-9	$23.50
Audio CDs (2)	978-1-4240-0968-8	$41.00
Lifeskills Video on DVD	978-1-4240-9568-1	$39.75
Lesson Planner (contains Activity Bank CD-ROM & Audio CD)	978-1-4240-1934-2	$32.75
Online Lesson Planner	978-1-111-03312-5	$40.00
Assessment CD-ROM with Exam*View*®	978-1-4240-0989-3	$113.25
Classroom Presentation Tool	978-1-4240-1855-0	$113.50
Technology Tool Kit	978-1-4240-6560-8	$150.00

Level 3

Text (208 pp.)*	978-1-4240-0260-3	$18.50
Grammar Challenge	978-1-4240-0993-0	$12.50
Reading & Writing Challenge	978-1-4130-0723-7	$12.50
Text/Audio CD Pkg.	978-1-4240-9304-5	$23.50
Text/DVD Pkg.	978-1-4354-3476-9	$19.50
Text/Grammar Café Pkg.	978-1-4240-2054-6	$23.50
Audio CD	978-1-4240-0970-1	$41.00
Lifeskills Video on DVD	978-1-4240-9570-4	$39.75
Lesson Planner (contains Activity Bank CD-ROM & Audio CD)	978-1-4240-1935-9	$32.75
Online Lesson Planner	978-1-111-03311-8	$40.00
Assessment CD-ROM with Exam*View*®	978-1-4240-0994-7	$113.25
Classroom Presentation Tool	978-1-4240-0992-3	$113.50
Technology Tool Kit	978-1-4240-6561-5	$150.00

Level 4

Text (208 pp.)*	978-1-4240-0262-7	$18.50
Grammar Challenge	978-1-4240-0996-1	$12.50

Reading & Writing Challenge	978-1-4130-0724-4	$12.50
Text/Audio CD Pkg.	978-1-4240-9306-9	$23.50
Text/DVD Pkg.	978-1-4354-3477-6	$19.50
Text/Grammar Café Pkg.	978-1-4240-2055-3	$23.50
Audio CD	978-1-4240-0972-5	$41.00
Lifeskills Video on DVD	978-1-4240-9571-1	$39.75
Lesson Planner (contains Activity Bank CD-ROM & Audio CD)	978-1-4240-1936-6	$32.75
Online Lesson Planner	978-1-111-03310-1	$40.00
Assessment CD-ROM with ExamView®	978-1-4240-0997-8	$113.25
Classroom Presentation Tool	978-1-4240-1856-7	$113.50
Technology Tool Kit	978-1-4240-6562-2	$150.00

Level 5

Text (208 pp.)*	978-1-4240-1781-2	$18.50
Grammar Challenge	978-1-4240-1784-3	$12.50
Text/Audio CD Pkg.	978-1-4240-9308-3	$23.50
Text/DVD Pkg.	978-1-4354-3478-3	$19.50
Audio CD	978-1-4240-1788-1	$41.00
Lifeskills Video on DVD	978-1-4240-9572-8	$39.75
Lesson Planner (contains Activity Bank CD-ROM & Audio CD)	978-1-4240-1937-3	$32.75
Online Lesson Planner	978-1-111-03309-5	$40.00
Assessment CD-ROM with ExamView®	978-1-4240-1783-6	$113.25
Classroom Presentation Tool	978-1-4240-1789-8	$113.50
Technology Tool Kit	978-1-4240-6563-9	$150.00

*Split Editions available. Ask your Heinle representative for details.

Starting Lines — p. 82

Text (144 pp.)	978-0-8384-5258-5	$32.50
Answer Key	978-0-8384-5259-2	$13.50

Step-by-Step Writing — p. 21

Book 1
Text (168 pp.)	978-1-4240-0400-3	$29.50
Teacher's Guide	978-1-4240-0499-7	$22.50
Assessment CD-ROM with ExamView®	978-1-4240-0513-0	$113.25

Book 2
Text (192 pp.)	978-1-4240-0401-0	$29.50
Teacher's Guide	978-1-4240-0500-0	$22.50
Assessment CD-ROM with ExamView®	978-1-4240-0567-3	$113.25

Book 3
Text (168 pp.)	978-1-4240-0402-7	$29.50
Teacher's Guide	978-1-4240-0505-5	$22.50
Assessment CD-ROM with ExamView®	978-1-4240-0526-0	$113.25

Step Up — p. 89

Book 1
Text (176 pp.)	978-0-618-35305-7	$29.50
Text/Audio CD Pkg.	978-1-4282-0305-1	$35.50
Audio CD	978-0-618-35307-1	$21.50

Book 2
Text (208 pp.)	978-0-6183-5306-4	$29.50
Text/Audio CD Pkg.	978-1-4240-8950-5	$35.50
Audio CD	978-0-6183-5308-8	$21.50
Instructor Audio CD (Books 1 & 2)	978-0-618-35314-9	$21.50

Steps and Plateaus, 2/e* — p. 70

Text (280 pp.)	978-0-0303-3987-5	$29.75

*Steps and Plateaus is Book 1 of the Steps to Academic Reading series.

Steps to Academic Reading series — p. 70

See individual titles: Steps and Plateaus, 2/e, Out of the Ordinary, Across the Board, In Context, 3/e, and Between the Lines, 3/e

Stories Worth Reading — p. 69

Book 1
Text (144 pp.)	978-1-4130-0853-1	$28.25
Text/Audio CD Pkg.	978-1-4130-6363-9	$34.25
Audio CD	978-1-4130-0854-8	$25.75

Book 2
Text (142 pp.)	978-1-4130-0856-2	$28.25
Text/Audio CD Pkg.	978-1-4130-6364-6	$34.25
Audio CD	978-1-4130-0857-9	$25.75

Books 1 & 2
Instructor's Manual	978-1-4130-0859-3	$33.50
CNN® DVD	978-1-4130-1826-4	$49.00
CNN® Video	978-1-4130-1515-7	$49.00
Assessment CD-ROM with ExamView®	978-1-4130-1827-1	$128.00

Strategies for Test-Taking Success: Math — p. 21
Text (224 pp.)	978-1-4130-0925-5	$19.50

Strategies for Test-Taking Success: Reading — p. 21
Text (224 pp.)	978-1-4130-0924-8	$19.50

Strategies for Test-Taking Success: Writing — p. 21
Text (224 pp.)	978-1-4130-0926-2	$19.50

Strategies for Test-Taking Success: Writing, Reading, Math — p. 21
Assessment CD-ROM with ExamView®: Math, Reading, Writing	978-1-4130-2863-8	$59.50

T

Talk It! series — p. 89

See individual titles: Talk It Up!, Talk It Through!, and Talk It Over!

Talk It Over!, 2/e — p. 89
Text (176 pp.)	978-0-618-14401-3	$26.00
Text/Audio CD Pkg.	978-1-4240-8895-9	$33.50
Audio CD	978-0-618-14404-4	$20.00

Talk It Through! — p. 89
Text (176 pp.)	978-0-3959-6072-1	$26.00
Text/Audio CD Pkg.	978-1-4240-8892-8	$33.50
Audio CD	978-0-618-21979-7	$20.00

Talk It Up!, 2/e — p. 89
Text (192 pp.)	978-0-618-14019-0	$26.00
Text/Audio CD Pkg.	978-1-4240-8893-5	$33.50
Audio CD	978-0-618-14397-9	$20.00

Tapestry Listening & Speaking — p. 90

Book 1
Text (288 pp.)	978-0-8384-0009-8	$32.75
Text/Audio CD Pkg.	978-1-4240-9316-8	$38.50
Audio CDs (2)	978-1-4240-1814-7	$43.00

Book 2
Text (256 pp.)	978-0-8384-0016-6	$32.75
Text/Audio CDs Pkg.	978-1-4240-9319-9	$38.50
Audio CDs (2)	978-1-4240-1815-4	$43.00

Book 3
Text (256 pp.)	978-0-8384-0023-4	$32.75
Text/Audio CDs Pkg.	978-1-4240-9318-2	$38.50
Audio CDs (2)	978-1-4240-1813-0	$43.00

Book 4
Text (288 pp.)	978-0-8384-0029-6	$32.75
Text/Audio CDs Pkg.	978-1-4240-9317-5	$38.50
Audio CDs (2)	978-1-4240-1816-1	$43.00
CNN® Video (Books 1 & 2)	978-0-8384-0007-4	$56.75
CNN® Video (Books 3 & 4)	978-0-8384-0026-5	$56.75
Instructor's Manual (Books 1 & 2)	978-0-8384-0008-1	$26.75
Instructor's Manual (Books 3 & 4)	978-0-8384-0027-2	$26.75

Tapestry of Language Learning, The — p. 119
Text (256 pp.)	978-0-8384-2359-2	$43.00

Tapestry Reading — p. 68
Book 1 (208 pp.)	978-0-8384-0568-0	$32.75
Book 2 (224 pp.)	978-0-8384-0056-2	$32.75
Book 3 (256 pp.)	978-0-8384-0050-0	$32.75
Book 4 (240 pp.)	978-0-8384-0060-9	$32.75
CNN® Video (Books 1 & 2)	978-0-8384-0051-7	$56.75
CNN® Video (Books 3 & 4)	978-0-8384-0057-9	$56.75
Instructor's Manual (Books 1 & 2)	978-0-8384-0052-4	$26.75
Instructor's Manual (Books 3 & 4)	978-0-8384-0059-3	$26.75

Tapestry Writing — p. 80
Book 1 (224 pp.)	978-0-8384-0033-3	$32.75
Book 2 (256 pp.)	978-0-8384-0038-8	$32.75
Book 3 (208 pp.)	978-0-8384-0042-5	$32.75
Book 4 (240 pp.)	978-0-8384-0045-6	$32.75
CNN® Video (Books 1 & 2)	978-0-8384-0030-2	$56.75
CNN® Video (Books 3 & 4)	978-0-8384-0043-2	$56.75
Instructor's Manual (Books 1 & 2)	978-0-8384-0032-6	$26.75
Instructor's Manual (Books 3 & 4)	978-0-8384-0044-9	$26.75

Targeting Pronunciation, 2/e — p. 96
Text (288 pp.)	978-0-618-44418-2	$37.50
Text/Audio CD Pkg.	978-1-4282-0303-7	$49.25
Audio CDs (5)	978-0-618-44421-2	$130.25

TeacherSource - The Ultimate Collection   p. 114
Includes all TeacherSource books 978-0-8384-4370-5 $302.75

Teachers' Grammar, A   p. 116
Text (166 pp.) 978-0-9067-1748-6 $38.00

Teaching Basic and Advanced Vocabulary   p. 112
Text 978-1-4240-6713-8 $28.00
Related product: See *Snapshot Online Assessment of Basic Vocabulary.*

Teaching and Learning Vocabulary   p. 119
Text (275 pp.) 978-0-8384-2863-4 $43.00

Teaching Bilingual Children   p. 115
Text (144 pp.) 978-0-8384-6098-6 $30.00

Teaching Collocation   p. 116
Text (246 pp.) 978-1-8993-9611-5 $38.00

Teaching Culture   p. 115
Text (192 pp.) 978-0-8384-6676-6 $30.00

Teaching English as a Second or Foreign Language, 3/e   p. 117
Text (592 pp.) 978-0-8384-1992-2 $56.00

Teaching ESL K-12   p. 114
Text (240 pp.) 978-0-8384-7901-8 $30.00

Teaching Language: From Grammar to Grammaring   p. 115
Text (180 pp.) 978-0-8384-6675-9 $30.00

Teaching Second-Language Writing   p. 114
Text (112 pp.) 978-0-8384-7892-9 $30.00

Teaching Vocabulary: Strategies and Techniques   p. 119
Text 978-1-4240-0565-9 $41.00

Tense Situations, 2/e   p. 60
Text (282 pp.) 978-0-0302-2517-8 $40.50

Themes for Today, 2/e*   p. 66
Text (240 pp.) 978-1-4130-0810-4 $28.50
Text/Audio CD Pkg. 978-1-4130-8731-4 $34.50
Audio CD 978-0-7593-9823-8 $25.75
Instructor's Manual with Answer Key (Books 1 & 2)* ..978-0-7593-9826-9 $17.00
Assessment CD-ROM with ExamView® (Books 1 - 5)* 978-1-4130-0132-7 $134.75
CNN® Video (Books 1 & 2)* 978-0-7593-9825-2 $71.75
Themes for Today, 2/e is Book 1 of the Reading for Today series.

Think About Editing   p. 82
Text (352 pp.) 978-0-8384-3976-0 $38.50

Thoughts & Notions, 2/e*   p. 65
Text (214 pp.) 978-1-4130-0419-9 $28.50
Text/Audio CD Pkg. 978-1-4130-6391-2 $34.50
Audio CD 978-1-4130-1334-4 $25.75
Answer Key and Video Transcripts (Books 1 & 2)* 978-1-4130-0609-4 $6.75
Assessment CD-ROM with ExamView® (Books 1 & 2)* 978-1-4130-0613-1 $119.00
CNN® DVD (Books 1 & 2)* 978-1-4130-1587-4 $53.75
CNN® Video (Books 1 & 2)* 978-1-4130-0610-0 $53.75
Thoughts & Notions, 2/e is Book 2 of the Reading & Vocabulary Development series.

Tools for Writing   p. 82
Text (240 pp.) 978-0-8384-5294-3 $38.50

Top 10   p. 78
Text (256 pp.) 978-0-618-48105-7 $34.75

Top 20, 2/e   p. 78
Text (320 pp.) 978-0-618-78967-2 $34.75

Topics for Today, 3/e*   p. 66
Text (320 pp.) 978-1-4130-0811-1 $28.50
Text/Audio CDs Pkg. 978-1-4130-8255-5 $34.50
Audio CDs (2) 978-0-7593-9827-6 $47.75
Instructor's Manual with Answer Key (Books 3 - 5)*....978-0-7593-9816-0 $17.00
Assessment CD-ROM with ExamView® (Books 1 - 5)* 978-1-4130-0132-7 $134.75
CNN® Video (Books 3 - 5)* 978-0-7593-9815-3 $71.75
Topics for Today, 3/e is Book 5 of the Reading for Today series.

20th Century American Short Stories   p. 70
Volume 1 (160 pp.) 978-0-8384-4850-2 $32.00
Volume 2 (160 pp.) 978-0-8384-4851-9 $32.00
Anthology (288 pp.) 978-0-8384-6146-4 $38.75

Two-Word Verbs in English   p. 60
Text (198 pp.) 978-0-1559-2506-9 $21.00

U.S. Citizen, Yes, 3/e   p. 47
Text (144 pp.) 978-1-4240-9599-5 $18.75
Audio CD 978-1-4240-3139-9 $20.50
Text/Audio Pkg. 978-1-4240-4752-9 $23.00

Understanding Language Teaching   p. 115
Text (160 pp.) 978-0-8384-6690-2 $31.50

Up Close   p. 48
Book 1
Text (144 pp.) with Student Audio CD ...978-0-8384-3136-8 $22.00
Workbook 978-0-8384-0541-3 $15.50
Classroom Audio CDs (2) 978-0-8384-2452-0 $59.00
Teacher's Edition 978-0-8384-0550-5 $29.25
Book 2
Text (144 pp.) with Student Audio CD ...978-0-8384-3258-7 $22.00
Workbook 978-0-8384-3274-7 $15.50
Classroom Audio CDs (2) 978-0-8384-2453-7 $59.00
Teacher's Edition 978-0-8384-3867-1 $29.25
Book 3
Text (144 pp.) with Student Audio CD ...978-0-8384-3285-3 $22.00
Workbook 978-0-8384-3878-7 $15.50
Classroom Audio CDs (2) 978-0-8384-2454-4 $59.00
Teacher's Edition 978-0-8384-3257-0 $29.25
Book 4
Text (144 pp.) with Student Audio CD ...978-0-8384-3393-5 $22.00
Workbook 978-0-8384-3827-5 $15.50
Classroom Audio CDs (2) 978-0-8384-2455-1 $59.00
Teacher's Edition 978-0-8384-3289-1 $29.25

Situation Cards (Books 1 - 4) 978-0-8384-0613-7 $86.75
CNN® Video (Books 3 & 4) 978-0-8384-3416-1 $59.75
Teacher's Resource CD Pkg. with ExamView®
   (Books 1 - 4) 978-1-4130-1504-1 $155.75

Visions: Literacy, Language, Literature, Content   p. 14
Basic
Student Book (210 pp.) 978-0-8384-0382-2 $53.50
Activity Book 978-0-8384-0385-3 $17.75
Teacher Resource Book 978-0-8384-0386-0 $77.50
Teacher Resource CD-ROM 978-1-4130-0643-8 $140.75
Audio CDs (3) 978-0-8384-0389-1 $95.25
Student CD-ROM 978-0-8384-0393-8 $77.50
Student CD-ROM Lab Pack (5) 978-1-4130-8009-4 $303.75
Assessment CD-ROM with ExamView® ...978-0-8384-5752-8 $142.75
Assessment Program 978-0-8384-5753-5 $142.75
Transparencies 978-0-8384-5885-3 $95.25
Intro
Student Book (400 pp.) 978-1-4130-1486-0 $62.00
E-Book (CD-ROM) 978-1-4240-4511-2 $66.25
E-Book (Online) 978-1-4240-4512-9 $66.25
Activity Book 978-1-4130-1487-7 $17.75
Grammar Practice 978-1-4240-1702-7 $20.00
Grammar Practice Answer Key 978-1-4240-1799-7 $3.50
Text/Grammar Café Pkg. 978-1-4240-2074-4 $67.50
Student CD-ROM 978-1-4130-1492-1 $70.50
Audio CDs (7) 978-1-4130-1490-7 $150.00
Teacher Edition 978-1-4130-1493-8 $107.00
Teacher Resource Book 978-1-4130-1494-5 $68.00
Teacher Resource CD-ROM 978-1-4130-1496-9 $133.50
Intro Online Inservice 978-1-4240-1791-1 $551.25
Assessment CD-ROM with ExamView® ...978-1-4130-1488-4 $47.50
Student CD-ROM Lab Pack (5) 978-1-4130-6823-8 $275.00
Assessment Program 978-1-4130-2179-0 $140.75
Remediation Tool 978-1-4240-1859-8 $238.00
Transparencies 978-1-4130-1495-2 $133.50
Book A
Student Book (420 pp.) 978-0-8384-5247-9 $62.00
E-Book (CD-ROM) 978-1-4240-4497-9 $66.25
E-Book (Online) 978-1-4240-4498-6 $66.25
Activity Book 978-0-8384-5284-4 $17.75
Grammar Practice 978-1-4240-0571-0 $20.00
Grammar Practice Answer Key 978-1-4240-1618-1 $3.50
Text/Grammar Café Pkg. 978-1-4240-2075-1 $67.50
Teacher Edition Hardcover 978-0-8384-5285-1 $107.00
Teacher Edition Spiralbound 978-1-4130-1007-7 $107.00
Assessment Program 978-0-8384-5297-4 $142.75

Teacher Resource Book	978-0-8384-5286-8	$72.25
Audio CDs (2)	978-0-8384-5280-6	$136.75

Book B

Student Book (432 pp.)	978-0-8384-5248-6	$62.00
E-Book (CD-ROM)	978-1-4240-4499-3	$66.25
E-Book (Online)	978-1-4240-4500-6	$66.25
Activity Book	978-0-8384-5334-6	$17.75
Grammar Practice	978-1-4240-0569-7	$20.00
Grammar Practice Answer Key	978-1-4240-1619-8	$3.50
Text/Grammar Café Pkg.	978-1-4240-2076-8	$67.50
Teacher Edition Hardcover	978-0-8384-5335-3	$107.00
Teacher Edition Spiralbound	978-1-4130-1008-4	$107.00
Assessment Program	978-0-8384-5341-4	$142.75
Teacher Resource Book	978-0-8384-5339-1	$72.25
Audio CDs (3)	978-0-8384-5332-2	$130.25

Book C

Student Book (432 pp.)	978-0-8384-5249-3	$62.00
E-Book (CD-ROM)	978-1-4240-4501-3	$66.25
E-Book (Online)	978-1-4240-4502-0	$66.25
Activity Book	978-0-8384-5346-9	$17.75
Grammar Practice	978-1-4240-0570-3	$20.00
Grammar Practice Answer Key	978-1-4240-1620-4	$3.50
Text/Grammar Café Pkg.	978-1-4240-2077-5	$67.50
Teacher Edition Hardcover	978-0-8384-5347-6	$107.00
Teacher Edition Spiralbound	978-1-4130-1009-1	$107.00
Assessment Program	978-0-8384-5350-6	$142.75
Teacher Resource Book	978-0-8384-5348-3	$72.25
Audio CDs (3)	978-0-8384-5344-5	$136.75

Books Basic – C

Student Handbook	978-0-8384-5840-2	$16.00
Placement Test	978-1-4130-2773-0	$12.50

Books A – C

Assessment CD-ROM with ExamView®	978-0-8384-5719-1	$142.75
Student CD-ROM	978-0-8384-5281-3	$70.50
Student CD-ROM Lab Pack (5)	978-1-4130-9150-2	$275.00
CNN® DVD	978-1-4130-1252-1	$178.25
CNN® Video	978-0-8384-5298-1	$178.25
Staff Development Video	978-0-8384-5357-5	$36.00
Staff Development Handbook	978-0-8384-5356-8	$29.75
Online In-service	978-1-4282-1144-5	$500.00
Teacher Resource CD-ROM	978-1-4130-0642-1	$142.75
Remediation Tool	978-1-4240-1858-1	$220.50
Transparencies	978-0-8384-5299-8	$95.25

Voices in Literature   p. 22

Bronze (Beginning)

Text (200 pp.)	978-0-8384-2283-0	$62.00
Skillbuilder 1 (142 pp.)	978-0-8384-1883-3	$25.25
Student Journal with Activity Masters	978-0-8384-2290-8	$15.75
Student Audio Tape	978-0-8384-7030-5	$41.75
Skillbuilder 1 Listening & Speaking Audio Tape	978-0-8384-2002-7	$28.00
Teacher's Guide	978-0-8384-2291-5	$29.00
Assessment	978-0-8384-2292-2	$114.25

Silver (Intermediate)

Text (224 pp.)	978-0-8384-7019-0	$62.00
Skillbuilder 2 (136 pp.)	978-0-8384-1890-1	$25.25
Student Journal with Activity Masters	978-0-8384-2293-9	$15.75
Student Audio Tape	978-0-8384-7023-7	$41.75
Skillbuilder 2 Listening & Speaking Audio Tapes (2)	978-0-8384-2030-0	$28.00
Teacher's Guide	978-0-8384-2294-6	$29.00
Assessment	978-0-8384-2295-3	$114.25

Gold (Advanced)

Text (272 pp.)	978-0-8384-7035-0	$62.00
Skillbuilder 2 (136 pp.)	978-0-8384-1890-1	$25.25
Student Journal with Activity Masters	978-0-8384-2296-0	$15.75
Student Audio Tape	978-0-8384-7027-5	$41.75
Skillbuilder 2 Listening & Speaking Audio Tapes (2)	978-0-8384-2030-0	$28.00
Teacher's Guide	978-0-8384-2297-7	$29.00
Assessment	978-0-8384-2298-4	$114.25
Teacher's Guide to Using the Heinle ESL/ELD Program	978-0-8384-7007-7	$29.75

W

Walk, Amble, Stroll   p. 99

Text 1 (176 pp.)	978-0-8384-3956-2	$34.25
Text 2 (192 pp.)	978-0-8384-2280-9	$34.25
Instructor's Manual/Answer Key (1 & 2)	978-0-8384-5985-0	$15.25

Weaving it Together, 3/e   p. 74

Book 1

Text (208 pp.)	978-1-4240-5603-3	$32.75
Text/Audio CD Pkg.	978-1-4240-4197-8	$38.50
Audio CD	978-1-4240-8739-6	$27.00
Assessment CD-ROM with ExamView®	978-1-111-00239-8	$128.00

Book 2

Text (206 pp.)	978-1-4240-5741-2	$32.75
Text/Audio CD Pkg.	978-1-4240-4198-5	$38.50
Audio CD	978-1-4240-8740-2	$27.00
Assessment CD-ROM with ExamView®	978-1-111-00240-4	$128.00

Book 3

Text (224 pp.)	978-1-4240-5740-5	$32.75
Text/Audio CD Pkg.	978-1-4240-4199-2	$38.50
Audio CD	978-1-4240-8741-9	$27.00
Assessment CD-ROM with ExamView®	978-1-111-00241-1	$128.00

Book 4

Text (288 pp.)	978-1-4240-5739-9	$32.75
Text/Audio CD Pkg.	978-1-4240-4196-1	$38.50
Audio CD (2)	978-1-4240-8742-6	$27.00
Assessment CD-ROM with ExamView®	978-1-111-00242-8	$128.00

Instructor's Manual (Books 1 & 2)	978-1-111-00237-4	$21.25
Instructor's Manual (Books 3 & 4)	978-1-111-00238-1	$21.25

Well Said series   p. 95

Well Said Intro

Text (240 pp.)	978-1-4130-0510-3	$35.75
Text/Audio CDs Pkg.	978-1-4240-9888-0	$47.00
Audio CDs (6)	978-1-4130-0716-9	$132.25
Instructor's Manual	978-1-4130-0719-0	$15.00

Well Said, 3/e

Text (240 pp.)	978-1-4240-0625-0	$35.75
Text/Audio CDs Pkg.	978-1-4240-8802-7	$47.00
Audio CDs (4)	978-1-4240-0781-3	$121.75
Instructor's Manual	978-1-4240-0783-7	$15.00

Working Week, The   p. 108

Text (136 pp.)	978-1-8993-9685-6	$32.25
Text/Audio Tape Pkg.	978-1-4130-5351-7	$55.25
Audio Tape	978-1-8993-9695-5	$29.00
Instructor's Manual	978-1-8993-9690-0	$26.00

Working with Teaching Methods   p. 115

Text (208pp.)	978-0-8384-7891-2	$30.00

World English   p. 42

Intro

Student Book with Student CD-ROM	978-1-4240-6335-2	$28.00
Student CD-ROM	978-1-4240-7987-2	$19.50
Workbook	978-1-4240-6302-4	$13.00
Online Video Workbook	978-1-4240-6318-5	$12.00
Teacher's Edition	978-1-4240-6298-0	$25.00
Audio CD	978-1-4240-6306-2	$36.00
DVD	978-1-4240-6310-9	$21.50
Assessment CD-ROM with ExamView® (Intro & 1)	978-1-4240-6327-7	$107.75

Level 1

Student Book with Student CD-ROM	978-1-4240-6336-9	$28.00
Student CD-ROM	978-1-4240-7988-9	$19.50
Workbook	978-1-4240-6303-1	$13.00
Online Video Workbook	978-1-4240-6319-2	$12.00
Teacher's Edition	978-1-4240-6299-7	$25.00
Audio CD	978-1-4240-6307-9	$36.00
DVD	978-1-4240-6311-6	$21.50
Assessment CD-ROM with ExamView® (Intro & 1)	978-1-4240-6327-7	$107.75

Level 2

Student Book with Student CD-ROM	978-1-4240-6337-6	$28.00
Student CD-ROM	978-1-4240-7989-6	$19.50
Workbook	978-1-4240-6304-8	$13.00
Online Video Workbook	978-1-4240-6320-8	$12.00
Teacher's Edition	978-1-4240-6300-0	$25.00
Audio CD	978-1-4240-6308-6	$36.00
DVD	978-1-4240-6312-3	$21.50
Assessment CD-ROM with ExamView® (2 & 3)	978-1-4240-6328-4	$107.75

Level 3

Student Book with Student CD-ROM	978-1-4240-6338-3	$28.00
Student CD-ROM	978-1-4240-7990-2	$19.50
Workbook	978-1-4240-6305-5	$13.00
Online Video Workbook	978-1-4240-6321-5	$12.00
Teacher's Edition	978-1-4240-6301-7	$25.00
Audio CD	978-1-4240-6309-3	$36.00

World English (continued)

Level 3 (continued)

	ISBN	Price
DVD	978-1-4240-6313-0	$21.50
Assessment CD-ROM with ExamView® (2 & 3)	978-1-4240-6328-4	$107.75

World Link p. 46

Intro

	ISBN	Price
Text (160 pp.)	978-0-8384-0661-8	$20.00
Workbook	978-0-8384-2522-0	$13.75
Combo Split A	978-1-4130-1080-0	$17.75
Combo Split B	978-1-4130-1081-7	$17.75
Online Workbook	978-1-4240-0699-1	$12.50
Text/Audio CDs Pkg.	978-1-4240-8800-3	$25.75
Text/Workbook Pkg.	978-1-4130-6507-7	$30.50
Text/Video Course Workbook Pkg.	978-1-4130-5043-1	$36.50
Audio CDs (2)	978-0-8384-4614-6	$48.75
Teacher's Edition with Presentation Tool CD-ROM	978-0-8384-2523-7	$27.00
Teacher's Resource Book	978-0-8384-2521-3	$45.50
DVD	978-1-4130-1073-2	$33.75
Video (VHS)	978-0-8384-4635-5	$45.50
Video Course Workbook	978-0-7593-9638-8	$20.50
Online Video Workbook	978-1-4240-0706-6	$28.25
Video Course Teacher's Guide	978-0-7593-9639-5	$19.25

Level 1

	ISBN	Price
Text (160 pp.)	978-0-8384-0662-5	$20.00
Workbook	978-0-8384-2533-6	$13.75
Combo Split A	978-1-4130-1082-4	$17.75
Combo Split B	978-1-4130-1083-1	$17.75
Online Workbook	978-1-4240-0700-4	$12.50
Text/Audio CDs Pkg.	978-1-4240-9874-3	$25.75
Text/Workbook Pkg.	978-1-4130-6504-6	$30.50
Text/Video Course Workbook Pkg.	978-1-4130-5045-5	$36.50
Audio CDs (2)	978-0-8384-4630-0	$48.75
Teacher's Edition with Presentation Tool CD-ROM	978-0-8384-2559-6	$27.00
Teacher's Resource Book	978-0-8384-2532-9	$45.50
DVD	978-1-4130-1074-9	$33.75
Video (VHS)	978-0-8384-4637-9	$45.50
Video Course Workbook	978-0-7593-9640-1	$20.50
Online Video Workbook	978-1-4240-0705-9	$28.25
Video Course Teacher's Guide	978-0-7593-9641-8	$19.25

Level 2

	ISBN	Price
Text (160 pp.)	978-0-8384-0665-6	$20.00
Workbook	978-0-8384-2561-9	$13.75
Combo Split A	978-1-4130-1084-8	$17.75
Combo Split B	978-1-4130-1085-5	$17.75
Online Workbook	978-1-4240-0701-1	$12.50
Text/Audio CDs Pkg.	978-1-4240-9875-0	$25.75
Text/Workbook Pkg.	978-1-4130-6505-3	$30.50
Text/Video Course Workbook Pkg.	978-1-4130-5057-8	$36.50
Audio CDs (2)	978-0-8384-4652-2	$48.75
Teacher's Edition with Presentation Tool CD-ROM	978-0-8384-2562-6	$27.00
Teacher's Resource Book	978-0-8384-2560-2	$45.50
DVD	978-1-4130-1075-6	$33.75
Video (VHS)	978-0-8384-4641-6	$45.50
Video Course Workbook	978-0-7593-9642-5	$20.50
Online Video Workbook	978-1-4240-0707-3	$28.25
Video Course Teacher's Guide	978-0-7593-9643-2	$19.25

Level 3

	ISBN	Price
Text (160 pp.)	978-0-8384-0668-7	$20.00
Workbook	978-0-8384-2564-0	$13.75
Combo Split A	978-1-4130-1086-2	$17.75
Combo Split B	978-1-4130-1087-9	$17.75
Online Workbook	978-1-4240-0702-8	$12.50
Text/Audio CDs Pkg.	978-1-4240-9872-9	$25.75
Text/Workbook Pkg.	978-1-4130-6506-0	$30.50
Text/Video Course Workbook Pkg.	978-1-4130-5026-4	$36.50
Audio CDs (2)	978-0-8384-4656-0	$48.75
Teacher's Edition with Presentation Tool CD-ROM	978-0-8384-2565-7	$27.00
Teacher's Resource Book	978-0-8384-2563-3	$45.50
DVD	978-1-4130-1076-3	$33.75
Video (VHS)	978-0-8384-4642-3	$45.50
Video Course Workbook	978-0-7593-9644-9	$20.50
Online Video Workbook	978-1-4240-0708-0	$28.25
Video Course Teacher's Guide	978-0-7593-9645-6	$19.25

	ISBN	Price
Assessment CD-ROM with ExamView® and Audio CD (Intro – 3)	978-1-4130-2768-6	$122.00

World Link Video Course p. 46

Intro

	ISBN	Price
Video Course Workbook	978-0-7593-9638-8	$20.50

	ISBN	Price
Online Video Workbook	978-1-4240-0706-6	$28.25
DVD	978-1-4130-1073-2	$33.75
Video (VHS)	978-0-8384-4635-5	$45.50
Teacher's Guide	978-0-7593-9639-5	$19.25

Level 1

	ISBN	Price
Video Course Workbook	978-0-7593-9640-1	$20.50
Online Video Workbook	978-1-4240-0705-9	$28.25
DVD	978-1-4130-1074-9	$33.75
Video (VHS)	978-0-8384-4637-9	$45.50
Teacher's Guide	978-0-7593-9641-8	$19.25

Level 2

	ISBN	Price
Video Course Workbook	978-0-7593-9642-5	$20.50
Online Video Workbook	978-1-4240-0707-3	$28.25
DVD	978-1-4130-1075-6	$33.75
Video (VHS)	978-0-8384-4641-6	$45.50
Teacher's Guide	978-0-7593-9643-2	$19.25

Level 3

	ISBN	Price
Video Course Workbook	978-0-7593-9644-9	$20.50
Online Video Workbook	978-1-4240-0708-0	$28.25
DVD	978-1-4130-1076-3	$33.75
Video (VHS)	978-0-8384-4642-3	$45.50
Teacher's Guide	978-0-7593-9645-6	$19.25

World Pass p. 46

Upper-Intermediate

	ISBN	Price
Text (176 pp.)	978-0-8384-0669-4	$20.00
Workbook	978-0-8384-2567-1	$14.25
Online Workbook	978-1-4240-0704-2	$13.25
Text/Workbook Pkg.	978-1-4240-9892-7	$31.00
Combo Split A	978-1-4130-1088-6	$19.25
Combo Split B	978-1-4130-1089-3	$19.25
Audio CD	978-0-8384-4687-4	$23.25
Teacher's Edition	978-0-8384-2568-8	$25.75
Teacher's Resource Book	978-0-8384-2566-4	$43.00
CNN® DVD	978-1-4130-1077-0	$32.00
CNN® Video	978-0-8384-4657-7	$43.00

Advanced

	ISBN	Price
Text (176 pp.)	978-0-8384-0670-0	$20.00
Workbook	978-0-8384-2570-1	$14.25
Online Workbook	978-1-4240-0703-5	$13.25
Text/Workbook Pkg.	978-1-4240-9411-0	$31.00
Combo Split A	978-1-4130-1090-9	$19.25
Combo Split B	978-1-4130-1091-6	$19.25
Audio CD	978-0-8384-4691-1	$23.25
Teacher's Edition	978-0-8384-2571-8	$25.75
Teacher's Resource Book	978-0-8384-2569-5	$43.00
CNN® DVD	978-1-4130-1078-7	$32.00
CNN® Video	978-0-8384-4693-5	$43.00

	ISBN	Price
Upper-Intermediate and Advanced Assessment CD-ROM with ExamView®	978-1-4130-2326-8	$122.00

Write from the Start, 2/e p. 82

	ISBN	Price
Text (144 pp.)	978-0-8384-4848-9	$32.50
Answer Key	978-0-8384-4849-6	$15.75

Write Ideas p. 82

	ISBN	Price
Text (128 pp.)	978-0-8384-3987-6	$36.00

Write in the Middle, 2/e p. 82

	ISBN	Price
Text (144 pp.)	978-0-0302-2297-9	$37.25
Answer Key	978-0-0300-6509-5	$4.50

Write Path, The p. 82

	ISBN	Price
Text (144 pp.)	978-0-1550-6519-2	$35.50

Writing Clearly: An Editing Guide, 2/e p. 82

	ISBN	Price
Text (336 pp.)	978-0-8384-0949-7	$38.50
Instructor's Manual	978-0-8384-0985-5	$28.25
CNN® Video	978-0-8384-0958-9	$62.50

Writing Essentials p. 82

	ISBN	Price
Text (336 pp.)	978-1-4130-0000-9	$37.00

Writing Practical English, 2/e p. 48

	ISBN	Price
Book 1 (168 pp.)	978-0-1557-0915-7	$12.50
Book 2 (168 pp.)	978-0-1557-0923-2	$12.50
Book 3 (168 pp.)	978-0-1557-0931-7	$12.50

Writing Workout p. 82

	ISBN	Price
Text (128 pp.)	978-0-8384-3960-9	$31.25

Writing Workshop p. 82

	ISBN	Price
Text (190 pp.)	978-0-8384-7973-5	$36.00

For customer support, call **(877) NEED-ESL** or visit **elt.heinle.com** ■ For pricing, ISBNs, and ordering information see pp. 122 – 144